EASY STRENGTH

How to Get a Lot Stronger than Your Competition —and Dominate in Your Sport

Dan John and Pavel

EASY STRENGTH

How to Get a Lot Stronger than Your Competition —and Dominate in Your Sport

Dan John and Pavel

A Dragon Door Publications, Inc production

Published in the United States by:
Dragon Door Publications, Inc
P.O. Box 4381, St. Paul, MN 55104
Tel: (651) 487-2180 • Fax: (651) 487-3954
Credit card orders: 1-800-899-5111
Email: dragondoor@aol.com • Website: www.dragondoor.com

ISBN 10: 0-938045-80-6 ISBN 13: 978-0-938045-80-9

This edition first published in October, 2011

Printed in China

Book design, and cover by Derek Brigham
Website http//www.dbrigham.com • Tel/Fax: (763) 208-3069 • Email: bigd@dbrigham.com

Dedicated to the memory of John Fass, Christian, warrior, American.

SOC (SEAL Operator, Chief) John Fass
KIA 2011, Afghanistan

The authors would like to thank the following individuals
for their suggestions about this manuscript:

Boris Bachman
Thomas Fahey
Steve Freides
Marty Gallagher
Rob Lawrence
Jeremy Layport
Chip Morton
Jeff O'Connor
Jack Reape
Mark Reifkind
Barry Ross

-TABLE OF CONTENTS-

FOREWORD

Minneapolis, Minnesota, 1997. My eye was caught by a series of brash ads in the local seminar-company's catalog. For $25.00 per three-hour class, a young émigré, Pavel Tsatsouline, was promising to challenge many of our Western World's most cherished fitness beliefs—and replace them with a rack of more practical, more scientific and flat-out more effective training protocols. Billing himself as the "Evil Russian", this mysterious "ex-Soviet Special Forces physical training instructor" offered a giddy set of powerful new "Iron Curtain Secrets" for rapid strength gains, dramatic stretches and iron abs.

With my 26-year background in Kung Fu, Chinese internal martial arts, yoga, qigong and traditional weight training, I was intrigued, to say the least. An eternal seeker for the Holy Grail of supreme fitness, how could I resist?

What if even 10% of Pavel's wild claims were true? I'd already be in like Flynn. And imagine if it was more?

When Constantinople fell in 1453 and its scholars fled across Europe, the resulting wisdom-blitz helped fuel the Renaissance of Western Culture. With the advent of Glasnost and the Fall of the Wall in 1989, we appeared to be witnessing a similar storming of the barricades of ignorance. The original vision of AK-47-wielding Russkies scything across Europe, morphed into a more stealthy invasion. Secret training-wisdom carriers, clutching tattered Cyrillic scripts, were spied snaking through the ripped Iron Curtain. Their objective: the Western Fitness Citadels and their deluded denizens—those woeful worshippers of ferns and mirrors, of aerobics, of Nautilus, of dieting and repping to failure.

And no such infiltrator brandished his promised secrets with more panache than this expat from the Evil Empire—now a self-declared "running capitalist dog" and proud of it.

So I signed up and showed up for the Evil Russian's Flexibility Training seminar. The room was packed with a startling spectrum: gnarly, tattooed gents of dubious pedigree were rubbing shoulders with petite ballerinas, soft-handed but quietly lethal martial artists, recovering bodybuilders, lil 'ol grandmothers and out-of-shape desk jockeys. Oh, and who was that man in black, in the corner, with shades and a frozen jaw?

But whoever they were, their attention was riveted on the colorful, charismatic Russian athlete who upbraided them for their current ignorance but promised them great and glorious gains—if they would only heel to his barked commands. "Comrades, it is not that you *will* stretch five more inches, it is that you *shall*—or else!" Not even the tattooed, scarred bikers or the grim Man in Black appeared ready to take on the "Or Else" part. 100% allegiance was demanded and secured.

The Evil Russian proceeded to lead his excited and obedient flock to a veritable Promised Land of flexibility and stretching breakthroughs. Everything the man said made sense—and everything he ordered us to do—worked in spades! How about that? The promises were real! 10% real? How about 110%?

Yet, for all his charismatic delivery and astounding results, I could see that the Evil Russian did still have one weapon missing in his bid for World Domination. The seminar handouts consisted of some shorthand hieroglyphs and chicken-scratch diagrams.

Hmmmnn...this needed to be remedied. With some diffidence—yet with a rapidly developing sense of kinship—I approached Pavel at the end of the seminar and asked him a set of three simple questions:

"Do you have a publisher?"
"Would like to have a publisher?"
"Would you like to have Dragon Door as your publisher?"

The rest is history—not to mention the beginning of a beautiful friendship.

Dragon Door collaborated with Pavel on a series of landmark titles that have contributed to a seismic shift in the Western World's fitness landscape: ***Super Joints, The Naked Warrior,*** the great strength classic ***Power to the People!***, and finally one of the most influential fitness titles of all time: ***The Russian Kettlebell Challenge***—which launched the modern world-wide Kettlebell movement in 2001.

Why has Pavel—the Evil One of yore—been SO successful? Well, I have many answers to that, but here are the most significant points:

Pavel has a remarkable ability to cull through the most arcane research and make glorious, practical sense of it for us lesser mortals. Pavel goes wide, to take us deep—very deep. He does the work for us, like a Master Chef, culling the best of the best—and he serves it to us on fine china, impeccably presented.

Pavel is a sponge for anything that truly works and has an uncanny eye for a method that can be tweaked and refined into a world-class, world-beating technique. Give Pavel the right ball and he'll run a mile with it. I've seen it over and over and over.

Pavel is a master of style: mixing succinct, brilliantly crafted text-play with superlative insight, extensive wisdom and unassailable research.

Pavel honors the masters of the past and pays generous respect to the modern greats—so, with him, we may stand on the shoulders of giants.

All of these qualities make Pavel the great teacher and author that he is. However, to me, his most admirable quality remains his generosity with peers and colleagues. Pavel is the Keith Richards of his métier, ever-eager to "jam" with like-minded artists of the strength game—while quick to acknowledge and give acclaim to those who have influenced him. And it is undoubtedly this admirable quality that led to the birth of ***Easy Strength.***

At Pavel's invitation and prompting, many stars have been encouraged to shine more brightly from the Dragon Door firmament. They have included greats like Gray Cook, Marty Gallagher and Ori Hofmekler. And they have included Dragon Door's elite cadre of RKC Masters and Seniors, both past and present. Well, as big a star as any in this Dragon Door pantheon, has got to be Fulbright scholar, National Champion athlete and coach-extraordinaire, Dan John.

Dan John—polyglot, polymath and all-around Renaissance Man—wears his experience and learning light, spinning his wisdom out in an almost aw-shucks manner, an Irish story teller who leans in to you across the table, nursing a Guinness, enlightening while entertaining. Dan is a man who has bitten deep into the apple. And Dan is a man who has willingly risked his own body, again and again, in the experiential quest for athletic excellence—like the never-let-go, never-say-die, Holy Grail seeker that he is. Dan is a leader whose battle scars are only matched by his impressive list of achievements. And, anyone who has been around the RKC knows Dan has been making a magnificent contribution to the development of this preeminent "School of Strength".

So, what do you know? Pavel and Dan became fast friends. Their mutual "love of the game", their mutual enthusiasm for the Quest, their mutual drive to push the envelope—and their mutual respect—led to long deep discussions into the late of night. The synergy of their intellectual excitement led to some profound insights and some groundbreaking conclusions. And surely, they should share these great insights with the world, as they had always been wont to do—in their own very different ways?

What to do and how to do it? Clearly, a book was sitting here that needed to be outed. Pavel called me and explained the dilemma: "But how on earth could two authors with such dramatically distinctive voices possibly co-author a book?"

You know, there have been attempts by great writers in the past to co-author works together, but I have yet to read one that I thought worked. Really worked.

This was a tough one...could this project be simply "inconceivable"? Born to die on the vine?

Then I remembered one of my favorite movies of all time: ***My Dinner with Andre***. By one of my all time favorite directors, Louis Malle. Starring one of my all time favorite actors, the inimitable hoot, Wallace Shawn.

"Inconceivable!" Wallace Shawn and Andre Gregory debate the meaning of their lives, in Louis Malle's masterly *My Dinner with Andre*.

In ***My Dinner with Andre***, two close friends meet for dinner and have an impassioned discussion that pushes both of them—and of course, the viewer—to reevaluate the meaning of their lives. The dialog is rich, volatile, intense, vibrant, funny, absurd, penetrating, entertaining, puzzling, astonishing, improbable, emotional and reflective. Actual friends, actor/playwright Wallace Shawn and Andre Gregory—an experimental theater director/playwright with spiritual links to Gurdjieff— play a kind of enhanced, dramatized version of themselves. The results are dizzyingly, engrossingly brilliant. They argue, they counterpoint, they banter, they agree to disagree. Wow!

Okay, well how about Pavel and Dan write their book using the ***My Dinner with Andre*** concept as their structure? Two friends, shooting the breeze as it were, about their subject of passion—and going deep as all heck in the process?

I overnighted Pavel a copy of ***My Dinner with Andre***. Pavel loved it. In fact, he watched it five times.

We were on. Yup, things were starting to look conceivable after all...

So Dan and Pavel embarked on exactly that organizational concept. One of them would make a statement, drop a pearl of strength-wisdom; the other would comment—elaborating, elucidating, extending the conversation. The other would respond back and so it would continue. And the more the conversation continued, the deeper they would go, surprising and inspiring each other with the gathering momentum of insight.

The concept worked liked gangbusters. More than I think any of us could have imagined. And I think I know what has made it so special. Despite all their differences in background, culture, experience and proclivities, Pavel and Dan managed to form one of those extremely rare creative partnerships, where two individuals combine to produce a work whose whole is truly greater than the sum of its parts.

Because *Easy Strength* is not a Socratic dialog, it's not a series of arguments, but rather two masters of the craft jamming together. It's the strength world's equivalent of Keith Richards and Mick Jagger at their peak writing and composing, say ***Sticky Fingers***—then unleashing it on an unsuspecting but deeply grateful and appreciative world.

"Conceivable!" Pavel and Dan, captured live at an undisclosed location, while creating their masterwork, *Easy Strength.*

Now, let me tell you, when you read the final masterwork that is *Easy Strength*, don't be misled by the almost magical smoothness of the Pavel-Dan dialogs. There was agony and there was ecstasy and it took two hard years to get it done. But that's great art for you.

The result, I proudly present to you: *Easy Strength*, a book of wisdom for the ages. A book by two "warrior athletes" I deeply admire.

Thank you, gentlemen.

May these two men and their *Easy Strength* inspire you—as they have so inspired me—to continue your own, never-ending quest for athletic excellence and supreme physical cultivation.

By John Du Cane
CEO, Dragon Door Publications

PREFACE

Not the ROLE of the Strength Coach but the IMPACT!

Dan John

> *"Begin at the beginning," the King said gravely, "and go on till you come to the end: then stop."*
> *—Lewis Carroll, Alice in Wonderland*

Although reviewing the influences in my athletic career might take an entire book (and it did!), the single most illuminating moment of my strength coaching career came to me in a nervous sweat in San Jose. Pavel had asked me to speak about "The Role of the Strength Coach" at the Russian Kettlebell Challenge (RKC) Certification. (For the record, I may be the only participant ever to have been asked to speak at his own certification.)

The role of the strength coach? Well, now, let's see: We get people stronger, we prevent injuries (maybe), we teach some skills, we do some of this and some of that, and—well, I don't know.

That was the problem! Literally, every fool knows the role of the strength coach: *to coach strength*. So, my workshop notes read simply this: "The strength coach teaches/coaches strength. Then play banjo, sing funny song, sneak out the back."

I have no issue with the fact that I am sitting at the feet of greatness when I speak of DeLorme, Hack, and Jessee, but the people who come to the RKC are often very tough characters. I didn't want to disappoint! As members of the RKC community began to drift into the room, I knew I had nothing. In my little moment of panic, I sat back and listened to two guys talk about how strength coaches can affect wins and losses.

Wait! The IMPACT on wins and losses? The *Bigger, Faster, Stronger* (BFS) magazine has remarkable turnaround stories in every monthly issue about struggling high school programs that go from 0 to 11 to being undefeated and state champs in a season or two. While I have great respect for BFS, I've always felt the turnaround in wins and losses usually comes from having commitment and enthusiasm—literally, some paradigm-changing event—not the decision to do 5 reps or 3 reps. (If you watch the BFS videos, I'm the guy in the power clean video.)

How does hiring the finest strength coach the world has ever seen IMPACT a team's win column? Well, it depends. Let's be honest: An American football team can have outstanding weight room numbers, staggering sprint times, and outstanding "conditioning" (whatever that means anymore) yet still lose a game because the football coach goes for it on fourth and one and tries a magnificent pass play that clanks to the ground or tries to trick the opponent with a double-reverse that leads to a fumble and thus the game. If football were played in the weight room or on the track, I could guarantee that each year, the team that won the championship would NOT be the team that won on the field of play.

And that is absolutely true in every sport and every game. It's a rare track meet that you don't hear someone rhapsodize about training numbers and then see him or her lose badly. In football, we have a phrase for this: "Looks like Tarzan, plays like Jane."

Sitting there in the overflowing classroom at the RKC, it came to me: *The impact of strength training on success in sports really depends on the sport!* If you want the world to listen to every word you say about weight training, then you must discover a way to increase the deadlift or the vertical jump that works for everyone, every time. "I can show you the secret to a 750 deadlift!"

The evidence for this claim would be, of course, a gym or a program with lots of 750 deadlifts (not the internet kind where you just type in the numbers either). As a coach, it is a rare week when I don't receive a letter, e-mail, poster, or catalogue promoting at least a few items that promise a vastly improved vertical jump (VJ) or deadlift (DL).

A small caveat here: Please don't send me any more items bragging how you got little Billy from a crappy 19-inch vertical jump to a 25-inch vertical jump. Improving from "awful" to "bad" is not a sign that anything is really happening. But give me a program or device that gets an elite athlete from a 38-inch VJ to a 43, and I am all ears!

As I sat there at the RKC, it became clear to me that anything that a strength and conditioning coach can do to increase the DL or the VJ is, well, clear. If changing the grip gets an athlete from a 455 DL to a 505 DL, then honestly, we can step back and say that that works.

A continuum began to form in my head. My brain works best in continuums—a way of seeing how things gradually transition from one state or condition to another, without any abrupt changes. I see the movements of the human body this way, as well as nearly everything regarding morality and the human condition. I can't help it.

So, when I thought about the exact OPPOSITE of the impact of strength coaching on a sport, I quickly came to American football. Strength and conditioning is one of the foundations of coaching football.

Until recently, weightlifting in some sports—basketball and baseball come to mind first—has been considered at best wrong, at worst flat-out evil. I have probably dozens of books on training athletes for football. Football coaches love the simple answer to strength work. Honestly, if you ever had to train 100-plus athletes, you, too, would embrace a straightforward approach using functional isometric contraction (a set of fixed racks next to the field), Universal gyms (one big machine and a whistle), or Nautilus equipment (big, shiny, blue machines that tire out an athlete in less than half an hour). There are problems with other approaches, including the Olympic lifts (proper coaching and time are needed to teach everyone the movements) and the powerlifts (it is a rare mom who doesn't blanch when she sees Junior pick up weights "with his back!"). Another challenge is the sheer number of athletes you need to make bigger and stronger.

But here is the rub: If you recruit, legally or illegally, five superior athletes into your football program, you will win more games. A few years ago, I worked with a high school student who scored a touchdown every sixth time he touched the ball. The correct response is "Well, why didn't they give him the ball more?" A great high school athlete can turn an ordinary five-yard gain into a game-breaking score.

Folks, that's "fuzzy," I know. Sadly, I can't yet coach genetics, but I wish I could. I can, however, give you some specific, time-tested advice: *You MUST strength train to compete in football, rugby, or any of the collision sports.* The sad thing—for me, anyway—is that it will be nearly impossible to gauge whether the winning record that results will be due to your commitment to doing 3 sets of 10 or the fact that your admissions office has absolutely no scruples.

Track and field is an interesting study. The shot put, for example, isn't affected by much, so anything that brings improvement is something I want to hear about. The discus, however, loves certain winds, hates rain and cold, and rewards the athlete with a great throw just for showing up under the right weather conditions. The discus—one of the great loves of my life—is a terrible mistress! She is "fuzzier" than the shot, so to speak.

Before you get too far into your journey of studying strength and conditioning, spend a moment thinking about the actual impact of strength training in your sport. Be careful in making your first judgment. A raw powerlifter can add weight to his bench press by simply purchasing and mastering some of the new "wonder gear," including bench shirts, elbow wraps, and wrist wraps. So even in obvious cases, putting in a few minutes of thought can work wonders.

My talk at the RKC was astounding, according to observers. (I blush!) As I told them, the clarity of this point shaped my coaching: *Everyone knows the role of the strength coach, but few have ever considered the impact of the coach on actual performance.*

Pavel and my goal in writing this book is to clarify the role and impact of strength training in fitness, sports, and life. We are committed to clarity, even though at times, it's impossible to navigate the sea of conflicting information regarding the lifting sports. Pavel's experience and research provides grounding and a confidence to "Do this!" as we often joke.

What can you expect from reading this book?

- You will learn some history. You will discover that almost everything discussed in the fitness industry has been done before—and often better.
- You will reexamine the role of strength training as it applies to sport. Doing so may serve as the greatest timesaver in history!
- You will find that, like a medical doctor, a strength coach must be committed above all to "Do no harm"—a pledge that's often disregarded.
- You will be exposed to the concept of systematic education and the need to build an athlete (or anyone!) using some kind of intelligent approach.
- You will be exposed to another educational system—along with a way to harness its powers—that will give you clarity into all the various fitness, health, and nutritional information being tossed at you daily.
- You will discover the tools for teaching an entire team to improve in a sport—and why these great tools may be of no value to you in your training!
- You will be exposed to what the best in sports do in the weight room, and you will discover why it will apply to everything you decide to do.
- You will learn many of the "champion's secrets" and be amazed at the simplicity, as well as the insightfulness, of what the best do.

CHAPTER 1

The Continuums and the Quadrants

"Look with favor upon a bold beginning."
—Virgil

So, what is the great insight? The impact of the strength coach on the performance of the athlete has always seemed simple:

Get the athlete stronger.

Recently, this idea has been sharpened up a bit, due mostly to the contributions of Gray Cook and Mike Boyle: *"Increase the number of quality workouts/performances."*

Not a bad idea, really, as many strength coaches think it's their God-given duty to smoke the athlete each and every time. Certainly, it is fun to do, but it leaves the athlete a physical wreck.

The great insight was this: Although we all "know" that every sport requires a different set of skills, strength and conditioning coaches were painting all their athletes with one color and one brush. And they knew if they got that right, their athletes would thrive. (Sometimes.)

Thinking about American football is what made everything clear. At the risk of repeating myself, let me say this again: If a college football coach has an admissions office with a very generous door, if the alumni are not afraid to bend the rules, if the coach is willing to turn his back on "little things", and if the program can get the biggest, fastest, wildest athletes available, then the team will win. Whether the strength coach does three sets of five or five sets of three doesn't really matter. Of course, if you lose a few games, the correct answer will be "Fire the strength coach."

In other words, the impact of the strength coach on football is fuzzy. So, I put football on the far end of one side of the continuum. On the other far side, I put the deadlift and the vertical jump. Listen, if you come up with a drill or idea that knocks the deadlift up in an experienced athlete by really any difference (I used to say 70 pounds, but really, 20 pounds is amazing), the lifting world will be buzzing about it tomorrow. Why? Improving the DL or the VJ is "perfectly clear," Mr. Nixon. If an upper-level athlete improves on something basic or simple, I want to know what you did.

Improving the shot put is clearer than improving the discus, for example. The discus is aerodynamic, the shot cares little about anything. Short-track speed skating, with its falls and collisions, is fuzzier than the long, smooth striding of long-track speed skating. If you take a few minutes, you can think through any sport. The more complex—the more factors, generally—the more fuzzy the strength coach's impact on this sport.

And that was pretty good, I thought. At least, I could explain to a fired coach, "Hey, man, your sport is so fuzzy!" But I also realized that there was something missing from the continuum. (I still use it as the continuum really gives one some clues concerning the role of training for various sports.)

So, I began thinking: What is needed for a football player? What is needed for a deadlift? The answer was simple: it's all about *qualities*.

Qualities are those things that we strive for in training: flexibility, stability, power, speed, technique, lateral movement, joint mobility, hypertrophy, prehab and rehab work—and the list, honestly, could take up reams of paper. In some sports, like rugby and American football, the list of qualities needed to perform is really long. In some things, like a deadlift specialist, the list would be shockingly short—like absolute strength.

So, I began to spin these ideas in my head. I realized that an elite discus thrower needs to be strong. But an elite powerlifter might laugh at those maxes. "Oh, yeah? Race me!" might be the throwers response, and I would bet on the discus thrower. But the powerlifter, even a subelite one, would outlift the best thrower. I began to see that there is a bit of relativity in sports and performance in the weight room. And that was the key: there are sports where "strong enough" or "fast enough" or "flexible enough" is, well, enough. The quadrants were born from that insight.

The four quads are determined by two simple concepts:

1. The number of qualities the athlete needs to master the sport

2. The relationship to the **Absolute Maximum** of each quality

The number of qualities needed by in some sports is amazingly high—football, rugby, basketball, probably all collision sports. In other sports, like that of this deadlift specialist we have invented, the number of qualities is rather low. If you want to be an elite sprinter or Olympic lifter (as far from fuzzy as you can probably get at the Olympics), we are probably talking about less than a handful of qualities.

Go ahead, raise your hand: "Um, excuse me, but shouldn't a lifter jog, so he can get his aerobic work in and so he can keep his cardio and his core functional?" Let the beatings begin! The answer is, "If the lifter wants to be the best: no." And this is what I found so refreshing about studying the quadrants. The world of sports training finally made sense.

The graph below is very simple: As you move to the right, you have a sport that requires less and less qualities. As you move down, the Relative Absolute Maximum goes higher and higher. What does that mean?

Well, at the extreme of QIV, we are thinking 1000 pound deadlifts and bench presses, sneaking up on 600 in the clean and jerk, and doing well over 40 inches in the vertical jump. In QII, think about the NFL player I recently worked with, who looked very lean but, as he said, "can't play in the league this light." He weighed 310 pounds!

Let's briefly highlight the quadrants. Here's the simplest way to think of each one:

Quadrant I (QI)

Physical education classes that honestly introduce games, sports, and movements in a broad and organized system

Quadrant II (QII)

The collision sports and occupations

Quadrant III (QIII)

Where most people are in life and sports—a simple yin-yang relationship between strength training and the goal at hand

Quadrant IV (QIV)

The "rare air"—the sport is so narrow and the level of competition so high that there is nearly total focus on one goal

QI: Lots of Qualities at a Low Level of Relative Max

Physical education classes that honestly introduce games, sports, and movements in a broad and organized system

This is what's done in a typical good high school PE class:

- Two laps and an obstacle course
- General stretching
- Push-ups
- A ball game with the rules covered—next week, another game!

Over the course of a year or four years, the youth will be exposed to lots of sports and games (probably including weightlifting) and will learn a variety of movements, rules of sport and the ability to enjoy many of them as an athlete and spectator for the rest of their lives.

There is probably just one rule: *Do no harm!*

> ***I swear by Apollo, the healer, and Asclepius, Hygieia, and Panacea, and I take to witness all the gods, all the goddesses, to keep according to my ability and my judgment, the following oath and agreement: I will prescribe regimens for the good of my patients according to my ability and my judgment and never do harm to anyone.***

There is NOTHING wrong with this quadrant! It's very important!

The Chinese have a saying: "A step in a wrong direction in the beginning of a journey takes you a hundred miles away from your goal." Start your QI training right by building a broad and solid base. QI is GPP time.

"America got into 'sports specific' training 15 to 20 years ago and forgot the fundamentals," laments leading sports physical therapist Gray Cook, RKC. "This created throwing athletes without legs and running athletes who could not do a single push-up correctly. It created swimmers who could not control their body on dry land and cyclists who could not stand up straight."

Soviet sports science made it clear: Premature overspecialization delivers a quick increase in performance followed by stagnation. Extensive research and experimentation have demonstrated that athletic specialization must be supported by all-around preparation. That means GPP.

But what exactly is GPP?

A little knowledge is a dangerous thing. When several of my books were translated into Russian (consider the irony), I asked to check the translations. What I discovered could have come out of the game "telephone." Almost every paragraph carried a meaning different from the original. Some went off on weird tangents, and some even stated the exact opposite of what I had written. It took me weeks to fix most of the damage.

I suspect that many Russian texts dealing with *general physical preparation (GPP)* and *special physical preparation (SPP)* have been translated into English by equally competent people, because in America, GPP has been mysteriously narrowed down to anaerobic smokers. "If it's not sled dragging or burpees, it isn't GPP!" Nonsense, Comrade!

GPP is not limited to a couple of subtypes of endurance but encompasses a wide range of physical attributes, including strength, joint mobility, work capacity, etc. What makes GPP different from SPP is its aim to "perform any physical work more or less successfully," according to Professor Nikolay Ozolin (whose name you will see again and again in this book), as opposed to improving strength or another quality specific to a given sport or task. SPP is what Americans know as *sport-specific training.*

I often ask this trick question at seminars: "The 3 RM deadlift—is it GPP or SPP?" Usually, the students give the answer that appears obvious to them: "SPP, because it's heavy and doesn't make you throw up."

The real answer is, "It depends." For a powerlifter or strongman, the 3 RM DL is SPP, because it is so close to his competition events. For everyone else, it is GPP—even for a weightlifter, because such a heavy pull has little in common with snatches and cleans. The fact that the load is heavy has no bearing on whether the exercise falls into the GPP or the SPP category.

One more time: General physical preparation* is training aimed at raising one's many fitness components applied to a wide range of tasks. Think Crossfit. I am not endorsing that training system but mentioning it because Crossfit's goal is clearly GPP: being ready for a wide range of challenges. GPP also includes addressing weaknesses and imbalances.

Another subtlety lost in translation is related to the relationship between GPP and SPP. In the Russian model, GPP is seen as the foundation on which SPP is built. An estimated 80% of a young Russian athlete's physical training is GPP. Practicing the specific without the general leads to short-term gains, usually followed by injuries and unavoidable long-term plateauing of sports results. Having a wannabe sprinter who can barely squat his bodyweight hang a kettlebell and lift his knee to strengthen his hip flexors ("I have seen it in a Russian book!") is irresponsible. Having him do "plyometrics" is even worse. As the youngster lands, his heels fail to roll back to the ground, his knees collapse inward, his back folds . . .

* Note that the proper word in this context is *preparation*, not *preparedness* (or *podgotovka*, rather than *podgtovlennost*, in Russian). We are talking about a process, not a static state.

Rubber-band-and-pulley functional stuff, while too light to injure, will not build an athlete. And those "speed camps" for weak kids ought to be banned and replaced with "strength camps."

GPP should constitute most of a young athlete's physical preparation. Work on general strength, endurance, etc., not on its sport-specific manifestations. Listen to Professor Nikolay Ozolin, a remarkable athlete who broke the USSR and European pole vault records too many times to mention and won an unprecedented 12 national championships—his last, at age 43. One year, he won the ski-jumping nationals, just for kicks and giggles. Ozolin is one of the founders of Soviet sports science, one of the mentors of young Yuri Verkhoshansky, and a Distingiuished Coach of the USSR. He is a man to listen to.

As Ozolin reminds us:

> *GPP contains the idea of all around physical development. Which is why the qualities developed by GPP may be called general as they express the ability of the organism and its psychological sphere to perform any physical work more or less successfully. Hence general endurance, general strength, general joint mobility, general coordination, general psychological preparedness.*

GPP presumes exposure to a variety of sports, games, and activities. Russian sports scientists point out that the bigger an athlete's "baggage" of movement skills, the easier he will master new forms of movement. Exposing a kid to gymnastics and martial arts will give him a great foundation for any sport—as long as the coach or instructor is a professional. An amateur will give him injuries to remember.

The strength portion of GPP is called GSP: *general strength preparation*. For a young athlete, GSP exercises should meet the following requirements:

1. **Safety.** Remember: "Do no harm!"

2. **Simplicity.** The young-un's attention span demands this.

3. **Teaching basic movement skills.** Squatting, hinging, bracing, crawling, jumping, falling, running, etc.

4. **All-aroundness.** A mix of static and dynamic loads, a mix of energy pathways, a mix of loading directions.

5. **Strength** carryover to as many applications as possible. GSP's focus on a wide range of attributes does not excuse using what Master RKC Mark Reifkind calls "random acts of variety." Seek maximally efficient exercises, which give the biggest bang for the buck.

Ozolin underlines that "general strength . . . is characterized by many-sided musculature development and expression of strength in different regimes, a variety of movements."

In our opinion, the following exercises fit the bill:

Top 16 Q1 GSP Exercises

- Plank
- Pull-up/chin-up
- Push-up
- Jump rope
- Barefoot running on uneven surface
- Kettlebell or dumbbell goblet squat
- Kettlebell get-up
- Kettlebell sumo deadlift
- Kettlebell swing
- Side-step swing
- Triple extension kettlebell swing
- Farmer's walk (single side)
- Bottom-up racked kettlebell walk
- Waiter's walk
- Kettlebell or dumbbell "batwing" (bench row for rhomboids) or TRX® body row
- One-arm dumbbell or kettlebell bench or floor press (the free hand is not holding on to anything)

Here is why: The plank teaches the essential skill of bracing and strengthens the midsection.

In the majority of athletic movements, the spine does not move, and the back and waist muscles do not generate power but stiffen up the spine and turn the torso into a "transmission" for passing force through the body—for instance, from the feet to the hands. This "tranny" must be stiff in order to maximize the transfer of force and protect the back. The plank is the first step in teaching and testing this ability.

Here is a stronger way to plank, as explained by physiologist Bret Contreras:

> *A while back, a colleague of mine named Joe Sansalone taught me how to do an RKC plank. Basically, he had me get into my normal plank position, and then made adjustments. First, he had me place my elbows slightly further out in front of me and closer together to increase the lever arm length and reduce the width of the base of support. He then had me forcefully lock out my knees by contracting my quads. Finally, he had me contract my glutes as hard as possible to the point where my pelvis posteriorly rotated. These adjustments left me quivering like a schoolgirl. I highly recommend experimenting with this new variation, as it blows away the core activation of a normal plank. (In fact, I suggest you stop reading right now, drop down to the floor, and try it for yourself.) Chalk up another one for the kettlebellers!*

Contreras took EMG measurements of the RKC plank compared them with those of the traditional plank. (An EMG measures muscle activation.) He discovered that while the lower back did not work as hard in the RKC plank, the internal obliques fired twice as strong, the abs three times as strong, and the external obliques four times as strong as in the traditional plank.

USAPL National Champion and IPF Team USA Head Coach Dr. Michael Hartle, Senior RKC giving "tough love" to Masters' IPF World Champion Doug Dienelt, RKC to improve the latter's RKC plank.

Although the push-up is as basic as it gets, don't touch it until the plank is on the level. It makes me cringe to watch kids—and adults—do "hungry cow" push-ups, with the lower back sagging and the scapulae sticking out. Gray Cook insists that stability must come before strength, and he knows what he is talking about.

Pull-ups not only build the "pulling" muscles but also develop the abs. I dare you to find someone who can do 20 strict reps and does not have rock-hard abs. Use many pull-up variations: change grips, do pull-ups off ropes and rings, etc.

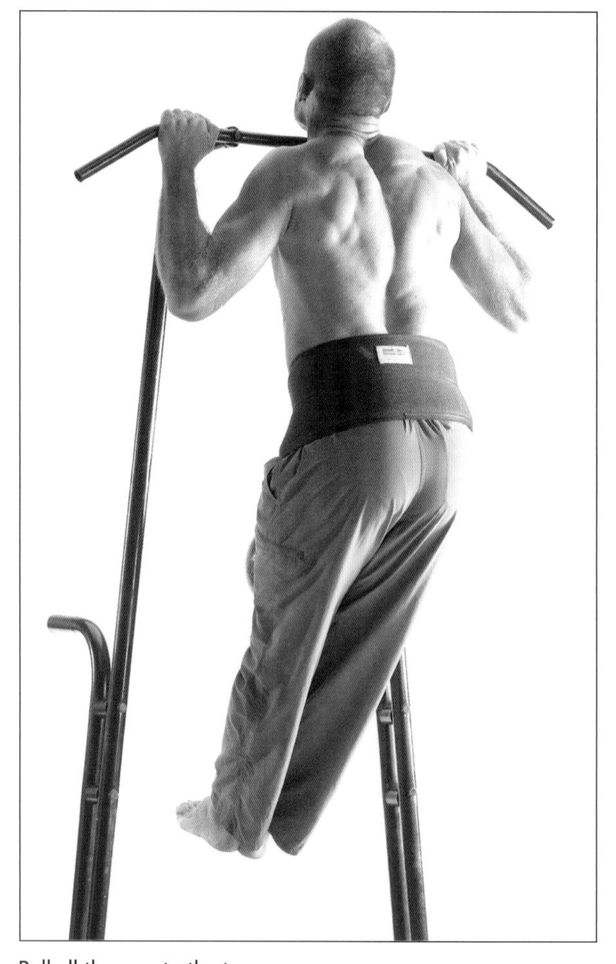

Pull all the way to the top.

Jumping rope will make kids light on their feet and prep them for more intense jumps. A few calf raises will not hurt, either. Professor Yuri Verkhoshansky explains the calves business:

> *If calf muscles are not the most important contributors to a high vertical jump, in any case, they are important because in the execution of vertical jump they are involved as an organic part of explosive legs extension movements in the last part of push up phase.*
>
> *The calf rises are not the main exercise for the vertical jump height increasing, but they cannot be eliminated in the training program. . . . The preliminary increasing of maximal strength of calf muscles is needed to assure the subsequent increasing of their explosive strength, starting strength and reactive ability.*
>
> *Calf muscles are strongly involved in the shock absorbing phase of run and bounces. The preliminary enforcement of calf muscles, before the use of jumping exercises, is needed also to avoid legs injuries (calf muscles strain).*

Running barefoot on an uneven surface will strengthen the feet and ankles and develop a natural running style. Vibram FiveFingers "foot gloves" and similar "no shoes" may be worn to protect the feet. Even if you are not a runner (and Dan and I certainly are not), Christopher McDougall's book *Born to Run* makes for very worthwhile reading.

In Gray Cook's instant classic *Movement*, he explains the benefits of barefoot running:

> *Self-limiting exercises make us think, and even make us feel more connected to exercise and movement. They demand greater engagement and produce greater physical awareness. Self-limiting exercises do not offer the easy confidence or quick mastery provided by a fitness machine. . . . The clearest example of self-limiting exercise is barefoot running. While running barefoot, the first runners connected with the sensory information in the soles of their feet. This works perfectly—this is the very reason the soles of the feet have such a uniquely dense distribution of sensory nerves. . . . The information provided by sensory nerves in the soles helps all . . . continually adjust their movement, stride, rhythm, posture and breathing to meet changes in the terrain.*
>
> *The modern running shoe allows us to ignore a sensory perspective of running that is only second to vision, and, as you know, the increase in running-related injuries paralleled running shoes development. When running barefoot, over-striding and heel striking is not an option—it produces jarring, discomfort and pain because it is not authentic. Is it not a bit peculiar that the quick twinges of pain refine the barefoot runner's stride to help avoid running injuries, while the comfort of the modern running shoe later exchanged those friendly twinges for debilitating pain? . . .*
>
> *Self-limiting activities should become the cornerstone of your training programs . . . as movement authentication—to keep it real. The limitations these exercises impose keep us honest. . . . Used correctly, self-limiting exercises improve poor movements and maintain functional movement quality.*

And if you add the requirement to breathe only through your nose to being barefoot, you will get an exercise that is twice self-limiting. More about that later.

K.C. Reiter, RKC II demonstrating a perfect goblet squat.

The goblet squat is the best way to teach the squat, bar none. Not surprisingly, it improves hip mobility. Surprisingly, it builds strength.

Dan likes to say that an athlete's body is "one piece." The kettlebell get-up is what puts the little pieces together into that big piece.

Senior RKC, Dr. Mark Cheng, is a get-up master.
Courtesy of *Black Belt* Magazine.

The sumo deadlift with one or two kettlebells will not only strengthen the hips and back and develop a useful "functional" skill, but it will start teaching the athlete jumping mechanics: stabilizing the spine and hinging through the hips.

The sumo deadlift is indispensable, a kilt is optional. Senior RKC Doug Nepodal.

The kettlebell swing introduces the dynamic strength component, further preps the kids for jumping and landing, and builds conditioning. The swing is as athletic as an exercise can get.

Master RKC Andrea Du Cane shows how the swing is done.

The side-stepping swing will teach the kids a thing or two about lateral movement in a safe yet loaded manner.

The triple extension kettlebell swing, developed by Master RKC Jeff O'Connor, is the last stepping stone before jumping. Once the athlete is competent at swings, have him elevate the toes and the balls of his bare feet on a 2 x 4. When he feels comfortable swinging that way, have him come up on his toes on the top of each swing. The drill mimics a vertical jump remarkably, both the take-off and landing, and teaches perfect extension timing—without the landing impact. Another subtle benefit: This swing style forces one to get a complete triple extension in a self-correcting manner. I anticipate breakthroughs in Olympic weightlifting coaching.

A young athlete coached by Jeff in the triple extension swing. Courtesy Jeff O'Connor

Single-arm farmer's walks will strengthen the grip, the traps, and the waist. Professor Stuart McGill is a big fan of this exercise, because it strengthens the quadratus lumborum—a pelvis-tilting muscle on the side of the spine. In his work with elite strongmen, the Canadian researcher discovered just how important this muscle is for performance and back health. And Dan dug out a study that concluded that QL strength prevents ankle injuries in girls, so we have a double winner.

Single arm farmer's walk.

"Kettlebell Goddess" and the bottom-up racked single kettlebell carry.

McGill also is a big proponent of the bottom-up racked single kettlebell carry, which lights up many muscles of one's midsection. So is Cook, who does strength magic with bottom-up kettlebell drills—like having a lady go from two to eight pull-ups almost immediately.

Overhead walks will develop shoulder stability while maintaining mobility. The kettlebell's offset center of gravity is of big help here.

The kettlebell lockout walk, Philly style, by Brian Petty, RKC. Photo courtesy Brian Petty.

The bench row or bodyweight row addresses everyone's weakness: the rhomboids. We do not recommend bent-over rows, as they are easy to cheat on and fatigue the lower back. We would rather fatigue our backs with something more useful, like swings or deadlifts.

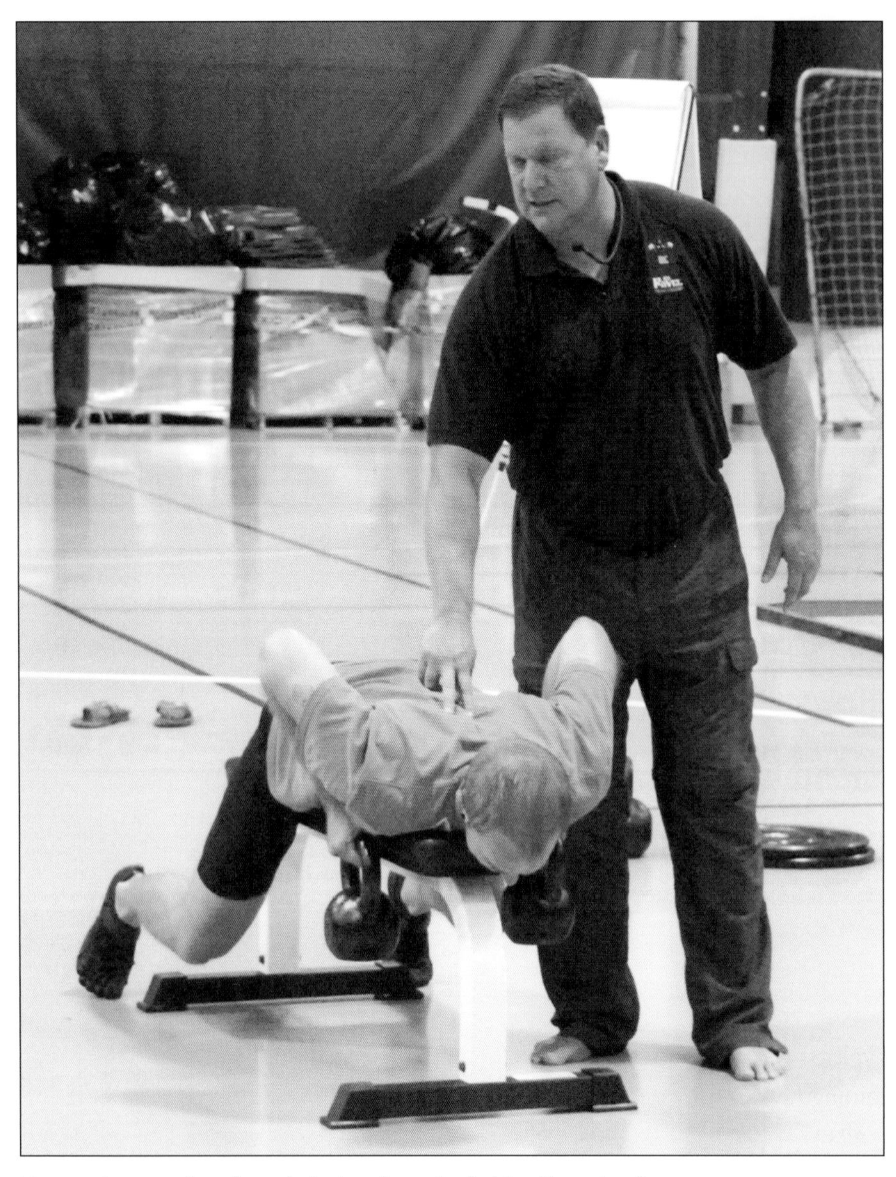

Dan putting a student through the bench row iso hold or "bat wing."

The one-arm supine press, Dan's favorite, will teach athletes not to flare their elbows in push-ups and barbell bench presses. It will also strengthen their obliques and teach them to root when benching. The free hand may not hold on to anything—this is the key. The drill may be done on a bench or, if you are in the field, on the ground. In the latter case, keep your legs straight and your feet shoulder width apart.

Senior RKC Shaun Cairns is doing the one-arm bench press under a stern eye of Master RKC Dave Whitley.

For the absolute novice and the completely detrained athlete, QI is the time to address qualities at a very low level of absolute relative strength. In other words, coaches and trainers must be vigilant in lowering standards to meet individual skill levels. Crushing a middle-aged man with a first workout filled with 400-meter runs and front squats may give him a ticket to the hospital or the morgue. And putting a younger athlete through a Marine Corps bootcamp-style workout might make the child swear off sports and fitness activities.

This is not an idle comment. My mother used to be a professional ballerina. She started training at the age of 6 and practiced for eight hours a day, in addition to doing her regular schoolwork, which was intense as well. (There is nothing feel-good, "Everyone is a winner" about Russian education.) When she graduated from the university, she quit ballet. She hates exercise to this day. This is typical of a great many Russian athletes, robbed of their childhoods.

Premature intensification, like premature specialization, does not pay off in the long run. According to Verkhoshansky, Soviet sprint coaches were guilty of that mistake for years. They were forcing the young sprinters' results:

> *This led to early mobilization of reserves possessed by young athletes which exhausted their capabilities and as a result, at 18–20 years of age, to stabilization of results in comparison to stronger foreign athletes.... The reason for Soviet runners staying behind ... is in the premature intensification of training.... At the same time it was established that on the beginning stage of sports specialization, improvement in the functional and physical preparation is the base for future mastery. With less intense but more varied exercises, not only was there no decrease in the level of increase in sports results, but it created better conditions for further sports improvement of young runners specializing in the short distances.*

In the beginning, a strength coach should focus on instilling in the youngster what Yuri Vlasov calls "muscle joy." If one develops a taste for movement and strength early on, adding intensity later will not be a problem.

Of course, this does not give you an excuse to go to the other extreme and treat your athletes like fragile wusses.

Everything needs progression in Quadrant I. A basic fitness test for general upper-body strength assessment is the one-minute push-up test. It is a good test and can be charted over decades of the individual's career. But with detrained and untrained athletes, it is wise to establish some kind of progression. The plank—an isometric position held for time—is ideal at this level. Ideally, we will build on this until the athlete can do much more with bodyweight than simply remain rigid.

An area often overlooked in schools today is tumbling. I have a short list on how to live longer statistically:

- Don't smoke.
- Wear a seatbelt.
- Learn to fall.

Oh, I agree that fish oil is great and a nice kettlebell swing is helpful, but these three rules will survive any hard look at the numbers. (I wonder what the Freakonimics guys take on this would be?)

Here's the actual progression I use in my class. After a basic orientation in falling and head position, we build immediately into this:

Tumbling

Forward roll from stand by SWAT officer Joey Williams, RKC.

Forward roll
- From stand
- With legs crossed
- Forward roll to a stand
- Cross-legged roll to cross-legged stand
- Roll into leap, turn, repeat

Shoulder roll
- Alternate shoulders in a series
- Shoulder rolls without arms

Dive rolls
- Walk into a dive roll
- Run into a dive roll
- Dive rolls over obstacles (crouched people, mats)
- Dive rolls for height (within reason)

Side rolls
- Monkey rolls

Leapfrogs

Wheelbarrows

Squat hand balance
- Head and elbow handstand
- Forward roll to squat hand balance
- Walk on hands

Head and hand balance

Hand balance
- Cartwheels
- Round-offs

Dan demonstrates a headstand.

Don't worry about the names or the specifics. Just about anything works to build confidence and skill on the mats.

Now, just for a moment, think about how many skills are necessary to simply bring a ball up a basketball court and make a lay-up. Progression is king at this level. Later, we will discuss the concept called accumulation. QI is all about *accumulation* of skills, movements, rules, and body knowledge.

Since **QUALITIES** (with a big S in the plural here) are being addressed, it is important to really be free to open the vast closet of experiences in the learning of sports, games, activities, and movements. This quadrant epitomizes the goals of a generalist, and there are three important lessons here:

First, *exposure* needs to be used in the classic sense. I have often wondered if I could have been a world-class kayaker or saber fencer. Alas, no exposure. Ideally, all the winter sports, the Olympic sports, the professional sports, and the lifetime sports would be given their due in a QI setting. If it sounds like a tough task, it is.

Second, *exposure* in the more common usage: when a group of 100 normal people get together, one person will simply be faster than the rest. Moreover, although my heart might be set on being in the NBA, my height is set on being a jockey. The more opportunities you have to be exposed, the more honest the process of discerning what sport might be right for you.

Third, if the participants are going to move through their careers to higher levels of a focused single sport or activity, the skills and rules of learning a variety of sports and games will carry over in two ways: One, there are some patterns and movements in sports that carry over from one arena to another, like feints, fakes, and double moves, for example. Two, just for simple variety and recreation, it is always nice to have the skill set needed to play any sport at some low level of ability.

QI is about *accumulation.* If I could highlight the single-greatest error most lifting enthusiasts make, it would simply be this: They have no variety. I'm not talking about using the decline, rather than the incline, for your pec development. I'm talking about doing nothing except going to the gym, walking on the treadmill, hopping off and doing a set of benches, playing with a machine or two, and hitting the steam room.

This is far from an overstatement. The first part of the AIT formula is "Accumulation" and doing just a few exercises a year is the antithesis of what I'm hoping you'll adopt in QI. Accumulation is actively seeking and learning new sports, lifts, moves, ideas, and games. One literally "accumulates" a number of new training moves and attempts a low level of mastery of each.

Accumulation is part of a simple method of looking at training that someone simply tossed out to me years ago. I was told in passing by Andy, a gym rat of mythical stature in downtown Salt Lake City, that the best way to look at training is *accumulate, intensify, and transform.*

I never heard Andy's last name. (He might not have one for legal reasons, or if I found out, he would have had to kill me.) But his AIT formula is the clearest way to look at "all of this." And what is "all of this"? It is the thousands of movements, machines, pieces of equipment, and games that we could possibly engage with.

The AIT formula works like this: You should *accumulate* lots of skills and tools and ideas and movements over time. Then, when you decide to focus on a specific goal, you *intensify* your work in the areas that will support the goal. The T stands for *transform*, and it can be one of two things: (1) simply having the confidence to allow the work to carry over into performance (or the wedding or the reunion, if it is a body composition goal) or (2) recognizing that it is time to reassess your goals and move in a different direction.

This might all be so obvious that you'll just shrug your shoulders and say "So?" Well, as Lee Corso would say, "Not, so fast!" The AIT formula is a simply elegant way to look at training. For the parent, it is a reminder to focus on multiple games and sports and not to "go specific" too soon for the young child athlete. For the elite athlete, it gives some clarity about adding all the new "toys" that show up in our industry every year. It is also a fine reminder for the older athlete to continue adding new ideas and insights but to use some kind of system to ensure intensity and transformation.

It is a simple tool. So, simple, you might ignore it!

Growing up, I did this naturally. In school, we'd play basketball or touch football during recess. During PE, we'd play kickball. After school, we'd hit the local playground, with its monkey bars, swings, tunnels, and variety of other dangerous contraptions that I'm sure have been banned from most of the United States today. Finally, we'd go home to breeze through whatever schoolwork was left.

Then, as fast as we could, we'd regroup and play street football, baseball, basketball, and a variety of games like tag, hide-and-go-seek, and "one foot off the gutter." By the time I entered organized sports, I'd probably been fouled 10,000 times, caught 100s of touchdown passes, and, for the record, run into one truck—that was still moving.

In school PE classes, we had speedball, volleyball, dodgeball, wrestling, basketball, crab soccer, soccer, swimming, and a host of other classes. In addition, I competed in several sports at the interscholastic, community, and church levels. Like all my friends, I was exposed to a myriad of sports experiences and soon discovered that the tricks in one sport often worked well in another.

So, you get the point: We need to add some variation to our training. But that is not the entire point. The idea of accumulation is to actively seek out new training concepts, not to add some simple variation, and to challenge our long-held notions of strengths and weaknesses.

This is quadrant I. It is the important—and perhaps even decisive—period of a young athlete's training, when every quality is developed at a minimal level. Throughout a long athletic career and the life well beyond it, the athlete will be able to enjoy a variety of sports and games as both a participant and a spectator. Moreover, some of the qualities will actually carryover to the mastery of the techniques of the elite athlete. Ball movement, for example, is a quality of both soccer (football) and basketball, but it also applies to handling the puck in hockey. Lessons learned "here" provide a ramp for lessons learned "there."

The key to QI is the courage of a coach (or parent) **NOT** to drool over the apparent edge that a young girl or young boy has at a skill or game at an early age. Oddly, I now believe that the person who struggles with a skill will actually eclipse the shooting star within a short time.

George Leonard's work on mastery has been proven to me in my years on the field, on the track, and in the weight room. It is odd to think that someone's natural talent might not manifest itself for years. While the new mantra is that 10,000 hours is the secret to being an "overnight sensation," my experience tells me that the easy learner stops improving after winning that first medal at the Middle School Track and Field Jamboree. Excellence demands time.

Dr. Ed Thomas has made a thought-provoking comment that things went awry in Americans' physical preparation decades ago when sports got organized. Athletes started getting in shape for sports by practicing those sports. The rich tradition of physical culture, with its gymnastic apparatus, barbells, dumbbells, kettlebells, and Indian clubs, practically died.

The absence of physical education in American schools did not help, and the final nail in GPP's coffin, in my opinion, has come courtesy of our "nanny" state education system. The principal at a California middle school banned the game of tag and even forbade all forms of physical contact between the kids, including pats on the back and handshakes. No more wrestling, no more fooling around, no more childhood, no more strength and health.

This notion of GPP is often linked to something that we now call variation in the weight room. The usual idea of variation looks like this:

1. I'll add wide-grip bench presses to my normal-grip bench presses.
2. I'll do decline bench press in addition to . . .

My idea of variation is much more in depth. For instance, an off-season track athlete might decide, "I'll enter an Olympic lifting meet." By taking on the challenge of Olympic lifting, certain things leap out immediately: "Do I know how to snatch and clean and jerk? Am I flexible enough? Are my legs ready for all of this? Do I know how to use the hook grip?" After these simple questions, another whole layer of questions emerges about registering for the meet, registering as a lifter, buying a singlet, buying lifting shoes, finding a place to train, and on and on. Taking on a triathlon at the same time would probably be too much.

Ideally, these out-of-the-way challenges ought to be undertaken by young children. But if you try on another sport for size as an adult, treat it as a noncompetitive "activity." You cannot serve more than one master, but you can sure dabble in a few other events. V. Gorinevsky wrote as far back as 1922: "One may not be a universal athlete. . . . Such universality is amateurism." L. Matveev added half a century later: "This principle [of specialization] states that a focus of time and effort on the chosen [sport] is the objectively necessary condition for achievement of elite results."

This is an excellent point. If you are focusing on being elite, especially in a QIV activity, then forget all of this or really cut back on it. When you serve two masters, issues arise.

For me, like several other former lifters who've moved into endurance events, my body fat went up. True, I lost weight, but my body fat percentage went up. This led me to believe that a high-carbohydrate endurance diet mixed with an enormous amount of low-intensity training doesn't lead to fat loss but merely weight loss. The numbers don't lie.

QII: Lots of Qualities at a High Level of Relative Max

The collision sports and occupations

Recently, I stood next to a professional football player. Actually, I stood below him. I am 6 feet tall and wider than most, and I barely came up to his chin. Moreover, his shoulders were wider than most people's ambitions.

There are sports that demand everything:

- Fat loss
- Hypertrophy
- Cardio
- Power
- Flexibility
- Agility
- Balance
- Skill
- Size
- Leverages
- Tactics
- Strategy
- Joint mobility

And obviously, the list goes on and on.

Sadly, most people think that quadrant II is the area to train all athletes in. Self-coached people almost always get the idea that this is the place for them to train. "I'm going to do this and that and this and that and this and that and this and that and this and that and fail miserably."

First of all, this quadrant is nearly impossible to thrive in without having massive support. Professional athletes and American Division I athletes have food, transportation, trainers, doctors, and other support systems that allow them to train so many qualities. Unless you have these supports, reconsider things. Years ago, I heard that the reason the Bulgarian weightlifting team moved to doing more and more workouts a day wasn't the result of some brilliant, insightful scientific breakthrough. Rather, it was due to the fact that young men with nothing to do find trouble. The coach added more workouts to keep an eye on them.

In QII, more than in any other quadrant, the strength coach and the sport coach have to deal with the interaction of different qualities. One issue is transfer. For instance, extensive aerobic training has a negative effect on power, while absolute strength has a positive effect (at least up to a point). For a given sport, one must find the optimal compromise of strength, endurance, and other qualities.

Note that I wrote *compromise*, rather than *balance*. Balance is achievable only in narrow specialist QIII sports, like powerlifting and marathon running. In QII sports, like football and decathlon, it is a compromise. (I hope your compromise will be more successful that the one achieved by a Russian couple. He wanted a car, and she wanted a mink coat. They finally agreed to buy the coat and keep it in the garage.)

The other challenge to deal with in QII is heterochronicity of adaptation. *Hetero* means "different," and *chronos* means "time." *Heterochronicity* refers to the different time periods required for recovering and improving different qualities, different muscle groups, etc. For example, you will retain a good portion of your strength even after a month's layoff, but you can kiss your anaerobic endurance good-bye. This means you need to carefully plot recovery from workouts focusing on different qualities.

Finally, there is the interaction of workouts with foci on different qualities. For instance, a low-volume/heavy-strength session performed before a sprint session has a positive effect on the latter. Elite sprint coach Barry Ross adds:

> *To do the opposite, running first then lifting, has negative effects. The reason for that is the amount of footfalls. A relatively slow runner would apply force at ground contact at two times bodyweight, or more . . . at every ground contact! Trying to lift sufficiently heavy weights to improve performance after a speed practice becomes very difficult.*

The following two books by Eastern European émigré specialists will be of great help to a QII coach or athlete who needs to juggle many qualities: *Block Periodization*, by Vladimir Issurin, and *Science of Sports Training*, by Thomas Kurz.

Although the focus of this book is strength, not endurance, QII is a good time to say a few words about the role of *aerobics* in the training of anaerobic athletes. For the record, American aerobics is synonymous with Russian *general endurance*, which is defined as "the ability to perform work of moderate intensity for a long time with global involvement of the muscular system."

The S&C world cannot help being influenced by its ugly cousin, mainstream "fitness." In spite of ourselves, we fall for fashions and trends. For a couple of decades, aerobics was the best thing since sliced bread. Today, the pendulum has swung to the other extreme, and aerobics has been banished from the training of all anaerobic athletes and fitness clients. The former ditched it because of its lack of metabolic specificity. The latter, because they have figured out that short and intense anaerobic workouts burn fat better.

Surprise: A little aerobics will do anyone good. In Russia, it belongs in the regimen of most athletes, even one-reppers. Thus spake Verkoshansky and Siff: "It should be noted that cooperation between the cardiovascular-respiratory and motor systems is important for improving work-capacity, not only in endurance sports, but in all sports." They added that aerobic training like cross-country running "improve[s] peripheral vascularization and recuperation after intense exercise."

Russian sports scientists and old-timer American boxers agreed: An aerobic foundation allows one to develop a greater anaerobic capacity. Steve Baccari, RKC, one of the best strength coaches in the MMA world, recalls:

> *When I was boxing, there were some real old-timers still in the gym every day. Some of them in their early 80s. One of them gave me the following roadwork routine after I cracked some ribs. He told me to walk at a comfortable pace for twice the amount of time that I would normally run. Example: I was running two times a week for 30 minutes, so I would walk 1 hour instead three times a week. Because I was not doing interval runs, we added one extra session. When I was able to start back running, my wind came right back very quickly. Also I gained very little weight. He told me fighters from the 1920s and 30s did this all the time, because fighting back then was more of a job and they had to train around their injuries. They couldn't just take a month off.*

"To rest is to rust."
—Jack Dempsey

And don't forget that a well-developed aerobic system will allow a football player or any other burst-and-rest athlete to recover faster between his anaerobic efforts. That means getting gassed less.

Even lifters and other one-rep athletes have something to gain from small doses of aerobics. Hübner-Wozniak et al. discovered that general endurance training sped up weightlifters' recovery and allowed them to train in their sport with more intensity. The key, of course, is to take it very easy with your long-distance training. I could not have said it better than Dr. Randall Strossen: a strength athlete's running should be as "hard core" as a runner's "lifting."

Fighters and other athletes from sports that demand "conditioning" also ought to take their aerobics in moderation in order not to compromise their power and strength. Russian full-contact karate master Andrey Kochergin cautions: "Run, definitely run! Run, but do not overload the heart, the maximal heart rate—no more that 120 BPM." One of his protocols calls for running 10K twice a week maintaining the same heart rate at the finish as 10 minutes after the start—ideally, 120 BPM. (This is about two-thirds of MHR for a 40-some-year-old Kochergin.) The other is an easy 2K every morning. I view easy running as an exercise in relaxation. Learn to turn into a rag doll on your jogs, and you will see a difference in your speed and sport-specific endurance.

Final bit of advice on aerobic training: go "double self-limiting." Run barefoot, and breathe only through your nose.

Back to strength.

Casey Sutera, one of the fine young coaches I work with in the weight room, came from an outstanding Division I football team. They were taught sprint work, agility work, every form of lifting, and much, much more. Here are a few concepts worthy of note from his experience:

Attention to Detail

I love this concept. It is one of the cornerstones of the RKC and, to be honest, every quality organization. If there is one lesson I have learned about QII coaching it is this: It always comes down to the little things. The best of the best programs insist on the little things. For example, today we wear the blue tops and the white shorts. If someone shows up in blue shorts and a white top, we punish them. Why? Well, I don't know why. But I know this: Under pressure, under stress, we revert to our training. If any aspect of our training is slipshod, our response to pressure will be the same. NFL games are usually decided by five plays. Often, the infamous stat "Missed Opportunity to Make A a Big Play" that decides whether a team lives on the bottom or wins the Super Bowl. Big Plays come from luck, but it takes a lot of discipline, work, and effort to get lucky in high-end sports.

Shrink the Gap

I love this concept, too. Casey's program used it as a way to relate the idea that the athletes with the lowest level of commitment to excellence had to be brought up to the athletes with the highest level. That gap is wide in many arenas. The movie *Office Space* is a wonderfully funny look at the restaurant and cubicle world, but the same gap is evident even in something that seems wonderfully self-motivating, like elite team sports. I took this concept into the weight room. I began to look at our award boards and our "big lift" charts and noticed something interesting: Our championship teams certainly were present in the lists, but our teams during problem years were actually better represented!

I have coached sophomore boys (age 15) who have benched 385. I have had two deadlift over 600 and another do a double from the floor with a 315 clean. These are outstanding lifts for any age, at any time. But to win in QII—which is, almost universally, team sports—*everybody* has to be strong. To "shrink the gap," we looked back over our standards and realized that we seemed to do best when the bulk of the players were at certain levels. For years, I had felt that when a boy can clean 200, he is strong enough for any varsity play.

We changed the numbers around just a little bit, as we have bumper plates with different colors: the 45s are black, the 35s are green, and the 25s are red. So, it makes a very colorful day when we line the lifts up for the Big Blue Club. The lifts are these:

Power clean	205 lbs.
Front squat	205 lbs.
Back squat	255 lbs.
Deadlift	315 lbs.
Power clean and jerk	165 lbs.
Military press	115 lbs.
One-armed bench press	32 kg kettlebell (five right and five left)

Most people ask about the bench press. If a boy can clean 205, rarely will he not be able to bench press it, too. My numbers may seem low in some areas (deadlift), but they are based on my discussions with Ethan Reeve of Wake Forest (who has a brilliant "gold standard" for collegiate athletes). Also note that the weights are all bumper plate selections—the 165, for example, is a 35 and a 25 on both sides. It certainly makes things a little safer and simpler to monitor.

When you have the bulk of the team in the Big Blue Club, you tend to meet your goals. It is possible to shrink the gap by simply raising the bar a little for everyone.

Although performing certain movements should be part of a general fitness class for school-age kids, QII athletes should have some advanced training on the key lifts. QII athletes should have some exposure to both the Olympic lifts and the powerlifts.

The Olympic Lifts

The military press should be a standard for every athlete in every situation, but it seems to have been replaced by the bench press as the standard of strength. It is my "one stop shop" that answers the question, "If I can only do one lift, what should it be?"

The snatch has made a tremendous comeback as the go-to exercise for explosive work. Many large athletes struggle with the wrists on the clean. Also, some athletes are taught the clean so badly that doing the snatch provides an appropriate "cleansing of the palate" after this abomination of teaching proper technique.

The clean and jerk is such a tremendous movement! In my perfect world, all my athletes would master a perfect squat clean and jerk with 150% of bodyweight. We would do quite well, I think, on the field of play.

The Powerlifts

I don't worry about people learning the bench press, until I see most people bench press. Proper technique in the bench press seems to be a bit like Halley's Comet: We seem to see it about every 76 years. It is well worth the time to master correct benching technique.

This exercise is either worshipped or condemned as "nonfunctional" and evil. Neither extreme view is correct. According to master's champion discus thrower Professor Thomas Fahey, the BP and the DL are the best predictors of a thrower's performance. Russian full-contact karate fighters bench heavy and hit hard. I believe these guys get a lot out of the bench for three reasons:

1. Powerful legs and hips
2. Flexible hip flexors that don't interfere with power transfer from below
3. Very strong midsection muscles that link the lower and upper body

Address these three and bench away.

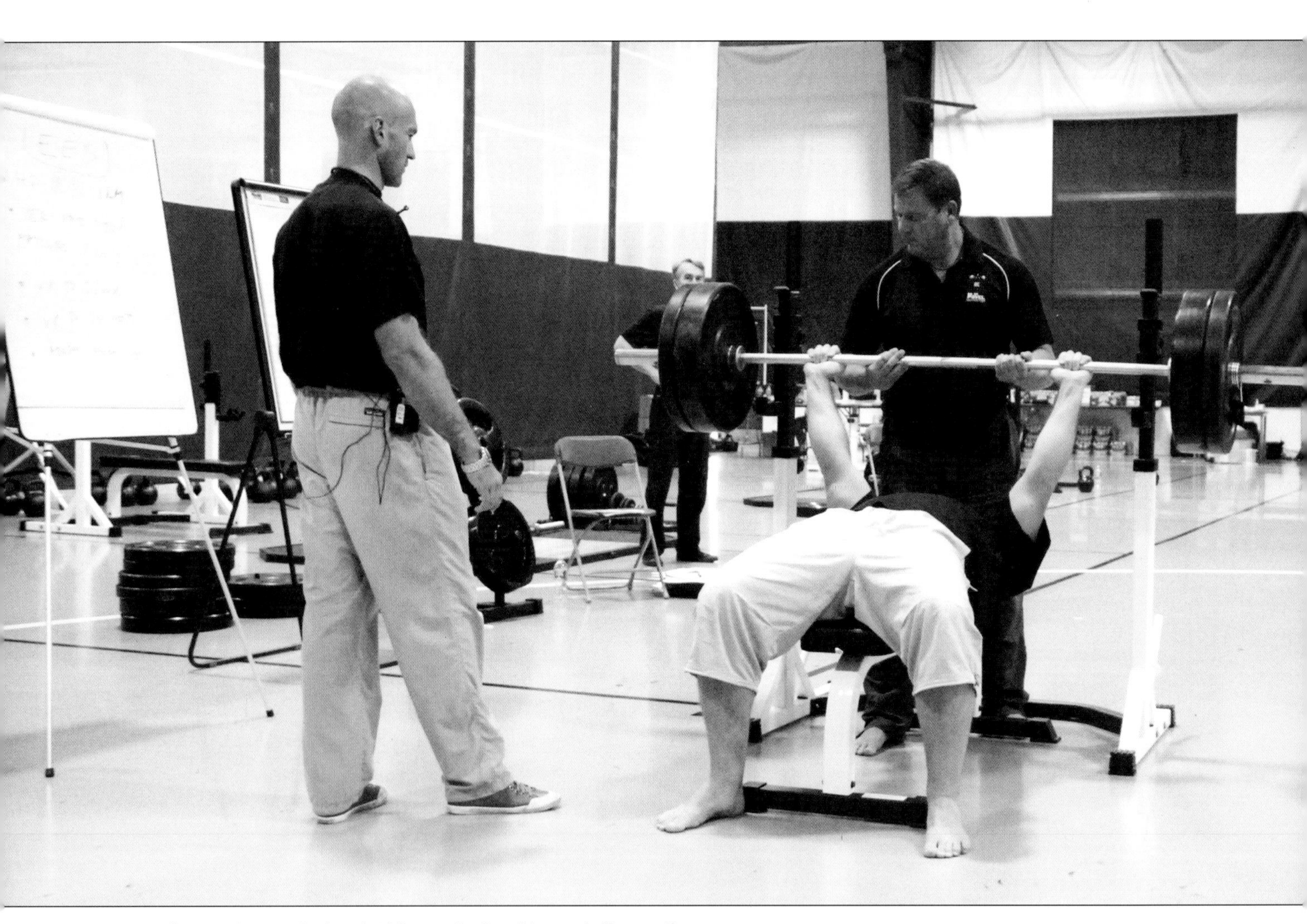

Shaun Cairns on the bench. This exercise is neither end-all nor evil.

The squat remains the most misunderstood and underappreciated movement in our pantheon of lifting movements. It's crucial to do it right. QII athletes can't afford to do it wrong—ever.

Athletes always find excuses not to squat. The most popular excuse today is "The squat is not functional"—whatever that means.

When I have no other choice, I lift at a public gym. A few months ago, I trained at a gym once known for strength. Not any more. The biggest "feat" I saw there was a 315 squat—by a guy who weighed about that much. It was a nose-bleed-high squat, too. Most patrons were busy doing "functional training." A dude was faking lunges. They looked like round-back deadlifts, because he was too weak to even stay upright and his bored personal trainer was counting reps while texting. A girl with too much makeup was standing on one foot on a balance board and doing rows with a Barbie weight. Horrified, I went to the corner and started deadlifting.

Above is a glaring example of functional training (FT) enthusiasts not paying any attention to what the Founding Fathers had in mind. Peruse Gray Cook's book *The Athletic Body in Balance*, and you will learn that the "balance" the author was promoting was a balance of development between different muscle groups. He was not referring to the development of equilibrium. The FT movement started with a great intention—to restore our God-given, fundamental movement patterns, like squatting, crawling, etc. lost to bodybuilding and machine training. Unfortunately, absolute strength was also lost—tossed out like the baby with the bath water, as people started doing circus tricks with laughable resistance.

This was never the point. All you need to do is look at the leaders of the FT movement to realize that you are doing something very wrong. These guys are strong. Gray Cook can breeze through a brutal RKC course that has been compared to the marine boot camp. Juan Carlos Santana benches close to 400. Paul Chek deadlifts almost five wheels, chins with either arm, and toys with heavy kettlebells. Sherlock Holmes would call it a "clue." Even Inspector Clouseau might.

Stop your complicated weakness, and get strong in the traditional sense of the word. Charles Staley once quipped that while you are knocking the "functionality" of the bench press, you would not want to be punched by a 600-pound bencher. A martial arts purist might scoff that it would be a push, not a punch, but that quaint difference would be lost on your broken ribs. Staley also warned that becoming enamored by the visual similarity of an exercise to a sport or life task will prevent you from doing some very productive exercises. In his words:

> *Wide stance ... squatting is used by members of Louie Simmons' Westside Barbell Club in powerlifting competition. Louie refers to this type of squat as a "wide stance good morning to parallel." Take a super-wide stance (at least double your own shoulder width), and initiate the squat by cracking your hips and sitting back rather than bending the knees. Try to lower yourself to the point where the tops of your thighs are parallel to the floor when viewed from the side, without allowing your knees to travel forward at all. This will be difficult at first, but as your adductor length improves,*

you'll eventually be able to do it. Focus on sitting back and pushing the knees out to the sides as you descend, keeping a neutral spine throughout.

This exercise is a great lesson in true functionality. While it does not outwardly resemble anything you'd normally do in sport or life, such as jumping, kicking, or running, in truth, it can improve your functioning in all of these skills . . . because the wide-stance squat promotes insane levels of strength in what kinesiologists call the "posterior chain," meaning the lower back, glute, hamstring muscles—the same ones that propel you in the activities just mentioned.

I am convinced that any athlete who tells me "Deadlifts make my back hurt" is missing something. What it is, I don't always know, but if this basic human movement is hurting the athlete, I really like to find the underlying cause. Is it movement issues? A CK–FMS (Certified Kettlebell–Functional Movement Specialist) screen and some correctives might be a simple way to address this quickly. Is it technical? If it is, it is important to reconsider the whole training process leading up to the hurtful deadlifts.

Although I joke about it, hurtful deadlifts indicate an issue. It could be one person in a program or an epidemic, but you still need to address it.

I have sung many praises to the deadlift, so I will not be redundant.

Brian Petty, RKC and the deadlift. If you are not deadlifting, you are not training.

Also, I can't imagine a press, pull, squat, or machine movement that would not need some exposure to the QII athlete. Your "quiver" of exercises has to be full, since "one size doesn't fit all" at the elite level of QII. You need to know a lot of things yet still have a basic philosophy.

Not long ago, an Internet guru noted that he could make D-I football players "a lot stronger." It was obvious from reading his work that either he was joking or he's a fool. When discussing athletes who are 6' 3", run the 40 in 4.4, bench 225 for 30-plus reps, and have a vertical jump around 40 inches, it's a fantasy, at best, to think that a simple tweak is going to make a difference. Yes, you can improve these athletes, but you had better be very, very good and very focused on one quality.

As you get into the powerlifts, Olympic lifts, and kettlebell lifts in QII, you need to remember one thing: "*There is a difference between lifting more and actually getting stronger.*"

These fighting words belong to Arthur Jones, not the Nautilus founder but a powerlifter who benched 563 pounds raw in the 242-pound class at the AAU Worlds. How can you lift more without getting stronger? By developing event-specific tricks. Sticking with the bench press example, an extreme arch would enable you to score a bigger lift. But if you are not a competing powerlifter and bench for some other sport—say, shot put—what is the point?

Sometimes, one has to modify the classic lifts of a given iron sport—PL, WL, or GS—to suit one's needs. For example, the Olympic barbell snatch builds great explosive power but requires a very long time to master and has at least two risky elements that are hard to justify for an athlete who is not a weightlifter. The two dangers are dropping into a full squat with a heavy barbell overhead, a skill with no margin for error, and using a wide grip that is hard on the shoulders. Did you know that after a snatch, weightlifting immortal David Rigert would toss the barbell up to bring his hands closer together before lowering it to spare his shoulders?

Russian athletes who are not weightlifters avoid the pitfalls of the classic snatch by switching to a narrower, clean, grip and not second dipping their knees at all. You get all the benefits with a much simpler and safer technique. You are forced to use a much lighter weight, but does that matter if you are a hockey player? Are you out to get stronger or to lift more weight?

Another example, this time from powerlifting: The deadlift is a terrific exercise for almost any athlete, but Russian wrestlers like to make it even more extreme and specific to their needs. That is why Alexander Karelin has worked up to an incredible ten 10 reps with 440 pounds in the Zercher deadlift. In the ZDL, the bar is held in the crooks of your elbows, which means you have to bend way over and be in a very awkward position—like wrestling.

The same logic applies to the *girevoy* sport. US Secret Service instructors did not like the traditional GS snatch requirement of switching hands only once during the attempt, as it prevented recruits and agents from going all out. The grip gave out before the lungs. Teaching the personnel kettlebell sport grip-sparing tricks made no sense. How does one justify taking time away from tactical skills to practice sport-specific techniques?

Counterterrorists are not interested in GS ranks; they are after the killer conditioning the kettlebell brings. So, the USSS kept the 10-minute attempt but allowed their operators to switch hands at any time and as many times as they chose and even to set the kettlebell down. Brilliant.

The test is as hard as one wants to make it. The top guys have no time to set the bell down, and the USSS record is in the high 200s, the total of both arms. The best-conditioned operators actively throw the kettlebell down to up their pace and greatly increase the difficulty of the snatch further. Yet by allowing the kettlebell to be parked, the test also becomes a gut check for less-conditioned recruits. One might only be able to do 25 + 25 snatches, abiding by the GS rules; now he has to suffer the full 10 minutes and do over 100 reps.

And you will still train your grip, don't you worry. The USSS snatch record holder laughed, "I am totally amazed by those that are claiming that a 10-minute snatch test is EASY! It doesn't test grip strength? Are you kidding me! After my last 10-minute ride with the devil, I couldn't even open up my hands for at least 10 minutes."

The USSS Kettlebell Snatch Test is a perfect example of intelligently adapting the tools of a strength sport to one's needs, rather than blindly copying them.

One must answer two questions when choosing an exercise for one's S&C regimen is: Is it simple to learn? Are there simpler ways to get comparable benefits? Verkhoshansky warns: "It is necessary to point out the ... mistakes in using strength means in special physical preparation.... Sometimes coaches simply mechanically copy the means and methods used in weightlifting or another sport rather than develop specialized exercises."

Do not confuse the means with the goal.

Who's Next?

Finally, a not-so-nice point: In QII, if you don't cut it, you're cut. Team sports are always looking for someone faster, bigger, and better. It's not just a Hollywood movie cliché—it's the reality of team sports.

The raging popularity of MMA and UFC has made many people believe that the way to fight is to work on everything all the time. Guys are racing marathons, doing yoga, learning the O lifts, and doing every feasible bodybuilding move. But they aren't getting on the mats. And when they do, they get schooled. The fighting arts probably have many built-in qualities, but to get them, you should be on the mat.

These guys who try to "prepare for everything" remind me of the Russian who leaves both a glass with water and an empty glass by his bed: the former, in case he wants a drink in the middle of the night, and the latter, in case he does not.

Contrast this attitude with the extreme minimalism of Steve Baccari's strength programs for fighters, which leads us straight into to the next quadrant: QIII.

The Hotel Workout

By Steve Baccari, RKC

Steve Baccari, RKC and Joe Lauzon back stage at UFC118 minutes before Steve's fighter stole the show. Photo courtesy Steve Baccari

The following workout is three exercises. They can be done in a slow circuit—which I'll explain later—or you can practice them one at a time.

Exercise 1: Stationary Handstand

1. Place your palms flat on the floor about a foot away from the wall.
2. Kick one leg up, then the other—until you're holding yourself in a handstand against the wall. Do not attempt a push-up; just maintain a stationary hold.
3. Stay in the position for as long as you can. Count slowly. A 10-count will feel like forever.
4. Breathe naturally and focus on the muscles in your shoulders and arms.
5. Come down slowly.

Note: This exercise is not only great for your entire upper body, but it also helps with your internal organs and bloodflow to your brain.

Exercise 2: Box Pistol

This is basically a one-legged squat from a chair.

1. Sit in a regular chair: one foot flat on the floor, knee bent at 90 degrees. Put your other leg straight out, and reach forward with your arms. Press all your weight on the heel of the foot that's on the floor, and stand up.
2. Slowly sit back down, and alternate legs. Do 3 to 5 reps per leg.

Exercise 3: Wall Walk

1. Stand with your back and heels flat against the wall.
2. Take two steps out, heel to toe, until you are 3 feet away from the wall.
3. Lean back with your hands stretched over your head until they hit the wall.
4. Slowly move your hands down the wall. Continue "walking" until your head lightly touches the floor.
5. Turn onto your side, and stand up. Do not try to walk back up the wall.

A couple of tips:

- Breathe naturally; do not hold your breath.
- Put a couple of pillows on the floor in case you lose it on the way down.

How to Do a Slow Strength Circuit

Perform exercise 1 (stationary handstand), exercise 2 (box pistol), and exercise 3 (wall walk) once. This is one trip through the circuit. Rest 3 to 5 minutes—longer, if you need to. Then make another trip through the circuit. Do 3 to 5 trips, and you're done.

Rule of thumb: Limit the amount of fatigue so that you can focus more on generating tension during each exercise.

Last rule: You can perform the same workout every day; you just have to vary the intensity. For instance, on your handstand holds, if you hold for 10 seconds one day, hold for 2 seconds the next day. With the pistols, you can do sets of 3 one day and sets of 5 the following day. With the wall walks, you can do more than one. Have a 100% effort day, followed by a 70% effort day, followed by a 50%, and then back to a 100% day.

QIII: Few Qualities at a Low or Moderate Level of Relative Max

Where most people are in life and sports: a simple yin-yang relationship between strength training and the goal in question

"If everything is a priority, then nothing is a priority."
—Rob Lawrence

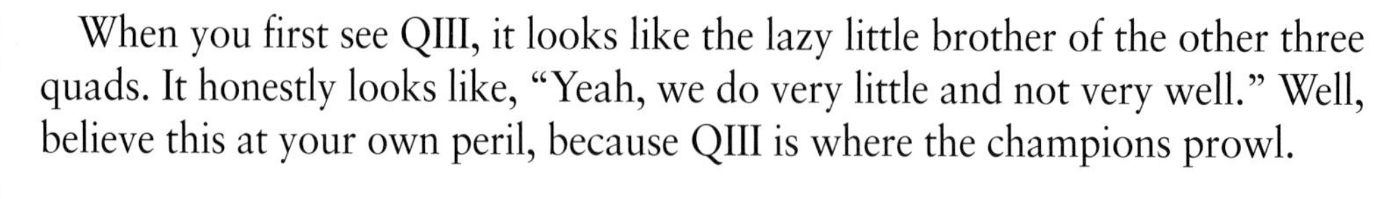

When you first see QIII, it looks like the lazy little brother of the other three quads. It honestly looks like, "Yeah, we do very little and not very well." Well, believe this at your own peril, because QIII is where the champions prowl.

Having the courage to focus on a few qualities is rare in sport, and as exercise-induced idiocy becomes more and more popular with the Internet, we can assume we will soon see the passing of QIII. Except that we won't. The great ones intuitively fig-

figure out that a high level of mastery in a few things brings extraordinary performance. The people I listen to in sport training, like Steve Baccari and Barry Ross, have figured out that you need to work on your sport. Then go in the weight room and get stronger. Rinse. Lather. Repeat.

This is the classic concept of yin-yang. As you get stronger on one side of the model, your technical base should improve, too. As you glide up technically, you should also be increasing your weight room lifts. Yes, there are those two small dots, where one can go into the gym and do a technical "shadow" move with weights or onto the field of play and do an overload—it may or may not help!

In QIII, the athlete needs eight types of strength, all simply developed with half as many exercises with a barbell, bodyweight, and a few kettlebells.

1. Real Strength

In the 1980s, when Soviet scientists measured the strength of high-level *karatekas*, they were dismayed to find out that these martial artists' strength was at the level of beginner track-and-field athletes. Since then, Russian fighters have learned their lesson. Today, no one on the full-contact karate scene in the former Soviet bloc is impressed with a double-bodyweight squat.

Strength will always be the king in sports. Russian scientists insist that it is strength that is the foundation of all other physical attributes. And don't let anyone baffle you with the argument that a weak fighter can beat a powerlifter. No one is suggesting that strength is all that matters. You still need the skills, conditioning, and other attributes of a warrior. But everything else being equal, the stronger fighter shall prevail every time.

A stale joke explains just how strong one needs to be: Two Russians were attacked by a bear and started running. One of them yelled, "Why are we doing this?! You can't outrun a bear!" The other one ran even faster and yelled back: "I don't need to outrun the bear. I just need to outrun you."

A fighter does not need to be stronger than a powerlifter, just stronger than other fighters.

2. Safe Strength

It is telling that the great sprint coach Charlie Francis removed power cleans from Ben Johnson's regimen because the athlete kept pulling the weight too far from his body.

No matter how "politically correct" a given exercise is in your circles, if it endangers an athlete, it has to go.

3. Strength Skill

There are two ways of getting stronger: by making your muscles bigger and by teaching them to contract harder. Some athletes can afford the former; some cannot. Regardless, both need the latter.

Learning to contract the muscles harder implies that strength training is a skill. A strength training session then must be viewed as a "practice", not a "smoker."

4. Easy Strength

"Lift heavy, not hard" is the motto of "easy strength" training. Such an approach allows the athlete to get strong without getting too sore or tired. We have dedicated a whole chapter to it.

5. Slow Strength

It is a long-established scientific fact that dynamic strength is built on a foundation of slow strength. If you want to jump high, you need to squat heavy first. No, this will not make you slow—at least, not until you become very strong.

6. Dynamic Strength

Plyometrics are powerful but also dangerous, if misused. Make sure to get strong before starting them, and keep their volume very low. Performing overspeed eccentric swings and snatches with a light kettlebell offers an excellent powerful and safe alternative to plyos.

7. Symmetrical Strength

According to the research of Gray Cook, a brilliant physical therapist and strength coach, asymmetrical strength and/or mobility between the right and the left sides of the body sets one up for an injury. Get symmetrical.

In his book *Movement*, Gray says a few kind words about my book *The Naked Warrior*, which I believe belongs in QII and QIII:

In the book, Pavel commits exercise book heresy by only discussing two exercises, the single-arm push-up and the single-leg squat, also known as the pistol. Since most people cannot do these moves, readers soon learn the book is about progression. These two exercises almost serve as a screen because the central premise is symmetry and movement competency with bodyweight.

I had the opportunity to perform a FMS [Functional Movement Screen] on the author, who at the time had never before heard of or seen the screen. His score was nearly perfect. Many people try to become as strong as Pavel but spend little or no time trying to be as flexible. The subtle theme suggested by his collective work us that good movement patterns are a precursor to good strength.

Obviously, one may have greater difficulty developing the push-up or pistol on one side compared with the other, and that is the point. Sometimes the best way to gain symmetry is to follow a non-symmetrical path.

Doug Nepodal and the one-arm one-leg Naked Warrior pushup.

Verkhoshanky and Siff's *Supertraining* offers another reason for such training:

Research has shown that the transfer of strength developed in bilateral training (e.g., using squats or power cleans) offers specific improvement in performance of bilateral events such as the squat clean and snatch in weightlifting, while unilateral training (e.g., with dumbbells or split cleans) enhances performances more effectively in unilateral activity such as running, jumping or karate.

Yet this is not an excuse to stop doing bilateral strength barbell exercises, as is fashionable these days in the "functional" circles. For athletes like karatekas, the powerlifts and Olympic lift variations were never meant to be SSP exercises; they are "big bang" GSP. Nikolay Vitkevich, a full-contact karate black belt and world-class powerlifter, clarifies the confusion:

You must clearly understand the difference between basic training and special physical preparation. Special Physical Preparation is different for everybody; one beats up on a tire with a sledgehammer, another does figure eights with a kettlebell, and someone incline presses. Basic training is roughly the same in all sports and aims to increase general strength and muscle mass. Powerlifting was born as a competition in exercises everybody does.

It bears repeating: "Powerlifting was born as a competition in exercises everybody does." And if they don't, they should.

Given the great number of muscle groups the powerlifts involve and the poundages they allow one to handle, the SQ-BP-DL greatly stimulates the neuromuscular and endocrine systems and makes one strong. Really strong. The sheer time efficiency of getting strong with the powerlifts demands that they be put on your list. I am not saying it is impossible to become an elite athlete without the Big Three—I am saying it will be a lot harder and you will have to spend a lot more time in the gym. "Strength is needed and the quickest and most available path to it is powerlifting," quipped Russian karate master and Spetsnaz vet Andrey Kocherghin, who is proud of his 462-pound deadlift.

For a number of reasons—including a favorable angle for the pecs and a modest stabilization challenge —the bench press allows one to handle a lot of weight. This translates into a great systemic, not just local, stress that powerfully stimulates muscle and strength gains in the upper body. And experience shows that great BP gains can be made with a very low volume of training. This is not the case for the military press, especially the one-arm version. Because the powerful pecs are almost out of the picture and a lot of effort is spent stabilizing the body and the bell, one cannot lift a heavy weight, relatively speaking. That is why the overhead press is a hard lift to improve and demands constant high-volume dues. The old Russian weightlifting saying, "To press a lot you must press a lot," did not come by accident.

The same case can be made for the pistol and the barbell squat, back, front, or Zercher. The former is a lot more "functional" for an asymmetrical sport, but the latter is a lot easier—in time spent, not in effort—to increase.

The answer is to train both the bilateral barbell lifts and the unilateral kettlebell and bodyweight exercises, although not necessarily at the same time.

Another type of symmetry is a healthy strength ratio between the agonists and the antagonists and between different muscle groups—for example, the hamstrings and the glutes. Narrowly specialized preparation usually creates heavy unbalances in the body. For instance, repetitive internal shoulder rotation destroys a swimmer's shoulders. And if the swimmer does nothing but swim, it will happen a lot sooner. A runner who does no exercise other than running will finish himself off as an athlete and a functioning human being even faster than the swimmer. You could ask Gray for details—or just visit a local race and watch the people who are moving in a spasmodic zombie fashion. (Now we know where they get all the extras for zombie movies.)

An elite athlete does pay for his titles with his health, regardless of the training regime. There is nothing healthy about repeatedly testing your body's limits—but with properly balanced strength training, the tab will not be nearly as high. Sometimes, finding this balance requires dedicated corrective exercises, but ideally, it should be achieved by intelligently selecting GSP exercises that address multiple goals. Kenneth Jay improved the shoulder health of swimmers on the Danish Olympic team by loading their shoulders in the opposite to sport-specific direction with double kettlebell cleans performed with the special technique described in *Return of the Kettlebell.*

8. Simple Strength

Steve Baccari has a simple rule: If 70% of his fighters do not pick up a strength exercise quickly, he discards it. You have better things to do with your training time than learn circus tricks. Find a limited number, two to five, of simple "big bang" moves, like barbell deadlifts and handstand push-ups. Practice them a couple of times a week, and make the competition take notice.

Mastery of the skill of sport takes lots of time and effort. The weight room can complement that effort. At surprisingly low levels of lifting, athletes can explode in their sports. And this is the danger of QIII. It is important to realize that increasing maxes in the weight room is probably easier than improving technical sport performance. The example I always give relates to my senior year in college. I had simplified my training to squat snatches, power cleans and an occasional back squat and bench press. I never went over 385 in the back squat for over a year (honestly, I was just sick of heavy training), and I threw over 190 feet. Years later, I drove my squat up to 605 for three (and limped everywhere) and tossed 184 feet. I know this is just one person's experience, but I have noted the same thing over and over in other people's logs and experiences, too.

QIII is all about balance. How important is cardio work to a thrower? Zero. Yes, I know health issues will come up, but we are trying to make a point here. Can six months of yoga help a downhill racer? Well, it is possible to become too flexible. Ideally, QIII, which probably includes the bulk of the Olympic individual sports, calls on certain movements in the weight room to be yoga-like. The goblet squat, the overhead squat, the dip, a proper pull up, bent presses, and windmills are all obvious choices, and other qualities will be inherent in the sport. An 800-meter runner probably has "cardio" covered. If you don't believe that, blast a 2-minute half mile and get back to me.

I have found that basic lifting movements, done correctly, are miles ahead of the junk most people do in their training. Combined with an obsession for technical perfection, QIII athletes can have long, healthy careers with a minimal number of qualities pursued.

This model may appear simplistic, yet I believe that Dan is spot on: "This is where the champions prowl."

An austere recipe consisting of 80% sport skill practice, 10% strength training, and 10% of everything else recognizes that the athlete's time, energy, and adaptive capacity are finite. One can always rationalize why adding some new exercise or training modality would help improving athletic performance. An aspiring powerlifter thinks, "I will work my calves so my squat set-up is more solid . . . I heard that the long head of the biceps flexes the shoulder, so curls must help my bench . . . I really should do some one-legged work to get 'functional' . . ."—whatever that means. Before you know it, he no longer gives it all to his competition lifts, saving himself for calf raises. This is "majoring in minors."

Consider the opposite approach: the QIII. Alexander Faleev dabbled with powerlifting for seven or eight years, then took a few years off. When he stepped back into the gym, he decided that he would not be content with mediocrity any more. He pored over years of his training logs looking for what worked. Then he returned to the platform with a vengeance and in just six months reached the coveted Master of Sports level in powerlifting.

Faleev has summed up his approach as "Nothing extra!" In one sentence, it is about doing only three exercises—the squat, the bench, and the deadlift—and competing regularly. That's it.

The system the Russian had developed for his strength and muscle mass breakthrough could have come out of *The 4-Hour Workweek,* by Tim Ferriss, RKC II. Among Ferriss's tools for getting the most out of life is Pareto's law. The essence of the law is that "80% of all results come from 20% of the efforts." Applied to strength, it means that if most gains will come from the three powerlifts, why waste your time and energy on curls and leg extensions?

Faleev stresses that doing additional exercises is worse than worthless. It is harmful, because it drains valuable energy that your body could have directed toward spectacular gains in the big three.

> *Get rid of the excesses and just do what is necessary.... When you give up the secondary ... exercises you will feel that you are not training enough. You will be leaving the gym totally fresh. This is it, the energy for an increase in the load in the basic lifts. This reserve is what will enable you to "shoot out of the gate"!*

You decide what you want: the process of enjoying the pump, the burn, and the variety, or results? Faleev walks into the gym, trains one lift, stretches, and hits the showers. Done! Since he dropped all the assistance exercises, his progress has been nothing short of spectacular. Ironically, his gym buddies who sweat for hours wasting time on meaningless exercises consider him a slacker. He does not care. The wily Russkie has the last laugh with his strength. As they say in Russia, "He laughs last who shoots first."

You might argue that everyone needs stretching, corrective exercises, a bit of cardio ... Fair enough, and all that can fit into the remaining 10% when you use an appropriate methodology, usually in the context of an intelligent (not to be confused with complicated) warm-up and cool-down. Follow Gray Cook's train of thought, and note my emphasis:

> *The physical presentation of differently trained bodies often provides a signature of the type and style of activity that developed it. Those who are exclusive in their activities seem more often be molded to their activities, and sometimes actually over-molded. These individuals can actually lose movements and muscles that would make alternate activities much easier.*
>
> *Some choose this path, and some are just victims. Specialization can rob us of our innate ability to express all of our movement potential. This is why I encourage highly specialized athletes to balance their functional movement patterns.* ***They don't so much need to train all movement patterns, they just need to maintain them.*** *When a functional movement pattern is lost, it forecasts a fundamental crack in a foundation designed to be balanced. The point is not that specialization is bad—it only presents a problem when the singular activity over-molds to the point of losing balance.*

Here are a few good examples of how to maintain all movement patterns from the training log of Master RKC Brett Jones and Dan's kettlebell warm-up:

Wednesday, July 14

Prep work—ASLR, arm bar
16 kg get-up x 3+3, 3+3
16 kg SLDL x 5+5
Behind-the-back deadlift
135 x 5
185 x 5
225 x 5, 5 [This is "even easier strength" training. Brett's best competition deadlift is 573 at 198 with a belt only—P.T.]
24 kg One-arm long-cycle clean and jerk
1 minute right arm + 1 minute left arm + 1 minute rest x 5 sets
Stretch

Courtesy Brett Jones.

Thursday, July 15

Morning session:
Behind-the-back DL
135 x 5, 225 x 5, 245 x 5, 225 x 5
Afternoon session:
Prep—ASLR, T-spine rotation
24 kg arm bar x1+1
24 kg get-up x 3+3
2/24 kg jerks x 4 reps at the top of each minute x 25 minutes
Mow yard
Stretch

Tuesday, July 20

Long-cycle jerks . . .
2/24 KG long-cycle clean and jerk x 5 reps x 20 sets
(1 minute rest between sets)
2# club swinging (20 reps of each of the 5 movements)
Stretch

I make a basic assumption before training an athlete (or anyone, really), and it comes in two parts. First, movements tend to trump muscles. I do not believe in an "arm day" or a "leg day." I think there are basic human movements that must be glided through each workout. Basically, they are push, pull, walk, squat, hinge (deadlift or swing motion), an explosive full-body movement, and the various rotary movements. Sure, they break down from here in vertical and horizontal and single limb and probably many more. But generally, I think we need to deal with these each day and certainly each training session.

Second, I think if something is important, it should be done every day. My warm-up progressions reflect this insight. Although there is a lot of "work" here, one can add or subtract the intensity very simply by changing the load or shortening the distance, time, or repetitions. Please don't worry about the terms, since often, they have little meaning except in a given context. (Ludwig Wittgenstein, I owe you that one!) The other day, I was told that the "tactical frog" is also called the "lion pose," but then someone else said that "this" is the lion pose and did a number of odd facial movements.

Don't worry about the names. Focus on the concepts:

- Waiter's walks, suitcase walks, heartbeat walks
- Light goblet squats/hip flexor stretches ("Make space")
- Planks (superman and one-leg variations)
- Bootstrapper squats ("Spread the load")
- Push-up position planks (superman and one-leg variations)
- Bootstrapper squats ("Pry loose")
- Horizontal shrugs ("Relax into the stretch")
- Maxercist rows ("Strength is a skill")
- Parked one-arm rows
- Alligator push-ups ("tick-tock, tick-tock")
- RDL stretches/timed push-ups/RDL stretches/timed push-ups
- Heartbeat squats
- Kalos Sthenos get-up series
- Swings and swing variations
- 1-2-3-Up goblet squats

Then, one set back to back of the following for 30 seconds:

- Planks
- Deadbugs
- Supermans
- Butterfly crunches

Recently, I have taken on a weekly free workout at a local park. The most important reason for doing this is to keep my coaching skills sharp. We do this warm-up in the open air with just one kettlebell each:

- Waiter's walks with weak hand (nondominant); then turn and walk backward with it. Repeat with dominant hand.
- Bottoms-up presses—Walk as far as you can. (With the 24 kg, I go nowhere!) Again, switch hands.
- Goblet squats—Get into the bottom position and make circles. Do a few curls, too.

- RKC hip flexor stretches followed by cross body lower back stretches, then a variation of the windmill, pushing the heart to the sky
- Goblet squats (Get into the bottom position and make circles. Do a few curls, too.)
- RKC hip flexor stretches followed by cross body lowerback stretches, then a variation of the windmill, pushing the heart to the sky.
- "Vents" (a Steve Ilg stretch for the toes)
- "Can opener" stretches (for the piriformis and the QL)
- "Tactical frog" stretches
- Windmills, emphasizing the straight back leg and driving into it
- "Scaps", or horizontal shrugs, push-ups.
- Downward dog pose (and move through it)
- Dolphin pose (and move through it)
- Elbow rotation push-ups.
- Get-ups to hips-high position.
- Windmills-on-high-knee drills

To make every exercise harder, if you wish, follow it with a set of 10 swings. And if you want to go even harder, make it 20!

You can learn this in a number of ways, and I'm very happy Pavel threw in that 10% for whatever the athlete thinks he needs to do, too. I've had athletes puke during a workout and leave sweat marks on the floor. After a few minutes of deep breathing and dialing 9-1 with my finger on the 1, waiting for the athlete to become coherent, it never fails to amaze me when little Billy will ask: "Can I do some curls (or lat pulldowns or whatever)?"

In the power sports, including American football and rugby, much of the specific training will wear down the athlete. Even in low-key practice situations, there are collisions. Add to that the immense amount of sprint work, and during the season, that is "enough. But like my puker, someone will say at the end of practice, "Coach, I gotta lift!" So, we end up again with an overtrained athlete, running on empty, building up for something else. There is no question that for an advanced athlete, maintaining strength is important, but it's probably more crucial to maximize performance in the actual skills themselves.

The yin-yang symbol always is appropriate. But watch out for the tendency to equate black, for example, with skills and techniques and tactics and white, for example, with lifting weights and all the other physical dimensions. Remember that skills and technical practices are work for the body. Repeating a drill or a play dozens of times is exhausting. It is sprint work. It is agility work. It is plyometrics. Don't add anything more!

So, when you look at the yin-yang symbol and the 80/10/10 rule, you are going to have a disconnect UNTIL you realize that practice is work! As one of my athletes famously said about this session, which I call "prepractice," "Coach, it is practice to me." It was a good reminder, as I

connect UNTIL you realize that practice is work! As one of my athletes famously said about this session, which I call "prepractice," "Coach, it is practice to me." It was a good reminder, as I thought doing drills for 30 minutes was just a good way to refresh and work technique. To my athletes, those 30 minutes of work was, well, work!

Err on the side of tactics, strategy, skills, and other techniques during the season or at the advanced levels of sports. Let me explain it this way: Many athletes do excessive victory celebrations when they score. But there is the rare great athlete who merely tosses the ball to the official or simply scores and jogs to where he needs to be. The explanation is usually, "I'm paid to score. I'm going to act like that is what I am supposed to do."

In other words, you ARE there. Act like you know it!

I find it ridiculous when an athlete spends 45 minutes on esoteric correctives, then half-heartedly lifts a baby weight in some sissy move. He has taken the worthy goals of health and harmony to such a ridiculous extreme that he has turned into a hypochondriac, constantly scanning his carcass for aches and pains, real and imaginary. I am seeing more and more of this type of behavior, and it is as counterproductive to athletic excellence as the other extreme: knuckle-headed heavy lifting through pain and a refusal to perform a minimal amount of joint mobility exercises and correctives.

Powerlifting great Dr. Judd Biasiotto.
Photo courtesy *Powerlifting USA*

It has been said that one cannot be healthy if one's goal is not to be sick. One cannot win if his goal is not to lose. An athlete preoccupied with his rehab/prehab and micromanaging his body will not have enough focus and spirit left to be strong. Dr. Judd Biasiotto, who squatted a world record 603 at 132 in minimalistic supportive gear of the 1980s, is a sports psychologist who has shrewdly used his knowledge that the nervous system does not operate in negatives. When a competitor of his would walk toward the platform, Judd would say to him, "Don't miss, Bob!" Of course, the only thing that the lifter's subconscious heard was "miss!"—which he often did while thinking that Judd was such a good sport.

QIII is about not majoring in minors. While QI and, to a lesser degree, QII are driven by the "Wouldn't it be nice to . . ?" question, QIII is about "What can I get rid of?"

In QIII, the strength coach must have a crystal-clear understanding of the Russian *principle of ratios*. According to its author, M. Nabatnikova, there is an optimal relationship between different components of preparedness (qualities) for a given athlete, corresponding to his or her sport, gender, age, level of mastery, and individual characteristics. Russian specialists have put forth the following seven rules for compliance with this principle:

1. The athlete must have enough strength to perform the techniques of his chosen sport.

2. The athlete must have enough joint mobility to perform the techniques of his chosen sport and the special exercises.

3. One must start by addressing the weakest link that demonstrates itself first during the performance of the competitive exercise.

4. The athlete must not have muscular rigidity and excessive tension.

5. The coach may not evaluate the ratio of the components in an athlete in the conditions of significant fatigue. This compromises the coordination, changes the ratio of the components, and makes it impossible to accurately identify the leading and lagging components.

6. The coach must remember the heterochronicity of adaptation: Different components develop and detrain at different rates.

7. The result in competition gives the final grade of the ratio of the components.

Russian coaches warn that overdevelopment of certain components may negatively affect other components; strength and endurance are an obvious example. Even if further development of a quality does not negatively affect other qualities, Russians advise against pushing the supporting qualities beyond a certain point required for elite performance. They do so for several reasons, one of them being efficiency: The body has only so much adaptive capacity. Why tap it with exercises that do not bring you closer to victory?

Note that all the qualities, main and supporting, need what Russians call a *functional component reserve*. This means having a little extra beyond what is needed in competition, just in case.

The second rule, "The athlete must have enough joint mobility to perform the techniques of his chosen sport and the special exercises," ought to be obvious but rarely is. Why are you snatching a kettlebell if you do not have enough flexibility to lock out? Why are you teaching a kid who cannot touch his toes the front kick?

The third rule deserves special attention: "The coach may not evaluate the ratio of the components in an athlete in the conditions of significant fatigue. This compromises the coordination, changes the ratio of the components, and makes it impossible to accurately identify the leading and the lagging components." Let us use the example of a boxer. There is only one way to evaluate his power or speed—in a fight. It would be completely wrong to attempt to assess these qualities after an exhausting 2-hour fighting practice—for the very simple reason that sanctioned fights do not last 2 hours.

This point segues into the professional approach to building endurance in QIII. Verkhoshansky and Siff speak up:

Metabolism is very specific to the intensity and duration of the sporting event, to the extent that excessive development of one type of may have a profoundly detrimental effect on another type of fitness. . . . It is vital to understand the metabolic specificity of each sport if any training program is to be effective and safe.

I firmly believe that many athletes are defeated not by their opponents but by their excessive and often irrelevant endurance training. If the amateur boxer in our example fights for three 3-minute rounds with 1 minute of rest between them, why should we smoke him with a 2-hour practice and the equivalent of 20 rounds (combined sparring, bag work, etc.)?

Not only does such training lead to inappropriate, not-specific-to-the-event intensity, volume, and work-to-rest ratio and metabolic and biochemical adaptations, but it makes the nervous system learn wrong lessons, as well. Practice brief efforts with a lot of rest, and it will adapt to concentrate all of its resources. Practice going the distance, and you will teach your CNS to pace its efforts in order to last. "So few recognize the dangers of a 'just trying to last' mentality," laments sprint coach Barry Ross. Our amateur boxer should not be saving himself for the twelfth round, which will never come.

Coaches rightfully want to make their athletes tough, yet few understand that there are different kinds of toughness. Who is a "better man": a powerlifter, a fighter, or a marathon runner? The one who is better at overcoming his body's unwillingness to keep going? And who would that be? The fighter usually comes to mind—pushing his body through crazy concentrations of lactic acid and all that. But what about the marathoner? He keeps overcoming himself for over 2 hours—even longer if he is less than elite. Now ask the runner to beat up a heavy bag, however inexpertly, for 3 minutes, and he will get completely gassed. The fighter will not look so pretty running 26 miles, either.

What about the powerlifter? Endurance athletes like to smugly badmouth (behind his back, of course) the big, strong dude who cannot climb two flights of stairs without huffing and puffing. Now consider this: A 700-pound deadlift requires an insane amount of willpower, fearlessness, and pain tolerance. An endurance athlete would not stand the chance of a snowball in hell of generating this level of mental intensity—not to mention of lifting half that weight.

And for the record, the powerlifts require a special type of endurance: neural drive endurance, the ability to keep up the nerve force for the duration of the attempt, which sometimes takes awhile. Steve Silver, a friend of former Coach IPF Powerlifting Team USA Mark Reifkind, once took 15 seconds (!) to lock out a 733-pound deadlift. If toughness means not giving up, this lifter exemplifies this quality. Such an extraordinary effort would have fried the brain of a mere mortal—or of any endurance athlete. Even a "normal" 5-second-max attempt feels like a very long time to a lifter. Endurance—like time—is relative. Einstein joked that a brief moment on a hot pan feels like an eternity. I have heard a full-contact karate national champion say that a 3-minute fight feels like a marathon. Don't knock a sport because its event is shorter than yours.

The bottom line is, toughness is event specific. It can be spread over hours and even days, as in the BUD/S Hell Week, or concentrated on the sharp point of a needle, as in a throwing event. I am anticipating an argument: Wouldn't you be even tougher if you pushed yourself in a variety of different ways? No, because your nervous system is not stupid, and it learns lessons from the challenges you throw at it. Whether you want it to or not, it will learn to spread the amount of toughness you possess over the duration that it is challenged. If you train a thrower as you would a Navy SEAL, you will compromise his throwing ability. You will have made him "tough" in some arbitrary sense—but another guy will win the championship.

Of course, this does not mean that you should never challenge your athletes' endurance beyond what they encounter in competition. "Hard in training, easy in combat," quipped great Russian military leader Alexander Suvorov. Yet the "hard" should still be in the ballpark, close to the parameters of one's sport. For instance, when Steve Baccari's boxers do running intervals, he tacks on an additional "round." If the upcoming fight calls for four rounds, Baccari will have them run five. But he absolutely refuses to stretch each interval longer than the competition rounds. He wants the fighter to maintain his target-punching frequency—read "intensity"—throughout the round, instead of learning to save himself for later.

Steve's exact protocol calls for three weekly interval run sessions at 70% intensity of an all-out sprint. He calls it a "comfortable strain." The lengths of the intervals and the rest periods match those of the competition, although walking around or easy shadow boxing is used for recovery instead of sitting. The number of the intervals exceeds the number of rounds in the upcoming fight by one until close to the fight, when the coach gets rid of the extra round and cranks up the intensity to 80% or 85%. One or two weekly 30-minute slow cross-country runs are a part of this conditioning plan.

By the way, why do so many coaches think that *supracompetitive exercises*, which impose greater than competitive demands, have to be longer? Why not more intense? In fact, Greco-Roman specialist A. Kolyosov has had great success with having wrestlers shorten their bouts in order to increase the tempo and the intensity while increasing their number. Russians have used the same technique successfully in boxing. Steve Baccari sometimes has his MMA guys go for 3 minutes, even though their competition calls for 5 minutes.

The above technique not only ups the intensity but improves endurance through building what Russians refer to as the speed reserve. Explains Professor Ozolin:

> *An important factor in endurance, especially special, is the "speed reserve." It has been known for a long time that if the athlete is able to cover a short distance very quickly, he will find it easier to cover a longer distance with lower speed. In this case the maximal speed on the short stretch speaks of a high level of development of strength, quickness, joint mobility, anaerobic capacity, and the CNS work capacity. Technical mastery also matters.*

This applies to boxing and wrestling, as well.

This book is about strength, not endurance, so we will stop here. Just remember: Excessive endurance training, aerobic or anaerobic, can make the athlete weak, sluggish, and slow. Don't fall into the common trap of turning every type of training—skill, strength, speed, and so on—into an endurance event. "You are weak! Do more reps ... Your skill is poor! Do more reps ... You are slow! Do more reps until you get faster." Yeah, right. There is much more to excellence than sloppy endurance, and freshness is essential for development of skill, speed, strength, and power.

Any idiot can smoke an athlete. But can you make him win?

Oddly, the game of American football, at the highest level, has abandoned its rich tradition of training endurance. There was a time—not long ago, either—when football coaches would try to make their teams "lean and mean" through various insane methods, including withholding water and doing long runs, countless windsprints, and drills designed to inflict pain. The problem with "lean and mean" was showcased in the early 1970s when one famous team's defensive players (we will protect the guilty here) were overrun by a running back who weighed more than any of them. Certainly, the defensive players had the conditioning to play several games in one day, but they couldn't stop an overwhelming physical force. Endurance training for football quickly joined the dustbin of history.

Training sessions should put you on the path of progress toward your goals.

I can't believe I had to write that—but it is true. The number of e-mails that I have read from wonderful young people struggling to find success in sports has clued me in to one thing: Most people haven't got a clue. The number of young Olympic lifters who have asked me questions about doing bent-over rows, improving their Concept II rowing times, and performing pull-ups has convinced me that most people don't ever realize that just because you CAN do this and that doesn't mean that you SHOULD.

The training focus I use with the athletes I work with comes from Olympic wrestling champ Dan Gable. He said, "If it's important, do it every day. If it isn't, don't do it at all."

I always use a simple scenario to clarify your answer to what's important. Let's say, for some reason, that you've found you can only train for a total of 45 minutes a week. Maybe you've become a political prisoner or something. You'll only be able to get in three workouts of 15 minutes each. What will you do? Think this through. This is going to be the core to your intensification program.

What will you do?

- Train your core on a large inflated ball?
- Be sure to stretch all your muscles so you don't strain anything?
- Walk on a treadmill and slowly let your pulse climb?
- Be sure to leave plenty of time to cool down?

If you answered "yes" to any of these questions, I'd suggest that you not read any of my work. Obviously, with only three 15-minute workouts, you're going to cut to the core of what you need. Here's the key: Whatever answer you gave in response to the "political prisoner" question is what you need to focus on during intensification. Yes, that can be hard. If your answer was front squats (not a bad answer, really), you're telling me that you need to take front squats seriously when you train from now on. Certainly, doing front squats three days a week is a challenge.

When I discuss this with throwers, they very often realize that "Throwers need to do full throws." Yet when they look over their training journals, they notice that very little of their training is dedicated to the full movement.

I asked a famous basketball coach this question a few years ago, and he instantly answered that the question ties into what he thinks wins games:

1. Free throws when you're tired.

2. Transition defense. (I have no idea what it means, but he nodded really hard.)

3. Make lay-ups.

Then after saying this, he smiled and said, "You know, I know this, but I don't think my athletes do."

If you know what to do, let's look at the million-dollar question:

How Do You Do It?

Here's how:

1. You can do the old Arnold trick: Work your weaknesses first in a workout, or work your priorities first in a workout. Either method will do. In this example, do the most important thing for your training first. I'd argue that perhaps twice a week, you do nothing but whatever lifts or exercises were your answer to the political prisoner question. My wife, Tiffini, has a one-line time management system: "If you have to eat a plate of frogs, eat the biggest one first."

2. Measure your workouts only by how you answered the political prisoner question. All the extra stuff is great, but it's only the icing on the cake.

3. Using the lessons you learned and the information you gathered during the accumulation phase, try to see if you're making improvements in the areas you found in need.

In describing their careers, people often say they have to be "prepared for anything." In my work with military forces, SWAT teams, police departments, and fire departments, I've picked up on little things. Stress-related health issues are the killers in these lines of work. As one officer told me, and I love the quote, "I have a gun and a car and a badge. Those three tend to deal with 99% of the problems in a career."

So, if you fit in this category, instead of getting caught in the spiral of being "prepared for anything," find one thing to improve over the next 3 months. Then you will only have to worry about "anything minus one."

Here is a curious aside for gun-carrying professionals. According to Hick's Law, the more stimulus-response alternatives there are, the slower the response time. For example, any possible move the suspect could make (a lunge for your gun, a tackle, etc.) is a stimulus, and any action you could react with is a response. The more combinations that are possible, the slower your reaction time.

There is an illuminating statistic that has quietly been around for a century and a quarter: Going from a single possible response to a threat to two increases your response time by more than 50%. And going from one response to three doubles your response time. You will be twice as slow if you entertain three choices instead of one! This fact may explain the popularity of Tony Blauer's SPEAR system in the tactical community. At the foundation of the system is a single reaction—the "spear"—naturally produced by the startle reflex as the response to any unexpected threat. It works. Very QIII.

Moving on from generalism in QI and QII to narrow specialization in QIII reflects the way human beings develop. Do you remember the many interests you had when you were a child? Aircraft modeling, baseball, skateboarding, guitar, boxing . . . What about today? What interests do you have, except, pizza, beer, and iron?

A young neural network is amazingly plastic and extensive. Synapses are budding everywhere, ready to service a wide range of new skills. Juggling three oranges? Here is a pathway, waiting to be opened up. Japanese? No problem—here is a groove. Just use it, and you will be fluent before your parent can say *"Mawashi geri jodan"*!

The incredible openness of a young human brain to learning a great range of new skills is called *neural exuberance*. It gives our species an edge in survival; we can adapt to almost anything. Dostoevsky wrote, "Man is a creature who can get used to anything, and I believe that is the very best way of defining him."

However, while a child can do or has the potential to do a lot of things, he cannot do any of them well. There are many pathways, functioning or ready to start functioning after a little use, yet none of them is really "grooving." Of the many synaptic connections, none is strong. The kid is an ultimate generalist. In a child, each muscle fiber is hooked up to multiple motoneurons, and each motoneuron synapses on multiple (more than in an adult) muscle fibers. As you grow older, the muscle fiber loses all the inputs but one. Other axons, which are command cables from the motoneurons, die out. At the same time, the motoneuron left in charge strengthens its connection and forms new synapses to solidify its control over the muscle fiber.

The process of training is similar to the process of maturation. The grooves that get heavy traffic get their synaptic connections reenforced and even form new synapses, something called *arborization*. Unused or infrequently used pathways shrivel and die out in the opposite process, appropriately called *pruning*.

The nervous system lives by the law of the jungle. Various pathways compete for synaptic sites, and only the strongest shall survive. It is the *law of neural Darwinism*. And the training of an athlete who has passed his beginner accumulation stage is a zero-sum game. This means that doing pointless exercises not only unnecessarily taxes time and recovery but also creates competition with the money lifts for synaptic sites. You have two choices: Concentrate your gains on your competition events and a handful of big payoff strength exercises, or spread them thinly over random acts of variety.

Balance is the sign of an amateur or a beginner. A professional does only one thing—extremely well. Listen to Tommy Kono:

> *The secret to Olympic lifting is quite simple. You are a specialist on the snatch and clean and jerk lifts, and not a "strong man" or someone with multitalent. If you happen to be good in basketball or track and field events without even practicing these events, that's fine. But you do not waste time and energy refining these unimportant areas, just like you do not specialize in extra-heavy squats if it was not going to help improve your lifts.*

Leave QI and QII behind you where they belong—in adolescence. Antoine de Saint-Exupéry was right:

> *Perfection is finally attained not when there is no longer anything to add, but when there is no longer anything to take away, when a body has been stripped down to its nakedness.*

Just do not interpret the above as the call to go to 100% sport-specific work in QIII. Extreme minimalism is not synonymous with total specificity. As Matveev clarified, *athletic specialization is narrow in its goal, not in its means.* This is why the best general strength exercises, like deadlifts belong in the minimalist regimen of a QIII athlete.

QIII does not exclude GPP. It simply zeroes in on a skeleton crew of the highest ROI general exercises. Dyachkov nailed it:

> *All-around physical preparation must not be ... unlimited and neutral. It must ... positively interact with the main movement skill and aid the development of special preparedness. Therefore all-around physical preparation acquires a clearly specialized direction.*

Bondarchuk added:

> *It should always be remembered that the GPP and SPP always form an interconnected unit. In some cases, the GPP and SPP may even be concurrent or the GPP may be largely indistinguishable from the SPP.*

So, there is only one rule in QIII: Do what you say you need to do.

Good luck!

QIV: Few (or One) Qualities at the Highest Level of Relative Max

The "rare air": The sport is so narrow and the level of competition so high that there is nearly total focus on one goal.

Unless you are chasing a 1,000-pound deadlift or really sneaking your 100-meter time closer and closer to 9 seconds, this might just be an interesting discussion. And it is.

The sports in quadrant IV are the least fuzzy of all sports. If something improves performance in QIV, the impact will spread to all other quadrants. If a drill or stretch increases the vertical jump of an NBA player or the leaping ability of a standing long jump specialist, it will work for everybody, everywhere. And maybe, that's the problem.

When you only have a quality or two, you don't have much to blame when things go wrong. As Andrew Carnegie noted, "Put all your eggs in one basket; then watch that basket very carefully." Coaching at this level is the realm of the best and brightest—or perhaps, someone who just got lucky and got it right. I believe in luck in athletic success like I believe in Harry Potter: fun to read and discuss, but I know, deep inside, it's not real.

The technical training and the specific exercises are nearly impossible to pull apart. We see this in the work of Anatoly Bondarchuk and the Chinese weightlifting team. There is a simple requirement that the coach be technically savvy AND an uncommon strength coach. Bondarchuk's ability to use weightlifting exercises as technical training and throwing movements as strength work makes it impossible for the outsider to see the difference. The Chinese coaches use their eyes to pick out lifters' daily weaknesses and then immediately address the issues with strength work. Having a lifter lift to get stronger has to be one of those concepts that is so simple to imagine but impossible to get across well enough to the unlearned masses.

To sharpen my thinking on the quadrants, I have done some traveling across the United States to give workshops on the ideas. As educators know, usually it is the teacher who does all the learning. As I sweep across from QI, with its fun and games and basic training approach, to the more-and-more emphasis of QII, most people intuitively think, "Hey, I'm a quadrant II athlete." At the end of the talk, I'm rarely approached by several people from the same sport who are begging for clarity here.

It's at that moment that a true elite will usually chime in: " You are so right! QIII is where the masters are. The unlearned play in QII." There's an old saying that "When the student is ready, the master appears."

You can quickly see that QIII is not very sexy. It is mat time and basic lifting for the martial arts. It is the ring and the deadlift and the press for boxers. For sprinters, it is quality sprinting and deadlifts with a touch of mobility work and maybe some box work. For throwers, it is lift and throw. At a recent workshop, a very scary fellow took me aside and told me, "These young guys, with all the fancy mobility stuff and the Olympic lifts and the plyos and the cardio on the rower. They think they can just step in and fight on the mat. They need to be on the mat."

QIV coaching and training is probably pretty rare. Years ago, Dave Tate entertained us in Washington, DC, but the punchline left me in tears. He asked, "How many of you can bench 200?" My hand shot up. Next, he asked, "300?" Me, again. "400?" I'm passing this test with flying colors! Dave then added: "The world record in the bench is now over 1,000. What percent is 400 out of a 1,000?" Uh, 40%? "Right," he said, "so a 400-pound bench sucks."

QIII can look awful when compared to the numbers in QIV. It also looks downright boring when compared to sexy QII. But it works. For years, Al Oerter, a four-time Olympic Gold Medal winner in the discus, trained with weights 3 days a week and threw the discus 3 days a week. He was busy with life but found some time each day to train. He didn't do anything fancy, but his success was historic.

On the topic of discus throwing, Dr. Tom Fahey once offered these numbers for someone to be strong enough to throw the world record and/or compete at the highest level:

- Bench press: 400
- Back squat: 450
- Snatch: 250
- Clean: 300

These numbers are modest—to a thrower, anyway. In fact, it wouldn't be unusual to find a high school athlete capable of doing at least three of the four numbers. Fahey once remarked to me in a conversation in Ohio: "Of course, once you get those four numbers, you just need to drive up your bench press and deadlift as absolute strength becomes the real issue." Good advice for anything, really.

The 300 clean is just a little over half what a superheavy weightlifter can do. The other numbers would all receive a failing grade in the classroom of lifting. But they are all pretty good lifts, especially for someone who iswho's also mastering a skilled technical event.

Honestly, it is a rare sport in which athletes won't be improved by a basic program of "just" lifting. QI was the "secret" of the 1950s and 1960s, when some sports exploded with new records. The cynics among us will scream "Anabolics!" but a simple look at the shot put record book will highlight the impact of lifting on the sport. Even though college football might demand a different kind of training today, all we have to do is leaf through the media guides of the 1940s to understand the difference that weight training has made on the sport. During that time, a guy who weighed 230 was often called something like "Tank." Today, with punters who clean over 300 and quarterbacks who weigh 240-plus, it is almost laughable to look at the bodyweights of some of the greatest teams of history.

So, "just" lift, but understand one quick point: *You have to move heavy weights.*

The problem with all the options in a modern gym (besides having too many options) is that we have no honest measuring system for the amount of weight. With the cams, the counterweights, and the plate-stacking systems, it is all too easy to trick ourselves into thinking that we are really moving iron. I'm not trying to brag here, but I went with my wife and daughter to a local gym and just went from machine to machine stacking the weights for safe, controlled reps. The max effort that you can do at this place is not really much of an effort for any typical high school athlete. So, you have to lift heavy.

Not long ago, Doug Dunagan talked with Brian Oldfield about his training. Brian is a legend in the strength sports—the first man to throw the shot 75 feet. Go ahead. Pick up something that weighs 16 pounds and throw it. If you measure half of Brian's effort, you are probably in the 1% club. Doug described Brian's lifting like this:

> *His lifting was done on Mondays and Thursdays and generally worked with 5 sets of doubles. On the push-press and front squat, he did triples. Sometimes he did 10 sets, because often he felt that his fifth set was the easiest.*

Lift	*Sets/Reps*	*Max*
Bench	*5 x 2*	*401*
Clean and press	*5 x 2*	*364*
Snatch (split and squat)	*5 x 2*	*250*
Front squat	*5 x 3*	*465 (500 single)*
Push-press/Jerk	*5 x 3*	*365–450*

Brian had a little formula that still makes sense: To add 1 foot to your effort in the shot put, you need to add 15 pounds to your max on each lift. Brian's workout was the same for this period: Tuesday and Thursday, he would repeat all five lifts.

Recently, Brian told me a little gem about counting reps for an explosive athlete. On a trip to Poland, he went to a local school and observed kids were in a PE class. They weren't just playing dodgeball, that's for sure. Brian watched the kids do overhead squats and count for each other: 10-9-8-7-6-5-4-3-2-1. So, Brian had the idea that for explosive athletes, the NASA countdown method reflected the real way we view lifting: as the launch pad for taking off! It's a small change, but try it. It really does work.

Vince Gironda said it best years ago: "It's not high reps that work. It's not heavy weights that work. It's high reps with heavy weights that works!"

And now, to really make things confusing, doing high reps with heavy weights is an issue. Here is the biggest problem with strength and conditioning coaches: What is their relationship to their athletes' goals? It's a problem because many team sport coaches expect a 1:1 relationship between weight room and sprint test numbers AND the number of Ws on the win-loss record. It is completely possible to take a group of athletes, drive their test results through the roof, and lose more games. Turnovers, bad genetics, poor tactical decisions, and just plain bad luck can make a team lose more games than their max deadlift numbers might suggest.

Barry Ross comments:

> *I would like to think the outcome would be close to the same in all sports and that the S&C coach would have greater impact. However, "extricating" the connection between the S&C coach and the event coaches is most often impossible. I've had too many athletes with remarkable performances in high school sink into mediocrity because the S&C coach will only follow what he thinks the head coach wants.*

A QIII approach to team sports is probably not bad, but its impact will be fuzzy, at best. It has been my belief since first feeling the iron in 1966 that this is going to be a journey to excellence. It is going to take some time—even for you.

In a recent interview, Stephanie Brown Trafton, the 2008 Olympic Gold Medal winner in the discus, stated this:

> *Fine-tuning the discus will take several years. You have to really develop a base for it, and then, after about 10 years of throwing, you get to the point where you're really solid in the technique that you have and you just need to have your little tweaking here and there.*

This insight alone will make most of us cry: After 10 years of training, you can go ahead and tweak things a little. Contrast this with all the hype that we read in most training advertisements. In fact, list the number of things you may have purchased through the years promising this or that in "as little as two weeks."

I have said the following about 10,000 times: Everything works. Everything works for about six weeks. In 10 years, there are a lot of "six weeks."

That's the simple reason I strongly recommend adding things to your training program every so often—just to shake things up a little bit. I have no problem with someone trying one of Ellington Darden's two-week focused training programs. Taking a minute to do a single dip or chin-up is well worth the effort, even if it is to simply discover how much intensity it takes to move a load at that rate of speed.

A strength coach cannot afford blind adherence to a single training modality. Professor Ozolin chuckles at the narrow-minded foci of the past:

- "Strength is more important than style." (1938–1940)
- "Technique decides everything." (1945–1950)
- "Isometrics is the best method." (1962–1964)
- "It is all about training machines." (1972–1980)

On the other hand, he cannot afford to be so open-minded that his brains fall out. Consider those trainers who are convinced that "Everything works" and "No system is better than another." Although any one methodology is limited, we still need simplified models in order to limit the variables we are working with and get anything done. For instance, although it has been proven that one can build muscles with high reps, I rarely prescribe more than 5 reps in hypertrophy programs, for a variety of reasons—one, being a reduction of the variables to juggle.

Bored with your training? Dust off Tom Platz's old squat workout. It's simple and fun: One day a week, you go really heavy on the back squat. The other day, you simply take a weight like 225 and do as many reps as you can. My best in the deep Olympic-style back squat with 225 pounds is 51 reps. I have heard that the record is 100 reps, not unlike the weight done by "someone's brother's friend's uncle." Go ahead, beat it!

If you are thinking that you have time to get your goals, you can experiment and try things that a narrow focus won't allow you to try. In my history book, called *My Training Journals*, I have found Nautilus training, bodybuilding, powerlifting, preseason prep for flag football, high-rep squats, triathlon training, and a host of other less normal ideas alongside my training for the Olympic lifts and the discus.

Once you have mastered the keys of your discipline, it might be time to begin the march up through QIV. What is the downside of QIV? Sadly, there is no balanced development. It doesn't follow the tradition of a healthy training lifestyle. It's brutally effective—but it's brutal.

Let me answer the question most commonly asked after someone has a grip on the concept of the quadrants: *Well, then, what should I do?*

Good question! If you are young (or a coach or parent of a young athlete or, honestly, any young person), dig your feet deeply into QI. Learn as many sports, games, and activities as possible. Experience the winter sports, the water sports, and all the games that populate professional and Olympic sports. Take a day to kayak, and find someone who can teach you to handle a saber. Try a martial art at the local community center, which is exactly how I learned judo.

If you or this child finds a niche in the collision sports and teams sports of QII, then climb up that ladder of intensity. One of the great insights of my career occurred when a football coach asked me if Pavel's *Power to the People!* (PTTP) program would work for American football. My answer was a staggering "Of course, but . . ." The coach never listened for the rest of my answer: PTTP is an excellent program, yet the football player needs more. He needs armor building, agility work, tumbling, speed training, and a host of other qualities. One final note: At some appropriate time in a QII career, move diagonally to QIII and simplify everything. I'm beginning to think this happens sooner, rather than later.

The hardest thing about moving up as an elite athlete is the discovery that you have to do so much less but all of it so much better. The PTTP template of deadlifts and presses is ideal.

Look at it this way: In your sport, do you need more absolute strength? Not all sports require this, by the way, and I'm sure we could chart it out in an interesting way. QIII sports tend to favor people with the courage to ratchet up their strength level the easiest way possible.

And that is *Power to the People!*. All the time you save by not doing extra work in the weight room could simply be transferred to mastering the key techniques or strategies for your goal or—and I wish I had known this when I was younger—doing nothing. Recently, one of the top US athletes told me that the numbers in the weight room were going through the roof and the performance was outstanding. But he also noted, "I can't believe how little time I spend training."

So, QIII training can almost "just" be PTTP. Few will have the courage to do that, but it would/could/should work. Like "greasing the groove," the program works so well that few athletes believe it is actually good enough for "someone advanced like me."

And that, in a nutshell, is why most people get stuck at a level for years and finally retire. Then, after a few months or years away, they come back to their beloved sport and discover they have lost little, if anything. At reduced levels of "training," their performance remains intact. Rather than mine their experience, most people tend to return to the old methods and end up tired and exhausted again. I'm only asking you to consider an easier, more effective way.

If this same young athlete finds success in a QIII sport, part of the job of preparing him for success is to quickly slide over to QIII and "doing few things relatively poorly." That's not true, of course, but the focus must be on the few qualities needed for the sport. John Powell and Ludwig Danek's axiom of "10,000 throws a year" is not hyperbole for a discus thrower, for example. I have a friend whose son is an outstanding wrestler, and he strives for 1,000 takedowns a week! My question was, "Who volunteers to be taken down that many times?"

Only a rare athlete will move up the ladder to QIV. A few sprinters and pure strength athletes may have the genetics to handle QIV. Honestly, most of us can simply stand in awe of performances at this level. Part of preparing this level of athlete is to add those qualities that will reestablish some balance and health (in all their meanings) to the individual at the end of his QIV career.

If someone lacks the background in QI or is simply interested in "feeling better" or "losing some flab," he should be put into QIII. Fat-loss programs involve only two qualities: adherence to some kind of eating plan and establishing some level of activity appropriate to support fat loss. Honestly, the program can be as simple as keeping a food journal and going for a daily walk. It can be made more complex, but that seems to help the profit line more than the waistline.

So, for personal trainers, you "should" live in QIII with your clients. The programs "should" be absolutely simple and repeatable, perhaps involving goblet squats, swings, and presses. Doing the basic powerlifts and some walking could also be extremely beneficial, as Marty Gallagher has proven with his clients. The problem, of course, is this odd need to be exciting and cutting edge and new wave and all of the rest of the nonsense that diverts people from the simple path of fat loss!

Kettlebell Exercises and Programs (and a Few Other Things) in Quadrants

Here's a look at the kettlebell world through the four quadrants. Remember, for most people and most uses, we should (as strength coaches) be directing them to QIII.

Quadrant I

Planks (star planks, push-up position planks, basic planks)
Push-ups
Pull-ups
HKC
Swings
Get-ups
Goblet squats

Quadrant II

RKC: The six movements

ROTK: The best armor-building program around

ETK: A balanced approach to achieving multiple goals

Quadrant III

Power to the People! (deadlifts and bench presses) for 2-week blocks

ETK program minimum (swings and get-ups) for 2-week blocks

Quadrant IV

GS: The sport of kettlebells

Viking Warrior Conditioning: If your goal is to increase VO2 max, this is a single purpose, single vision.

Barbell Moves (and a Few Other Things) in Quadrants

Here's a look at the kettlebell world through the four quadrants. Remember, for most people and most uses, we should (as strength coaches) be directing them to QIII.

Quadrant I	Quadrant II
General calisthenics **Basic lifting movements:** Power cleans Military presses Front squats Bench presses **Introduction to the sports of lifting:** Olympic lifting Powerlifting Girevoy sport Strongman Highland games	**Powerlifts:** Squats Bench presses Deadlifts **Olympic lifts:** Presses (even though not part of competition since 1972) Snatches Clean and jerks **Basic bodybuilding movements:** Classic strength movements Gymnastic and sports movements related to strength and conditioning (bar work, tumbling, hurdles and the like)
Quadrant III	**Quadrant IV**
Deadlifts **Benches or military presses** **Other lifts as necessary—and keep it limited!**	**Olympic lifting** **Single-event competition in the powerlifts**

CHAPTER 2

Where Are You? How Do You Measure Up?

"They can conquer who believe they can."
—Virgil

I hate to say that something is driving me crazy without any hesitation—especially something that many will argue has been going on for years. The issue involves youth sports clothing, of all things.

In Utah, lacrosse is becoming a popular sport. The club coaches, who make quite a bit from this part-time job, sell a great deal of equipment and clothing to their athletes. And, I notice, that nearly every single shirt has the term "Elite" or "Select" printed on it. So, it seems that if you have a deep enough pocketbook, your child can be an "Elite" athlete.

When I was a kid, real-deal athletes trained in old sweats. Team USSR members might have shown off their blue Adidas tracksuits, with the Soviet Union coat of arms, and the white Sambas with three stripes that every kid dreamed about at some social occasion. But in the gym, they were all business in cheap, worn-out duds.

It is amusing that because everyone is "elite" these days, they are so weak. We mention several times in the book that at some point in one's athletic career, adding more wheels to the bar becomes a liability. Comically, amateurish coaches and lazy athletes have taken statements such as the above out of the elite context and interpreted them as "Grinds are bad for all athletes whose sports require speed." In other words, they went straight back to the Stone Age brilliance of "Weights make you slow and muscle bound" and proceeded to do their "sport-specific speed training" with pink bands, because "Gym strength just does not translate to the field." Pray that this is what your competitors are doing.

Until you squat double bodyweight, rock bottom in a "no-no-no" fashion and put up same league numbers in a few other key lifts, you should have no fear. Strength will not make you slow. Just the opposite. European research and in-the-trenches experience on both sides of the pond show that there is no simpler means to drive a kid's vertical jump up to the border of respectable than pushing up his squat poundage.

And to continue my streak of candor, this has been happening for a long time. It has always been possible to get little Junior a leg up by buying him into a camp or club. Even something as simple as having more ice time can make a huge difference for someone in hockey.

Quadrant IV is all about real elite. It is difficult at this level to have a skill set that goes beyond more than one basic human movement. This level defies normal thinking. In the clean and jerk, a superheavy would need six big plates on each side to break the world record. In the deadlift, four figures must now be considered the target. The javelin had to be reconfigured to keep the spear in the stadium. There are few sports that a normal person can compete in with any hope of success. As I mentioned earlier, I know a 300-pound NFL lineman who was told he was too light to play.

There was a discussion about adding a fifth quadrant, but that had issues from a pure math standpoint. There was also an additional question: Why even discuss elite training?

I recently made a joke about something I have been doing for literally years that has recently become popular:

"Oh, really? Well, on this one, I'm on the beach. I have a cold beer with a lime in it. Why? Because while everybody else is trying to find the wave, I took the wave, rode the wave, had a pretty girl in a bikini pat my skin down and bring me a beer."

The issue concerned shoes, but the point is this: In elite performance, QIV work, if you are reading this now, you are looking for the wave while the "select" are watching you from the shore. So, why even discuss the issues?

Because.

That is a pretty good answer, but let's add a bit to it. I think it is often a good idea for self-coached individuals or the guys and girls who attempt to support and train each other to stand back and ask the big, global questions—for instance, What would it take to get to the top? Simply asking a very positive question like this has great value.

The issue of self-coaching has always been difficult to nail down in the strength and conditioning world. Quite simply, it's like we say about lawyers: The lawyer who represents himself has a fool for a client.

Although it is possible for an independent athlete to put together a solid training program and even learn basic and correct lifting techniques, the role of a coach should not be ignored. Even something as simple as attending an annual workshop or conference can be helpful. It has been said that the third RKC is the one where everything comes together.

Self-coaching is often a reality and a necessity. But where do you find the most important thing a coach can give you: constant vigilance concerning your weak points? If it were possible to provide a simple summary of "good coaching," it would be "constant vigilance" in addressing the athlete's weak points. As Master RKC Mark Reifkind once stated, "Train your weak points, but compete with your strong points!"

Strong points are easy to find. Just ask yourself this question: What are the things you like to do? Almost universally, they are your strong points! Generally and as close to universally as possible, you cannot hate your strengths. In football parlance, you need to "Dance with the girl who brung ya!" The fastest kid in the school probably wants to prove himself with a sprint race, a distance runner will define *health* with a 10K run time, and a strength athlete will want to talk about max attempts.

Your strong points may be so obvious that listing them seems worthless. But one of the secrets to long-term success is taking the time to honestly access what you do well. For a high school football program, it might be something like this:

1. All-weather football field
2. Excellent strength training facility
3. Solid six-year youth football league that runs the same basic offense and defense
4. Little turnover in coaching staff
5. Stable community, not impacted by highs or lows in the economy

That's not a bad list to build from as you approach each season. For an individual, the list might be more basic, but the idea is the same:

1. Fully equipped home gym
2. Member of a communally run weight room with powerlifting friends
3. Supportive family, afternoons free to train
4. Strong genes, family members in the NFL and Division I sports
5. Great levers for sport of choice

If the kid's sport is boxing, a "supportive family" means having an older brother and parents who buy the two of you one toy to share.

"Strong genes" and "great levers" have to be put in a context. A long waist that makes a swimmer kills a deadlifter. Long arms that kill a powerlifter make a thrower. Long legs make a kickboxer and bring down a wrestler.

Almost everybody could be a contender at something. It is just a matter of making an honest professional analysis to find the event that perfectly matches your body and your head. Dreaming to play in the NHL just because every kid in your northern Minnesota town does may not be the best goal for you, even if ice time does not seem to be a problem.

With this list, most adults can succeed in reaching their basic goals and beyond! Again, it is impossible to hate something like a fully equipped home gym; it is simply too much of a good thing!

Discussing your strong points may seem obvious, but it is well worth the time. Notice that some points may be missed, and we might simply take them for granted. An outsider's point of view might be helpful in assessing your list. Call me.

This, of course, leads us to the more elusive issue: what are your weaknesses. Like Inspector Clouseau might say: "There are 'clews' here." Success and failure tend to leave tracks, clues, and it is possible to sort through them.

Cleau/Clew/Clue Number 1

What do you hate? Seriously, when you go into the gym, what do you skip MOST of the time? It could be a body part, for example. That explains why so many lifters train wearing really baggy pants: They don't want to reveal their pencil-thin calves or thighs. You could also skip a component of training, or you might ignore a part of a game or sport that just gets under your nerves.

There you go: There is a hint here. You have taught yourself to ignore something rather easily, because you hate it. A good coach will insist that this is what you focus on! There is a rule here that shouldn't be missed: *This weakness must be within the parameters of your sport or focus.*

If an event takes less than 2 seconds, like a throwing event, then having the cardiovascular capacity to run a marathon won't help you. It's OK to be out of breath after making a world-record toss. Ignore this simple point at your own peril! Many losing teams have claimed to be in "better shape" than the team that defeated them. The correct response is, "So?"

In "better shape" for what? is a good question. You had better reread the last two paragraphs. An elite rock climber is likely to be pathetically weak in the back squat with this exercise's max poundage in the ballpark of his best weighted pull-up. As Wolff's Law states, "Function precedes structure." Rock climbers get it and like saying that an ideal rock rat has Popeye forearms, the lats of a flying squirrel, and the legs of a starved chicken. Aggressively attacking this "weakness" will quickly take the "elite" out of the climber who has gained the weight. He has absolutely no business taking on the rock. His best squat may be 135, but that happens to be enough to propel him up the wall. *This weakness must be within the parameters of your sport or focus.*

Cleau/Clew/Clue Number 2

If you are lucky, an honest, skilled observer will be able to quickly point out your technical and training weaknesses. There is often nothing better than "fresh eyes" to save you literally months of work in the wrong direction. There are gym rats and training partners with the skills to do it, but, with all due respect, most people in most gyms are as myopic about weaknesses as looking in the mirror. By the way, you will see pecs, abs, and biceps. For the record, work all the muscles you DON'T see in the mirror!

So, how do you find these skilled observers? For many, a camp situation is often best, especially at a place that might not follow the same exact method that you are currently doing. A multiday camp setting, with several sessions a day and many sets of fresh eyes, will help most people. Otherwise, clinics and workshops and even a private session or two might be helpful. Even your competitors might be able to give you insight into what glaring weaknesses you may not be seeing.

But you have to be careful about which feedback to take to heart. Marty's and Dan's insistence that I use more legs in my dead is something I listen to. The "Head up! Get your head up!" yells I get from the audience are not in the same league. While it is not a bad general recommendation and an element of many successful pullers' technique, it does not fit everyone.

Franco Columbu—who happens to be not just a bodybuilder but a 700-plus-pound deadlifter and a doctor of chiropractic—told me that he looked at a spot on the platform about 8 feet in front of him at the start of the pull, because cranking his head up would have pinched some nerves and weakened some muscles. Powerlifting coach extraordinaire Marty Gallagher told me that Hugh Cassidy used to look down when he squatted in order not to get distracted by the crowd. Some of today's top deadlifters, like Konstantin Konstantinov, look straight down at the platform to get a powerful start.

Smirnov and Dubrovsky explain that tipping your head down or forward increases the tonus of the knee extensors, thanks to a "pose reflex" originally meant to help you reach your food with greater ease. When you listen to advice, make sure that it fits the context of your particular technique and methodology.

Powerlifting legend Hugh Cassidy (center). Photo courtesy *Powerlifting USA*

Cleau/Clew/Clue Number 3

Assessments are both over- and underrated. True, little is learned during most annual physicals. Height and weight might indicate nothing, but an annual blood test might show how changes in diet are affecting the body. Many of the items that can be assessed give almost no insight into health issues or performance indicators. Often, the key factor that's missed is the assessment of the assessment.

A quarterly battery of assessments can be suggestive about performance. There is a video of German Javelin throwers measuring odd kettlebell throws, including one where the bell hangs off the toe and is "kicked" for distance. One can assume that an athlete that improves in ten measured kettlebell throws of various skills should also see an increase in javelin performance.

That's the issue with assessments: They probably need to be assessed more closely than actual physical test. Some tests—like the famous flexibility test called "the sit and reach"—are so easy to manipulate that any measurement that's made is probably more reflective of specialized coaching than actual physical ability. The 225-pound bench press for reps test ceased to be of value the first time it was implemented.

Russians test the potential of would-be javelin throwers with a small stone throw: any way you want it, with any pre-run. According to Olympic javelin throwing champion Yanis Lusis, "He who will throw the stone 60 m I will get a 'satisfactory' grade, 80 m will be 'good,' and the one who will throw 100 m or more could be an Olympic javelin throwing contender in 3–4 years of preparation."

The standing vertical jump is a great predictor of quickness in all movements, not only leg explosiveness. According to Russian coaches, 70 to 80 centimeters (28 to 32 inches) for young men and 60 to 70 centimeters (24 to 28 inches) for young women predicts success in speed-strength sports.

For athletes who have already reached the elite level, Russian coaches have *models of sport-specific motor abilities:* goals that give those still climbing to the top something to shoot for. For instance, the model for the Russian national gymnastics team includes climbing a 4-meter rope (with the arms only, of course) in 5 to 5.5 seconds, holding a cross on the rings for 5 to 6 seconds, and doing a 60- to 65-centimeter standing vertical jump, among other things.

Here is an example from another sport. A male world-class javelin thrower has a height of 185 to 195 centimeters, a bodyweight of 95 to 105 kilograms, a "wing span" of 195 to 205 centimeters, a SVJ of 95 centimeters, a bodyweight-plus 15-kg snatch, a two-times bodyweight squat, and so on. The women's corresponding numbers are 170 to 180 centimeters, 70 to 80 kilograms, 175 to 180 centimeters, 70 centimeters, bodyweight-plus 10 kg, and 150% bodyweight.

Evgeny Zagorulko, Distinguished Coach of USSR and Russia, describes a model high jumper as "skinny, mean, and strong." You will do yourself a favor interviewing elite coaches in your sport to learn everything you can about that model athlete.

But there needs to be ongoing assessment. The hardest part of finding weaknesses is the natural human tendency to find ways around doing things we do poorly. Many college graduates proudly acknowledge that they never took a writing course or a math course in getting their degrees. Athletes can master the same skills and ignore their weak subjects as well, if not better, than anyone. A naturally stiff athlete will have few flexibility assessments, and a strength athlete will rarely have a pull-up test as part of a quarterly assessment.

Improvement in quadrant IV is all about assessing and addressing weaknesses. To acknowledge weakness is simple to say, "I'm X, and I have way too much fat or poor hamstring flexibility." Dealing with this realization to the point that the issue disappears is a whole different story, however.

For the QIV athlete, the most crucial assessment is simply this: Is my primary goal (and my only goal) improving? At this elite level, no matter what is tried—no matter how far fetched—any improvement is **RIGHT**. A whole battery of assessment tools that all indicate improvement will be tossed out if the primary goal does not improve. Such is the life of the QIV athlete.

The QIV athlete needs to assess to discover weaknesses, and then those weaknesses need to be addressed. If, however, the primary goal, the only goal, doesn't improve, he needs to toss out the assessments. No, it is not very clear.

John Price—noted Masters thrower and member of the University of Washington's track program back in the day—often talks about a swim coach who gave him the key to proper training for athletes in the weight room. The key was this cliché: "A chain is only as strong as its weakest link." Price observed that successful athletes seemed to have some inner guide that allowed them to constantly hone in on this simple insight and find ways to deal with their weaknesses. For a power athlete, the tests listed below seem to have some validity.

But before you even try the movements, I strongly recommend having a full FMS screen. My first screening only took about 10 minutes, but the review took half an hour. Screening your mobility is essential, as those tiny compensations made for injuries really add up over time. If you are "locked down" here and compensate there, you are not only risking injury, but in addition, these compensations are inhibiting progress in your sport.

So, **GET SCREENED**, and then test yourself on the following (Thank-you to Wil Heffernan for teaching me most of these):

- **One-minute plank:** If you can't do this, stop worrying about anything else until you can!
- **Push-ups in a minute:** Note how many at the 30-second mark, too. Real power athletes will do a lot in the first 30 seconds but not so many in the next 30. If you can't do 45 in a minute, well maybe you need to do some push-ups.
- **Horizontal rows in a minute:** Again, note the 30-second number. Consider 24 as a minimum, or half the number of push-ups for most people.
- **A flexibility test:** I like the simple overhead squat with a light stick. Again, the full FMS screen probably has more value.
- **Bodyweight bench press for reps:** Up to 15. Anything more is just overkill.
- **Bodyweight back squats for reps:** Up to 15. Again . . .
- **Pull-ups:** Should equal the number of bench press reps.
- **A measured jump:** I suggest the three jump. If you can do over 30 feet, you are in rare air. Strive for at least 21.
- **A measured throw:** Anything is fine—med ball, kettlebell, shot, or whatever.

Let's pause and look at the wealth of information you can mine from just the first assessment: the one-minute plank. For the absolute novice and the completely detrained athlete, quadrant I is a time to address qualities at a very low level of absolute relative strength. In other words, coaches and trainers have to be vigilant about lowering standards. As noted earlier, overdoing things, especially early on, can send a middle-aged man to the hospital or drive a young athlete away from sports and fitness activities.

Everything needs progression in QI. A basic fitness test for general upper-body strength assessment that I have used for years is the one-minute push-up test. It is a good test and can be charted over decades of the individual's career. With detrained and untrained athletes, however, it is wise to follow some kind of progression. The plank—an isometric position held for time—is ideal at this level. The standard plank is also a brilliant means of assessment. By itself, it can provide the trainer with wonderful insights.

The task is to hold a one-minute standard plank. If the person fails to hold the plank for a minute, he or she obviously needs remedial work before participating in a more advanced training program. If someone can't plank a minute, how can he or she do honest push-ups for a minute? Remedial work should include the following:

- Various planks
- Various weighted walks
- Core movements of the Turkish get-up
- Sumo deadlifts with kettlebells

After successfully completing the one-minute plank test, the individual should be asked some follow-up questions concerning "Where did you feel it?" The plank test can give insights into certain issues. Shaking, by the way, says very little about the athlete's general conditioning or fitness issues. Extremely well trained athletes often shake doing the test, especially those who have mastered the use of tension in their sport.

After doing the plank test, young females and males with weak upper-body pushing and pulling strength often display extreme armpit fatigue. This is a simple indicator that can be cross-checked with later tests.

Hamstring cramping and fatigue is often an indicator of what Janda referred to as gluteal amnesia. Although many trainers will recommend hamstring stretches to address the issue, a much better course is to wake up the glutes with goblet squats and Bulgarian split squats (or intelligent single-leg variations), plus an introduction to proper sprinting techniques.

Quad cramping almost always indicates tight hip flexors. Having tight hip flexors is part of a whole package of issues: gluteal amnesia, a beer belly, tight hamstrings, and too much time sitting. Everyone—at every level and every quadrant—should stretch the hip flexors.

An odd insight gained from experience involves the issue of cramping calves. Usually, someone with this ailment has nutritional or dietary issues that need to be addressed. If you want to be shocked, ask a trainee for an honest two-week food diary. You will be stunned by the sheer volume of sugar and sweets. The hidden amount of salt in fast foods also produces calf issues, in many cases. By the way, this conclusion is simply based on the observations of hundreds of athletes, not hard science, but the evidence is there.

If the athlete survives the one-minute plank test, then we can take our time to honestly review the results of the other tests.

If the individual scores low on one test, spend some extra time on that movement. Ideally, that should lead to an improvement in that area, and THAT should help reach the singular goal. If it doesn't, it might be time to assess the assessment. There is always a need for general joint health and a certain intangible feeling of being healthy and most athletes understand it is also important to be able to get out of a car unassisted. However, and this will sound insane to all but quadrant IV thinkers, being healthy is still secondary to the primary goal.

Obviously, this is not a lifetime plan.

It's a wonder that we even discuss strengths. It should be so crystal clear, but let's look at the Cleau/Clew/Clues:

The first is simple: What do you love? What's the first thing you like to do when you enter the gym or stadium? Few people work on defensive footwork drills (see the earlier discussion of weaknesses), but many kids will pick up a ball and start shooting threes. A pick-up game will last forever with little coaching, although the skills will be at a low level. But in the pure joy of the game, you can find strengths. Don't dismiss what you like to do. It provides real insight into your success.

You are probably doing what you like to do if you're a QIV athlete. It might be getting old, though, and you might even be looking forward to the end, in terms of retirement or the off-season. But remember: This is "the girl who brought you to the dance."

The other insight about strength is, once again, fairly obvious: your performance. Are you a national-level or international-level competitor in something? That's a clue. The Soviets had a massive ranking scale that a young athlete could use to figure out his standings across several sports and then naturally slide into the sport in which he was most successful. In the martial arts, the belt scales could be very helpful. Yuriy Sedykh once noted that an advanced athlete simply improved year to year over a 10- to 12-year period in measurable increments.

Two quick caveats: First, Chris Long, a noted American educator, has often stated, "It's like being the best opera singer in Rock Springs, Wyoming." Nothing against this fine town, but it's important to focus on the point: If you can find a small enough pond, you'll be certain to be the biggest fish.

Second, there are approximately 20 powerlifting federations. This means that it's possible to be the national champ if you either join the sport very early in its inception or wait until the sport splinters in a dozen groups. The role of a good coach is to discern if you truly are among the elite. So, how do you build on this?

Every time I write an article or give a workshop, someone asks me, "So, uh, Dan, do you think I should do it five times a week, or should I do it twice a day?" It doesn't matter what "it" is—one-arm lifts, Tabata front squats, Olympic lifts. I always get the same perplexing question. I understand perplexity. As the father of two teenagers, being perplexed defines most of my life. But only recently have I understood the issue from both sides. Questions like the one above mystify me, because I have been training since 1967 and can obviously discern whether or not something works.

Perhaps more importantly, I understand the steps needed to add something (an exercise, training protocol, a supplement, etc.) to my training. Some people have no idea how to do this. If you're one of them, then this next part is for you. I'll give you a hint: You must begin by understanding how we learn. To begin, imagine asking a 5-year-old to figure out how many square yards of burnt-orange shag are needed to carpet a room. You will run into several issues:

- **Issue 1:** This 5-year-old still counts "one-two-free-four-five-uh . . ."
- **Issue 2:** Not only does this young scholar not know what a *yard* is, but he also thinks a *foot* is something intended only for kicking a ball.
- **Issue 3:** Sure, it's a simple issue of length times width. But asks the kiddo, "What's times mean?"

To learn math, you followed a progression that we call systematic education. Math skills were based on first learning the numbers in the correct sequence. (Now, this doesn't apply to me when I'm doing high-rep squats. I count by fives when I get tired.) Second, we might approach simply adding two numbers together to get a sum. I have 33-inch arms, for example. After learning addition, we learn subtraction and then multiplication. Finally, we learn about feet and yards, so we can figure out problems like our carpet question. Take the width and multiply it by the length, only to discover that no one still sells burnt-orange shag. However, you will find a lovely lime-green rug on sale. A systematic education offers the best way to learn anything. But how the heck does this relate to chunking weight around in the gym? So, young Billy, who wants to impress his 14-year-old female classmates, buys a bodybuilding magazine, takes it home, drags his older brother's weights out from under the bed, and tries to follow Mr. Greater Jupiter's training program. In a few years, Billy has done every curl imaginable, and his elbows hurt from hours of bench dips to the "max."

Billy then joins the local fitness center and discovers bench pressing five days a week and the indisputable fact that "Squats hurt the knees"—which is, of course, quite disputable. By this time, Billy has also joined an Internet forum and become an expert on biochemical reactions inside the human body, "trash talking" beginner's questions, and making fun of old guys who do Olympic lifts.

Then, Billy goes to a workshop or, even worse, reads one of my articles. You see, Billy doesn't have a systematic education. He never learned to squat correctly, deadlift correctly, or learn the basics of the sport. He doesn't eat breakfast because he's on the "Warrior Diet," he drinks five Super Huge Gulps of cola a day because he heard that was the best way to get creatine to work, and he thinks the only way to get a bodyweight bench press is to be on drugs.

And maybe they ask me to speak at this workshop, and I explain the joys of sprinting with heavy boulders, tossing long wooden poles end over end, and mixing chains, rocks, thick bars, kettlebells, and isometrics into one exercise. Young Billy stares up at the ceiling after the workshop. He just doesn't have the time to train on the Olympic Lifts two hours a day, train to be an Olympic gymnast, train to become a Highland athlete and a terror in the neighborhood, or continue training for the Mr. Greater Guns, Novice Amateur Class.

You see, Billy doesn't have the background to discern what to do and when to do it. He "knows" a lot, but he can't sift through the process. Billy is right: He doesn't have the time to do all the things he learned at the workshop, nor should he attempt to do them. So, what should he do?

The problem with systematic education is that it takes a long time. Now, the fact that you can read this shows the value of the process. But unless you had an extraordinary elementary physical education teacher, opportunities to train in a wide variety of sports, an elite-level high school program, and the finest college coaching in the world, it would be difficult for you to pick up all this info in the typical gym.

Systematic education is based on understanding a simple model. You can use the image of a ladder as a basic model, but as the cliché goes, be careful when you get to the top of the ladder, because you might have it placed against the wrong wall.

When it comes to Billy's education in general strength preparation, for the lack of the best alternative—such as being personally coached by a professional—he could settle for the second best. Find one author whose methods have been tested in the fire, such as Dan John or Marty Gallagher, and do exactly what this authority says, one of his programs at a time. Until a level of high proficiency, if not mastery, has been reached in one system, education in other systems is unnecessary at best, harmful at worst. If you have picked Gallagher, ignore Simmons, and vice versa.

When Hidetaka Nishiyama was asked whether a student of karate should study other martial arts, the late master replied: "You must first reach a certain level in your own art before studying other arts. Too much looking around is not good as it becomes confusing. You must have a strong base of knowledge."

And Billy must do exactly what his one chosen authority has prescribed without trying to "improve" it.

A lyrical aside: Back in the USSR, we loved jokes involving the "Armenian radio". Every joke was structured the same way: The Armenian radio received a question—rhetorical, stupid, or politically incorrect—and responded with its famous witty sarcasm—for instance:

What is the difference between the Soviet Constitution and the US Constitution?
—Both guarantee freedom of speech, only the latter guarantees freedom after that speech.

What is the exchange rate between rubles, pounds, and dollars?
—A pound of rubles is worth a dollar.

Here is a joke from that series that perfectly describes your typical Internet forum–dwelling muscle head:

Is it true that Azaryan won 10,000 in the lottery?
—Pretty much ... Only it was not Azaryan, it was Karpetyan, and not in lottery but in blackjack, and not ten grand but two rubles, and not won but lost ...

A forum thread usually goes like this:

BigGuns1995: *I have been on PTP and it is not working for me. Should I get PTP Pro?*
Coach: *How many times a week are you deadlifting and what is your max?*
BigGuns1995: *I have replaced the deadlifts with power cleans. I do them once a week.*
Coach: *Do you floor press or bench press?*
BigGuns1995: *No, I do Convict Conditioning for my upper body.*
Coach: *What else do you do?*
BigGuns1995: *Kettlebells and TRX three times a week.*
Coach: *And you say that you are doing Power to the People?! [Logging off]*

One of the hardest things for me to deal with as a coach is a parent who is pushing his or her kid to do stuff that, well, the kid can't do or doesn't wanna do! I got a call from a dad who was trying to push his daughter into using one of my roughest training programs, The Big 21, and having nothing but problems. She simply wasn't strong enough to be able to use the weight changes required. She barely could lift 45 pounds, and the program demands lots of plate changes.

A couple years ago, I did a workshop for some very good high school throwers, and the first question came from a dad. So, I put together this short list of some basics of being an "elite athlete":

What Is an Elite Athlete?

1. The athlete is no longer on a steep learning curve. In other words, the athlete is no longer improving in quantum leaps from year to year or season to season. Lifts, for example, no longer double over two years. Improvement is slow.

2. The athlete has a year-round approach to one sport.

3. Each year, the athlete uses some form of intense training camp or focused training of some kind.

4. The athlete uses a high level of strength training before competitive periods. Except for lifters, as the strength level goes down, performance should improve.

5. The athlete has made a personal choice to be elite.

It is a simple list, but it seems that number 5 is the issue for many people. Let's talk about number 4 in this next chapter.

Chapter 3

The Magic of Easy Strength and Realistic Reps

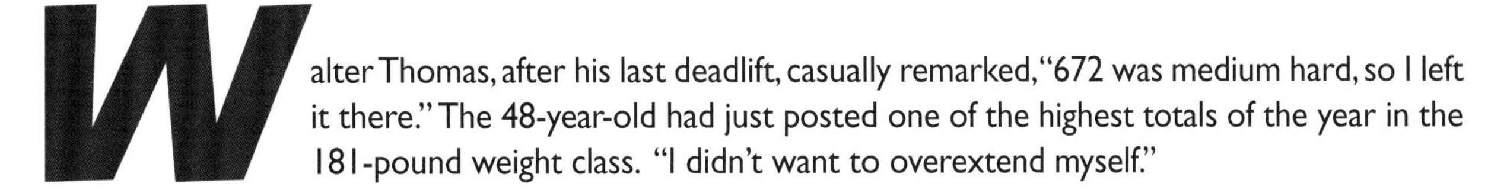

Walter Thomas, after his last deadlift, casually remarked, "672 was medium hard, so I left it there." The 48-year-old had just posted one of the highest totals of the year in the 181-pound weight class. "I didn't want to overextend myself."

"Easy strength". Marty Gallagher coined this expression after observing Thomas, Coan, and other powerlifting greats who never missed a training lift and hardly ever missed a competition attempt. *Easy strength is training and setting PRs without maxing.* It's a good strategy for a powerlifter and a great one for an athlete from another sport.

Easy Strength in a Nutshell

- Lift heavy.
- Keep your reps and sets low.
- Stop your sets and your workout before you get fatigued.

Competitors, especially fighters, often miss the point of strength training. The barbell is not there to make you a better man by testing your mettle; that is what the mat, the ring, or the kettlebells are for. And you are not training to become a weightlifter or a powerlifter. Iron is the means, not the goal.

Walter Thomas, a great lifter. Photo courtesy Powerlifting USA

Your goal is to excel at your own sport, and you lift to get a strength advantage over an opponent of equal skill. And if you hope to be a contender, practicing the skill of your sport must dominate your schedule. Strength training, as much as you dig it, must take up as little of your time and energy as possible—all in the name of leaving you as much gas in the tank as possible for sparring, hitting the bag, and other skills and drills of the trade.

That is the point many S&C coaches and athletes miss somehow: Strength training ought not interfere with the practice of the sport. *The strength regimen must deliver great strength gains without exhausting the athlete's energy or time.*

Marty Gallagher (left), one of the greatest strength coaches of all time.

Fighters need to be strong, too. Conditioning is great, but given equal levels of conditioning and skill, the stronger man shall win. Top Russian Kyokushinkai *karatekas* routinely bench three wheels and squat four to five. Yet, to quote Steve Baccari, coaches of MMA fighters keep confusing "strength and conditioning" with "conditioning and more conditioning."

It is a lot easier to smoke an athlete than to make him stronger. The late Dr. Mel Siff put it well:

> *To me, the sign of a really excellent routine is one which places great demands on the athlete, yet produces progressive long-term improvement without soreness, injury or the athlete ever feeling thoroughly depleted. Any fool can create a program that is so demanding that it would virtually kill the toughest marine or hardiest of elite athletes, but not any fool can create a tough program that produces progress without unnecessary pain.*

Brian Petty, RKC—a colorful Philly gent behind whose scarred-by-bare-knuckle-boxing mug hides razor-sharp intelligence and wit—has a few things to say on the subject of doing smokers for the sake of being smoked:

The difference between exercising and training is having a point. Exercise is done to waste energy—burn calories—or to "blow off steam," excess mental and physical energy, and tension. Training is done in order to improve something—strength, endurance, neuromuscular control, etc. Exercise is a singular event with an immediate goal.

The success of training can only be judged by changes over time in performance. Exercise doesn't have a point beyond the immediate session—if you leave the gym a sweaty mess, it was a good exercise session or "workout." If you show up every day and breathe hard and get tired and sweaty, you may consider yourself to be successful at exercise. By contrast, training can only be judged as a

Brian Petty, RKC. Photo courtesy Brian Petty

success if it works—that is, if after an appropriate amount of time you can clearly show improved capacity for physical work. You may show up every day and push and pull and grunt and sweat and even limp to your car—but be terribly UN*successful at training, if over time you are not getting any stronger, faster, leaner, more agile, better at your chosen sport, etc. . . .*

Swinging a weight around with the express goal of becoming extremely fatigued is what I would do if I had a lobotomy. With a frontal lobotomy destroying my ability to plan over the long term, I would believe that the goal of exercise was achieving a certain specific response—I would search for the immediate effect of exercise. I would forget that as biological organisms, we not only respond in the short term to a stimulus but also adapt in the long term to the sum total of stimuli we are presented with—so long as we are able to recover. The idea that anything that made me horrendously fatigued, to the point of nausea, vomiting, dehydration, hyponatremia, and even rhabdomyolosis, would constitute an effective—or "killer"—workout would appeal to my zombie-like, short-term-thinking mind. I would strive in my workouts for "failure," or forcing my body to stop working. Fascinated by the immediate effects of exercise and unable to plan, I would work at top voluntary intensity every time I exercised, always attempting to maximally disrupt my body functions. I would also be unable to follow a program, so I would change exercises constantly, attempting to "confuse" my body and prevent it from "getting used to" my exercise sessions. I would change aimlessly, regardless of whether the exercises were useful or dangerous, choosing them solely based on how bad they made me feel. . . .

If you want pain, learn Muay Thai. If you want to learn about failure, play golf. If you want to vomit, drink syrup of ipecac. If you want to become stronger and more fit, train appropriately.

A rare coach who understands this is Steve Baccari. He coaches top boxers and MMA fighters in Boston, and his fighters have had great success with *Power to the People!* Norman "Stoney" Stone, the trainer and manager of World Heavyweight Champion John Ruiz commented that Baccari's program "leaves your boxer feeling fresh and ready to fight instead of sore and burnt out." Check out Baccari's adaptation of *Power to the People!* below to get an idea what a professionally designed easy-strength program looks like, and then we will give you 10 guidelines for putting together one of your own.

"If brute force doesn't work, you're just not using enough." Steve Baccari's T-shirt says it all. Photo courtesy Steve Baccari

Power to the People! Deadlifts for Boxers and MMA Fighters

By Steve Baccari, RKC

This is how I teach deadlifts to my fighters. We have had very good strength gains with no injuries. This is a summary of months and months of notes. This is not a powerlifting program.

1. Do sets of 2–3 reps. Never more than 3 reps.
2. Stop each set with your best rep.
3. Stop your training session with your best set.
4. Use rest intervals as long as you have the time for.
5. Start with a very short range of motion, 3–4 inches.
6. Start with a heavy weight. Because your ROM is so short, there is a much smaller risk of an injury.
7. Decompress your spine between sets by hanging on a pull-up bar.
8. Increase your ROM slowly, so slowly that you hardly notice it.
9. Never increase the ROM and the training weight in the same session. For example, for the first two weeks keep the ROM the same but increase the weight. Then in the next two weeks, keep the weight the same but increase the ROM. See-saw back and forth until you are pulling from the floor.
10. If you cycle the deadlift in and out of your routine, start each cycle this way.

1. Use a limited number of "big bang" exercises.

"Focus on two or three lifts," advises former Senior RKC Rob Lawrence. "That many enable 'all-aroundness' and focus." For example, focus on the deadlift and the floor press.

Zatsiorsky classified exercises as *global* (at least two-thirds of the muscles are involved), *regional* (one-third to two-thirds), and *local* (up to one-third). While some local exercises may be needed (e.g., wrist, grip, and neck work for fighters), focus on the first two categories.

2. Lift two to three times a week.

Nikolay Ozolin was one of the pioneers who advised Soviet weightlifters to train daily. He explained that high training frequency (e.g., five times a week) is most effective when the goal is improving neuromuscular coordination with low reps. Nevertheless, the scientist typically recommended strength training only three times a week, with heavy loads and doing special exercises—including technique practice—on other days. Effective as it is, daily strength training is hard to balance with the demands of one's sport.

Of course, three times a week is just a guideline, not a law. Two weekly days of iron is a standard practice with many top Russian fighters. Some of Dan's plans and mine feature four to five weekly strength sessions. Elite shot putter John Brenner did one lift per day: squat, bench press, power clean, and power snatch. Dan's One Lift a Day program is well known. Training each lift once a week on a split routine is acceptable, as long as it does not produce excessive soreness.

There is nothing wrong with a split if you are not using it as an excuse to have a bi's and tri's day. Ben Johnson lifted six times a week: three for the lower body and three for the upper body. He cut down to four days when felt the need to back off. I like Charles Poliquin's weekly strength plan for MMA fighters: five days of lifting a week, only two exercises per workout.

Relatively easy exercises for small muscle groups may be practiced more frequently than three times a week. On some days, Steve Baccari has his fighters "grease the groove" with Captains of Crush® grippers throughout the day. Then he would have them do neck and wrist exercises. In Russia, it is not unusual for power athletes to work their feet and hands twice a day, in separate mini-workouts. Whether this is an efficient use of your time and energy is up to you to decide.

3. Keep the volume around 10 reps per lift.

Ten reps per workout, as advocated by Dan John and by *Power to the People!* is smack in the middle of the rep range recommended by Russian strength authorities like Ozolin, Medvedev, and Vorobyev: 3–6 sets of 2–3 reps.

Dan has observed that after 10 reps, athletes start compromising intensity or technique, hence his "rule of 10 reps." The coach's favorite set-and-rep schemes are 5 x 2, 2 x 5, 5 x 2, 3 x 3, and 6 x 1. When singles are used, Dan makes an exception and cuts the volume to 6 x 1. The man has coached thousands of athletes and could not help noticing that six good singles is all you can expect from an athlete before the quality suffers.

Not surprisingly, the in-the-trench observations of this strength coach extraordinaire are in line with Soviet research. The famous Prilepin's table gives almost the same number of optimal reps in the 90% 1 RM plus intensity zone: seven. And according to Verkhoshansky and Siff, the energy expenditure from a series of singles is 35% more demanding than the same number of reps done in sets. Subtract 35% from

10 reps, and you will get 6 or 7. Of course, only the top couple of singles in the 6 x 1 will approach the maximal weight.

Some other set/rep schemes to consider are 343, 424, 1234, 4321, 1423, and 12321. You may stay with the same weight or vary the weight from set to set. You may change the sets and reps every workout.

The above does not mean that higher volumes are not effective in building strength. Quite the contrary. However, the muscle mass gain, fatigue, and soreness that accompany high-volume training make it inappropriate for most athletes. Take the iconic Smolov's squat cycle.* This 13-week nightmare calls for a gruesome 136 reps per week during the first month! The cycle delivers beyond anyone's wildest dreams: One man I knew added 105 pounds to his squat in 13 weeks of Smolov and peaked in the mid-600s drug free—and his gains are typical. But it takes its toll. You will be so sore and exhausted that the only "sport" you could practice at the same time is chess. The Smolov is a specialist program for an athlete who does not have any skills to practice outside the gym. An exception might be an athlete who must gain a lot of muscle mass in the off-season—for instance, a football lineman.

The same thing applies to the "Russian Bear," the muscle-building workout from *Power to the People!* Straight PTTP, on the other hand, is an example of Easy Strength training. The classic 5 x 5, which lies in between when it comes to volume, is still too much if one uses the same weight in all sets. For a fighter or a thrower, a total of 10 reps is just right.

Ten reps is where we are and have been for several years, reports Barry Ross. "This allows are athletes to leave exhilarated rather than exhausted. It also allows them to exit the weight room and start immediately on event training."

4. Keep the reps in the 1–5 range, emphasizing doubles and triples.

Soviet weightlifting champion and authority Robert Roman demonstrated that recovery is rapid and soreness is minimal after low-rep, low-set heavy lifting. Just what the doctor ordered for an athlete.

High-rep training can be painfully ineffective and inefficient in building absolute strength. A friend of Dan's undertook a valiant effort of pushing his deadlift to 405 x 20. When he tested his 1 RM, he got—425.

Strength and power gains are superior with heavy low-rep training. Dyachkov had two groups of athletes squat. One repped out to failure with 70% 1 RM, and the other did low reps with near-max weights. When it was all said and done, the high-rep group improved their squat by 13,7 kilograms and the low-rep group gained twice as much: 26,3 kilograms. The standing vertical jump was measured, as well. The "reppers" improved by 8,7 centimeters and the "near-maxers" by 13,3 centimeters.

* See my article titled "Another Russian Super Cycle: Add Up to 100 Pounds to Your Squat in Thirteen Weeks," on www.DragonDoor.com.

Professor Thomas Fahey, one of the top American sports scientists, wrote:

> *A few years ago, I did some experiments with the college basketball team that involved them only doing single, doubles, and triples for whole body lifts (cleans, snatches, overhead squats, bench press, standing press, etc). They got very strong but had plenty of energy for playing basketball. They were in and out of the weight room in 20–30 minutes.*

Prof. Thomas Fahey is one of the leading strength scientists in the US.

Steve Baccari is a stickler for perfect form, and he discovered that none of his fighters could do 5 perfect deadlift reps. Doubles hit the spot. Some fighters with perfect technique are allowed to do triples. Interestingly, 2 is the most preferred rep choice of the Russian National Weightlifting Team.

Two or three is a great rep range to emphasize in an Easy Strength program. Four or five is where neural training and muscle building meet, which means you could end up with some hypertrophy. This is out of the question in sports like boxing.

Singles, doubles, and triples are pure nerve force training. Singles, however, are very demanding on the nervous system. Do a few, but don't abuse them. Dan John lifts ten times in two weeks. Only two of these workouts are singles and only one comes close to his max.

Hence, doubles and triples rule when it comes to Easy Strength with zero mass gain. But if your sport does not punish muscle gain, don't be afraid to train with fives more often. Regardless, go easy on the singles.

5. Rest approximately 5 minutes between sets. Practice *Fast & Loose* relaxation drills in between.

Tommy Kono, a weightlifting legend held in the highest regard in Russia, has the following advice for your squat strength workout: "Avoid 'pumping' muscles up. Try to relax the muscles completely between sets so you are 'fresh' when you begin each new set."

Baccari's recommendations for rest between sets are unique by boxing and MMA standards. He demands that fighters rest long enough to "forget" their last set. Steve's bruisers usually take a full hour to complete 5 sets of doubles! Not only do these breaks allow for nearly complete energy replenishment in the muscle, but they also allow the athlete's nervous system to recover, which is very important for continuous gains. The fighters hang on the pull-up bar to decompress their spines and simply hang out and relax. Again, they take up to an hour to complete 5 sets of 2 deadlifts!

If you want to excel in your sport, you must get over the pump-and-burn bodybuilding mentality.

6. Train in the 80% to 95% 1 RM intensity zone. Always leave at least 1 or 2 reps in the bank.

The influential Soviet *Boxing Yearbook* offered the following strength program design recommendations:

Russian Boxers' Max Strength Training

Weight:	80%–95% 1 RM
Sets:	5–7
Reps:	1–3

If it does not look like a lot of work, it is supposed to be that way. The idea is to build as much strength as possible while staying as fresh as possible for boxing—or track, or tennis, or whatever. When I worked with Maria Sharapova, I had her do a few singles, doubles, and triples of pull-ups, pistols, hard push-ups, modified Janda sit-ups, and nothing else. The future Wimbledon star had plenty of conditioning from her daily tennis practice, and the last thing she needed was adding fatigue from her strength regimen. Pure QIII to QIV training.

Barry Ross, sprint coach extraordinaire.
Photo courtesy Barry Ross

Barry Ross—the world-class sprint coach who took Allyson Felix to the women's fastest 200 meters in the world at the age of 17—follows a low-rep, low-fatigue regime. He prescribes the *Power to the People!* deadlift plus a bench press workout with a slight volume reduction. Ross's athletes lift 2 or 3 x 2 or 3 with 85% to 95% of their 1 RM with 5 minutes of rest between sets and never to failure. Explains Ross:

> *The benefit is much more rapid strength gain. By keeping sets and reps low, timed and without lifts to failure, lactic acid was minimal or non-existent. . . . The athletes felt exhilarated and ready for a full-event workout after lifting.*

Ross believes that the short set/rep scheme combined with a 5-minute rest between sets has other advantages beyond just strength training. According to him:

> *It's not unusual for pro and collegiate runners to have 2 or 3 hours of training twice per day over 5 or 6 days. Felix worked out once a day for a maximum of 5 days. The longest workouts occurred three times per week and consisted of a combination of sprint and strength training which rarely exceeded 2.5 hours.*

Allyson Felix, USA, and Monique Williams, New Zealand, racing in the world championship in Berlin. Photo courtesy Barry Ross

Another one of Ross' athletes, J. Marks, one of the fastest female high school runners in California, pulling a mean deadlift. Photo courtesy Barry Ross

The Ross strength training protocol allowed on-track training immediately after strength training. This eliminated the need for the daily split training time so often used. Says Ross:

> Power to the People! *showed me more then just another simple workout. What I realized from reading the book was that I had overcomplicated strength training for athletes. I bought into an existing system 30 years ago that was flawed to begin with.*

7. Go for a PR, single or rep, when you are feeling exceptionally strong, but stop short of an all-out max. Set a "sort of max." Always back off after a PR for at least two weeks.

Canadian track coach Charlie Francis's approach to strength training his infamous charge Ben Johnson is very educational from the Easy Strength point of view. The sprinter stayed with low reps and low volume—for example, to 600 x 6/2 (reps/sets) in the below parallel box squat and 385 x 2/3 in the bench press. The 173-pound Johnson eventually benched over 400 pounds, and Francis was convinced he was good for 440. But—pay attention!—the brilliant coach never maxed his athlete to avoid injury. This obviously did not prevent Johnson from breaking his PRs—without maxing.

Dan John has a great name for the type of a max you need to push up: a "sort of max." Clarifies Charlie Francis:

> *There's a huge difference between 95 and 100% performance.... The difference in output and effort is unbelievable. Even though it's in the 95th percentile and qualifies as high-intensity work, it's a joke. Keep in mind this only applies at the highest levels. If a kid gets a personal best, so what? We're talking about world record levels.*

Not surprisingly, the Russians have a term for this method of strength training: the *large-effort method,* not to be confused with the *maximum-effort method.* The latter is something to pull out once in a blue moon. The former is the way to train on a regular basis.

Every time Johnson set a personal record, be it in the gym or on the track, his coach made a point of backing off immediately. He literally stopped the workout. Then he had Johnson back cycle for 10 to 14 days. Francis points out that it takes an elite athlete that long to fully recover from a PR effort, even if it is not a true max (Ozolin puts that number at three weeks minimum. It is possible that Francis's obsession with not pushing to the edge allowed his charges to recover quicker.) The experienced coach had observed that most athletes get hurt the workout after their PR, and he would not allow this to happen to his prized athlete.

Two of Rif's famous corollaries, numbers 4 and 5, are appropriate here:

- The next step off a peak is always down.
- One should step down rather than fall off.

Francis never hesitated to cut back on the weight or drop the strength session altogether either when Ben was tired from sprint training. Insists the coach:

> *If there is any degradation in training, stop. If there is any doubt about one more rep or run, don't do it. If you are trying to learn with reps, you won't get it later if you haven't already. Leave it and come back to it.*

8. Vary the intensity every workout, either through cycling the powerlifting style or through less structured advances and retreats.

Some of the coaches I have mentioned cycle their athletes' loads in the classic powerlifting fashion. Others simply vary the loads, pushing and backing off constantly. Speaks Francis:

> *If the previous workout has been spectacular, I will pull back and force an easier workout as a matter of principle. The athlete will usually want to build on a spectacular workout and train even harder.... As this can lead to overtraining and injury, it is always better to err on the light side—do too little rather than too much.... Ninety percent of my time is spent holding athletes back to prevent overtraining, and only 10 percent is spent motivating them to do more work.*

Dan John likes the following sequence: 3 x 3 (heavy), 5 x 2 (heavier), 2 x 5 (light), 6 x 1 (work up to a "sort of max"), 5-3-2 (moderate). Sometimes the workout after "sort of maxing" his athlete, John would have him do only one very light set of 10 and nothing else. A 400-pound squatter, for instance, might do something like 165 x 10. Although the reps climb high, they will not make the athlete sore because the weight is so light. When Francis wanted to spare Johnson's CNS after a series of hard, heavy workouts, he had him do 10s, too—once in awhile.

9. Don't stop strength training in season, but reduce the volume by two-thirds to one-half. For example, do 3 x 2 instead of 5 x 2 or 3 x 2 instead of 3 x 3. You may switch from three to two strength workouts a week.

Francis's in-season strength training is in line with the Russian school. Ozolin warns that once you stop training, your strength will drop in as soon as two weeks and advises maintaining it with 2 or 3 sessions a week. The Russian specialist recommends cutting back to two-thirds of the volume without reducing the weight.

Francis took an even bigger cut, he downshifted Johnson from 2 sets of 6 with 600 in the squat to 2 sets of doubles or triples—a one-half to two-thirds reduction in the already low volume. This reduction allowed Johnson to get extra fresh for the season without losing his strength. Francis quipped, "Ben was never far from strength and speed." Indeed, he was not pushing as hard, but he was still handling 600 pounds.

10. Finish your workout feeling stronger than when you started. Stop the workout if your performance is less than perfect, and come back another day.

Five sets of doubles are what Baccari's fighters usually end up doing, but if an athlete hits a perfect set earlier, the jig is up. Elite coaches from different sports think remarkably alike. Charlie Francis might prescribe five repeats of a sprint drill but stop the athlete if he hits a PR on the third.

Tommy Kono has a powerful insight:

> *After each repetition, erase any flaw detected so the next repetition will be even smoother.... If you perform a total of 20 repetitions of snatches in a workout, your twentieth repetition should be the one most efficiently performed! That is productivity! If fatigue (of mind or body) is setting in by the twentieth, it is better to quit snatching, because you begin to fail in refining your technique.*

I would underline Tommy's final words: *It is better to quit, because you begin to fail in refining your technique.*

In the classic text on training the prototypical power athlete, the high jumper, Dr. Vladimir Dyachkov offered a timeless recipe for Easy Strength training. The Distinguished Coach of the USSR advised to stop the strength training session when the athlete *starts* feeling fatigue or starts experiencing a loss of speed or a decrease in muscle elasticity. Dyachkov stressed that high-caliber jumpers have no business training to failure. He also recommended that the athlete limit his reps with heavy weights to 1 or 2 and to stay with 3 or 4 even with light weights.

By the way, Vladimir Dyachkov was no armchair quarterback. He was the USSR champion and record holder in the high jump, the 110 m sprint hurdling, and the pole vault. Dyachkov won his last national title at the age of 41, and his showdowns with Ozolin in the pole vault are legendary.

Easy Strength Training for Athletes: 10 Rules of Thumb

1. Use a limited number of "big bang" exercises—for example, the deadlift and the floor press from *Power to the People!*
2. Lift two to three times a week.
3. Keep the reps in the 1 to 5 range, emphasizing doubles and triples.
4. Keep the volume around 10 reps per lift or 6 when using only singles—for example, 5 x 2, 2 x 5, 532, 3 x 3, 343, 424, 1234, 4321, 12321, 6 x 1, and so on. You may stay with the same weight or vary the weights from set to set.
5. Rest approximately 5 minutes between sets. Practice *Fast & Loose* relaxation drills in between.
6. Train in the 80% to 95% 1 RM intensity zone. Always leave at least 1 or 2 reps in the bank.
7. Go for a PR, single or rep, when you are feeling exceptionally strong, but stop short of an all-out max. Set a "sort of max." Always back off after a PR for at least two weeks.
8. Vary the intensity every workout, either through *Power to the People!* style cycling or through less structured advances and retreats.
9. Don't stop strength training in season but reduce the volume by two-thirds to one-half. For example, do 3 x 2 instead of 5 x 2 or 3 x 2 instead of 3 x 3. You may switch from three to two strength workouts a week.
10. Finish your workout feeling stronger than when you started. Stop the workout if your performance is less than perfect, and come back another day.

Now you know how to build great strength while staying focused on excellence in your sport. The bottom line is, *Lift heavy, not hard.*

Will you get as strong as a powerlifter who does more volume, either in the primary lifts (the PTP Bear, Sheyko) or in assistance exercises (Westside)? No. But your strength will be head and shoulders above your competitors' in boxing, tennis, or whichever sport you have chosen to excel at. And your skills will be superior if you have wisely invested the time and energy saved through state-of-the-art easy strength training into relentless and perfect practice of your sport.

Concludes Steve Baccari:

> *In my opinion easy strength training is the only productive way a competitive fighter can strength train. But most people think if you don't break a sweat, it must not work. This used to bother me a lot, but not any more because I think it is one reason why my fighters win so much.*

Training sessions need to be repeatable.

I have joked for years about a workout I did in June 1979. Here it is:

- Back squat 315 for 30. Rest.
- Back squat 275 for 30. Rest.
- Back squat 225 for 30. Rest.

And, as I have often stated, "I will repeat this workout as soon as I have recovered."

You see, this was a workout that was unrepeatable. Yes, I threw my lifetime best in the discus at that time, but I also crashed emotionally and physically for a long time after these workouts. For an elite athlete, one could argue that the crash is just part of the price, but for the bulk of us, I would argue that sustained progress is a much better goal.

Recently, I increased my thick bar deadlift from 265 (this is a seriously thick, thick bar) to 315 pounds. I also used this same program to match my best incline bench press in a decade, without ever going hard for even one workout.

What is this miracle? Well, give me 40 days.

A few years ago, Pavel outlined a simple program for me. Be wary! This program is so simple that you'll ignore its value.

1. For the next 40 workouts, do the exact same training program every day. (For the record, I find that most of my goals are reached by day 20 or 22, so you can also opt for a shorter period.)

2. Pick five exercises. I suggest you do a squatting movement like the goblet squat or overhead squat as part of the warm-up, as you don't want to ignore the movement. But it might be fun to focus on other aspects of your body.

3. Focus on these five movements:
   - A large posterior chain movement (the deadlift is the right answer)
   - An upper-body push (bench press, incline bench press, military press)
   - An upper-body pull (pull-ups, rows, or, if you've ignored them like me, heavy bicep curls)
   - A simple full-body explosive move (kettlebell swings or snatches)
   - Something for what I call an anterior chain move (an abdominal exercise)—I think the ab wheel is king here, but you can also do some other movements best suited for lower reps.

4. Only do 2 sets of 5 reps per workout for the deadlift and push/pull exercises, and 1 set of 20 to 50 for the explosive move. Do a solid single set of 5 reps for the abs.

5. Never plan or worry about the weight or the load. Always stay within yourself and go heavy "naturally."

6. Don't eat chalk, scream, or pound on walls. Simply do each lift without any emotion or excitement, and strive for perfect technique.

So, the workout might consist of these five movements:

1. Thick bar deadlift
2. Incline bench press
3. Heavy biceps curls
4. Kettlebell swings
5. Ab wheel

For the record, this is exactly what I recently used in my workouts. I often did this five days a week and found that my lifts naturally waved up and down throughout the week and the full 40 days. Sometimes, something like a 250-pound incline bench press would feel so light for both sets of 5 that I had to hold back on the excitement to do more sets and reps.

The secret to the program is that you get your volume from doing up to 10 sets of a lift in a week. The load increases as you naturally feel like the weights are easy. It's that simple.

The first time I tried this program under Pavel's direction, I added 15 pounds to my lifetime incline bench press during the twenty-first workout, approximately a month after starting the program. I did this max with no spotter, and I got the lift for a double. It was a 15-pound improvement over my lifetime best with an extra rep as a parting gift without doing a single hard workout. Just 2 sets of 5 anytime I entered the gym.

Let's just stick with this simple plan. Actually, it's a variation I used a few years ago to go from a 265 thick bar DL to 315. You have to try a thick bar deadlift (and the diameter makes a huge difference) to understand how amazing any progress can be in this difficult movement.

Coming into the program, my 1RMs on these movements were as follows:

1. Thick bar DL: 265
2. Bench press: 405
3. Heavy biceps curl (cheat curl): 315
4. Kettlebell swings: 200 swings with 24 kg under 10 minutes
5. Ab wheels: Easy from knees; goal is to do from standing to full extension

Week 1

Day 1

Thick bar deadlifts	6 singles with 205
Bench press	2 x 5 with 205
Cheat curls	2 x 5 with 135
KB swings	2 x 25 with 24 kg
Ab wheels	1 x 5 from knees

Day 2

Thick bar deadlifts	2 x 5 with 185
Bench press	2 x 5 with 185
Cheat curls	3 x 3 with 205
Kb swings	1 x 50 with 24 kg
Ab wheels	1 x 5 from knees

Day 3

Thick bar deadlifts	2 x 5 with 185
Bench press	2 x 5 with 185
Cheat curls	2 x 5 with 165
Kb swings	2 x 50 with 24 kg
Ab wheels	1 x 10 from knees

Day 4

Thick bar deadlifts	5 x 2 with 225
Bench press	5 x 2 with 255
Cheat curls	2 x 5 with 135
Kb swings	2 x 25 with 24 kg
Ab wheels	1 x 5 from knees

Day 5

Thick bar deadlifts	2 x 5 with 135
Bench press	2 x 5 with 225
Cheat curls	2 x 5 with 135
Kb swings	1 x 25 with 24 kg
Ab wheels	1 x 5 from knees

Week 3

Day 1

Thick bar deadlifts	5 x 2 with 225
Bench press	5 x 2 with 255
Cheat curls	2 x 5 with 135
Kb swings	5 x 20 with 24 kg
Ab wheels	1 x 5 from knees

Day 2

Thick bar deadlifts	6 singles: 135, 185, 205, 225, 245, 270 (easy!!!)
Bench press	6 singles: 135, 225, 255, 275, 295, 305
Cheat curls	2 x 5 with 185
Kb swings	1 x 50 with 24 kg
Ab wheels	1 x cautious attempt(s) from stand

Day 3

Thick bar deadlifts	5 x 2 with 205
Bench press	5 x 2 with 225
Cheat curls	3 x 3 with 205
Kb swings	2 x 50 with 24 kg
Ab wheels	1 x 10 from knees

Nikki Shlosser, RKC II had been stuck on a 24kg kettlebell strict one-arm military press and a pistol with the same kettlebell for a couple of years. Following the 40-Day Workout she pressed 28kg, a weight she could not even budge in the past, and pistolled 32kg.
Photo courtesy Nikki Shlosser

Day 4

Thick bar deadlifts	2 x 5 with 135
Bench press	2 x 5 with 205
Cheat curls	2 x 5 with 135
Kb swings	2 x 25 with 24 kg
Ab wheels	1 x 5 from knees

Day 5

Thick bar deadlifts	5 x 2 with 245
Bench press	3 x 3 with 315
Cheat curls	2 x 5 with 205
Kb swings	2 x 25 with 24 kg
Ab wheels	1 x 5 from knees

Some observations:

1. You will notice, it isn't much. Really? The volume is actually staggering, with, for example, 23 sets of thick bar deadlifts in the third week. The secret, like all the great secrets of strength

training, is the repetitions. Instead of pounding the max lift up with a sledge hammer, we are attempting to coax up our 80% efforts. And, like all the great secrets, this one is so obvious that most of us miss it.

2. There are almost no efforts done on nerve. Every lift, every set flows easily. Because of the way we are built, doing something like thick bars is really hard on the CNS. Too much grip work can easily lead to an odd kind of overtraining where the athlete simply loses grip power. If the grip or finger dexterity (think typing skills) suddenly erodes, it indicates to me, as a coach, that some serious overtraining has been allowed.

3. When you do decide to max in this program, it's almost laughably easy to break your old marks. This "can't miss" mentality seems to be the key to "greasing the groove." It's so simple, you won't do it.

Forty Days of Life

by Tim Anderson, RKC II

I recently finished Dan John's 40-day workout. The workout was said to be an easy, easy way to build strength. Dan said the program was so simple, you wouldn't be able to trust that it would work.

At the time, it sounded like a fun challenge and a fresh change of pace, so I decided to give it a try. Basically, the premise of the workout is that you pick four to five exercises that you want to focus on, and you do them roughly everyday for 40 days. Oh, and you only use 40% to 80% of your one-rep max, and you keep your reps at or below 10 for each exercise!

Yes, I know. It already sounds way too easy to work. Guess what? It worked. I got stronger, a lot stronger, with almost zero effort. The program is *simply* amazing. Not only did I grow stronger, I grew wiser, as well. Let me explain. I gained wisdom because I learned several life lessons while following this fantastic 40-day program.

I know it seems crazy. I'm talking about learning life-changing lessons from a simple strength training program. But it's true. For example, I learned about having integrity. Everyday, I had my doubts about this program. But everyday, I showed up and did what I was supposed to do. Why? Because I had made a commitment to do so. It would have been easy to say, "This is crazy, I'm going to do something else." But I didn't. I wanted to finish what I started. I wanted to do what I said I would do. If I can not commit to a simple 40-day workout and stick to the commitments that I make to myself, how can I expect to have integrity with anyone else? This idea, this integrity, has spilled over into my personal life, and I am now more aware of my commitments. I want to be the guy who does what he says he will. I want to be the guy that his wife and kids can depend on. I want to have integrity.

I also learned about humility. I knew too much for Dan's 40-day program to work. I've been training for almost 22 years. There is NO WAY deadlifting 135 pounds for 10 reps is going to help me dead lift 350 pounds 40% of my max? Really? Yes, really. I was wrong. Lifting 40% of your max can increase your max. So, I learned a little something about humility. I don't have all the answers. Maybe I don't have any. Maybe I should keep an open mind and realize that there are lots of people out there that have a world of possibilities to offer. Maybe I shouldn't make opinions about ideas or concepts until I at least try them. Maybe I should think less of myself and more of others. Maybe I should strive to have humility.

A huge lesson that stood out to me from Dan John's program is the lesson of faith. Faith is the hope for things uncertain and unseen. Believing I could get stronger, even when I was unsure in the method, was an act of faith. Dan said the program would work. He said I would struggle with the idea that the program would work. But Dan said, so I did. That is faith. I know having faith in something so small as a strength training program seems trivial. But how could I have faith in something huge, like love or God, if I can't even have faith in something simple like a strength training program? Faith, like strength, needs to be exercised, too. Faith in little things can yield faith in larger things. A man walks a mile one step at a time, all the while believing each step will take him closer to where he wants to go even when he can't see past the horizon. We could all use a little faith. Without it, we are just staring at the horizon.

I learned some other lessons, too. Perhaps not as "out there" as integrity, humility, and faith but diamond, nonetheless. For instance, training to win. One of the cool things about Dan's 40-day workout is that you are training to win. In other words, you are not training to failure. By keeping the workouts easy and always making your lifts, you are teaching your body how to win, how to succeed. So when you do lift heavy, you make your lift. I think that is an awesome lesson that should be carried much further than simply strength training. I know we can't always avoid failure, but we can always strive for success. We can always choose to be our best. I have to believe that if I always give my best, then those around me will get my best. That is training to win, and nothing bad can come from that.

Perhaps one of the most important lessons I learned following Dan's program is this: If it is important, do it everyday. Dan John credits this saying to Dan Gable, but Dan John is the man who brought it to my attention. And I have to say, it is simply brilliant. In Dan's 40-day workout, you are supposed to focus on five things you really want to improve upon—five important things—and you do them everyday. Then, like magic, they improve! There is a huge lesson here that goes far beyond the weight room. *If it is important, do it every day.* Tell your wife you love her everyday. Hug your kids everyday. Say your prayers everyday. You get the point. I think this is so brilliant. With this one concept, a person could change the world. If it is important, do it everyday....

There it is—life lessons from Dan John's 40-day workout. To sum it all up, you pick four to five important things—like integrity, humility, faith, and giving your best—and then you consistently work at them every single day.

Oh wait, I think I've got that confused. That must be Dan's 40-day, life-changing program. Come to think of it, after 40 days and 40 nights, the rains stopped and the world was forever changed.

Thank you, Dan!

You can certainly come up with your own variations, but try to stick with the basic five movements, and don't stray far from 2 sets of 5. You will be amazed at how quickly your strength will improve after just a few weeks. Also, notice the element of randomness in this workout.

The key, that seems to be missing is the idea to ramp it up when it feels right. So, for me, I would max out on some random day or go heavy 3 x 3 because the bar was leaping off the ground. It's not just the easy days, but those are the keys.

If there's a secret to weird strength (goofy, top-end strength), it's the ability to ramp it up when you need to ramp it up. People want a program with percents and magic and guidelines, and yes, this works. But then what?

The original 40-day recommendation was based on German research by Neumann, who studied the dynamics of adaptation for over 20 years and came to the conclusion that complete adaptation takes at least six weeks. (Neumann's research led to the East German practice of planning elite athletes' training in six-week units.) However, as seen from Dan's and many others' experience, three-week strength blocks can deliver PRs even to elite athletes.

Jeremy Layport, RKC Team Leader, is convinced that "anyone with proficient technique and strength should be fine from shorter 3- or 4-week cycles." He "tried Verkhoshansky's 'American football' program (crazy volume and intensity, as I'm sure you're aware) and PR'd in the fifth session." These are not beginner's easy gains. This strength coach is one strong hombre.

Jeremy Layport, RKC Team Leader.

I bet you are familiar with the simple and reliable powerlifting tactic of going all out for three weeks and unloading for one. Thanks to Westside Barbell and Metal Militia, this elegant approach to cycling has become very popular in the last decade.

Thanks to Dr. Vladimir Issurin, we know of its origins. The Russian scientist cites three relevant studies. Sharobayko (1984) had elite athletes working on their maximal strength for 20 weeks. They gained 5.9% strength in the first three weeks, another 1.6% in the second three, and then the gains became negligible. "Exhaustive intense training elicits a pronounced stress response as the athletes approach the upper limit of biological adaptation after three–four weeks (Steinacker et al., 1998). Continuation of such a program may lead to overtraining (Hooper et al., 1995)."

So, neural strength blocks can be as short as three weeks. German scientist Dr. Ekkart Arbeit explains:

> *For the mesocycle the [three-week rhythm] is decisive.... From the daily praxis we know, that three-week holidays are most restful, as elite athletes we know, that we need for a training camp in the altitude minimum 21, better 24 days. A medical cure has a duration between 21 and 27 days. All this based on the [three-week rhythm].*

After finishing all 40 days or when you feel your strength has come up to a level that make more advanced training methods are appropriate, feel free to move on. The short time you invest in focusing on strength building will do wonders for your muscle mass as you begin to attack supersets or whatever you deem important.

Well, the 40-Day Workout is an organized "grease the groove." The hardest part of the program is simply not trying to overreach. It's easy to say but hard to do.

Should we call what Dan has just described "even easier strength"?

He spent ridiculously low amounts of energy on this plan—the energy that was saved for practicing the skills of his sport.

How "Even Easier Strength" Training Differs from Easy Strength

- Lighter weights, 40% to 80%
- Usually stopping the set very far from failure (e.g., 10 reps with 50%)
- Increased frequency, up to five times a week
- Allowing higher reps, up to 10
- Allowing very short rest periods

Russian scientists used to firmly believe that while beginners can get stronger with weights as light as 40% and even 30% 1 RM, advanced power athletes must at least reach the 80% threshold and train in the 80% to 95% intensity zone. But they are not so certain any more. Speaks out Olympic champion hammer thrower Dr. Anatoly Bondarchuk:

> *According to our deep conviction, training loads in the zone of 95% to 100% are significantly stronger (we are not speaking of effectiveness) than 75% to 80%. If we consider the strength of the training effect coming from the weight lifted in a barbell exercise, then this is without question true. If, however, we look at this from the point of view of the long-term effectiveness of the 95%- to 100%-of-max zone and the zones of 75% to 80% on the neuromuscular system, then here it can be said that the second zone is somewhat stronger than the first.*
>
> *We did not come to this conclusion by chance. We accumulated a sufficient amount of experimental material showing that the duration of the training effect of the barbell exercises with the use of low zones of intensity can fully rival and even supersede the strength of the effect of the higher-intensity zone. We have in view that for the exercise executed—as, for example, in the 75% to 80% zone—where the number of repetitions in one set varies from 8 to 10, the strength of the effect can be higher than from those that are executed in the 95% to 100% zone, with the number of repetitions from 1 to 2. All of this once again indicates that the problem of training transfer should be looked at first of all on the neuro level and only after this on the "functional" level.*

Recall what Dan said earlier: "Coax" the 80% poundage up, instead of forcing the 100%. This is the patient approach of a professional. Marty Gallagher ponders a similar tactic—this time, with an even-lighter 50% poundage—in his classic *The Purposeful Primitive:*

> *I once received a lesson in power and strength that lasted less than 10 seconds and provided me mental fuel that has burned for twenty years. In the mid-1980's I was coaching a friend at a powerlifting competition. Coaching another lifter was George Hechter. George was a smart, sharp guy who came up as a protégé of iron icon Bill Starr. . . . On this particular day George weighed 360 pounds. He and I and a hundred other athletes and coaches were backstage scurrying around getting lifters ready to lift. George and I had just gotten through the emotional rollercoaster of squats and were filtering backstage, drained and spent. George and his athlete were walking ahead of me. As we passed the warm-up area, a squat bar still sat on the racks loaded to 505 pounds. It had been the last weight one of the lifters had used to warm-up. George walked over to the loaded bar, dipped under it, stood erect, took a step backwards and did ten perfect, no sweat reps. He wore street clothes. No belt, no warm-up, no spotters, no knee wraps, no dramatic psyche up and no big deal. He repped the weight and replaced it before anyone noticed. I noticed and as he fell back in step to catch up to his lifter I said, "You could have asked for a spot George. Shouldn't you have warmed up a bit?" I prodded. He was dismissive, "It was only 500 pounds Marty." That hit me like the old Zen joke: "What is the sound of one hand clapping?" The answer? "A slap across someone's face."*
>
> *A few weeks later I saw George squat 975 pounds at the Potomac Open as if it were 500. He was good for at least 50 pounds additional pounds on that day. In the intervening years I've replayed that 500 squat set in my brain, so casual, so easy, so effortless—still it was 500 pounds! The lesson I took from it was this: George had built his absolute strength upward to such an astounding level that 500 was "only" 50% of his single repetition maximum. To put that in context, I myself could squat 50% of what I am capable of at any point in time for 10 reps without any warm-up or drama. I would not need spotters nor would I be in any great danger with 50%. So what's the lesson?*
>
> *What if, over a protracted period rather than attempt to raise the absolute strength ceiling, the I rep max, you sought to raise the 50% base strength level? Would this reverse approach, over time, allow you to increase the absolute I rep maximum? If you could squat 400 x I and could squat 200 x 10, could you increase the 400 x I limit by working the 50% 200 x 10 limit to say 250 x 10 over time? Would tweaking the 50% poundage translate into increased absolute strength? I've deliberated on this Zen Koan for decades and it's provided me with mental fodder I still ponder.*

Indeed, even 40% to 50% weights—and even lighter, as witnessed by the Wilson-Workman deadlift routine I have written about elsewhere—can build strength. Among the groundbreaking conclusions of the famous German work by Hettinger are these two:

- The maximum training benefits are derived from using muscle tension of no less than 40% to 50% of one's 1 RM.

- Maximum training effect does not require prolonging muscle tension to the point of fatigue.

What Verkhoshansky and Siff have to say about the above is remarkable: "Although these points have been modified and extended by more recent research, they still offer useful information for the general strength training world today".

Onto the reps. If you are familiar with my work, you might be surprised to see me recommend anything over 5 reps for strength work. There is no inconsistency. When sets are pushed to RM, higher reps encourage poor technique, develop lack of tightness, and promote soreness. That is why I do not like them. When you do 10 reps with a weight you could have lifted twice as many times, none of the above is a problem. In Boris Sheyko's training plans, you will occasionally see things like . . . 60% x 9, 50% x 11. Obviously, the fastest-twitch athlete will not be challenged with the above and will keep perfect form—which is the idea.

Following are a few effective "even easier strength" (EES) plans. The first is a terrific QIII deadlift plan taught to me by John McKean, an accomplished powerlifter who has been at it since the birth of the sport. I called John after reading his article about deadlifts with bands in *Milo.* McKean did not claim to have invented anything new, but his übersimple approach caught my eye. Normally not a fan of explosive deadlifts, I was experimenting with them at that time. I had always been a "grinder," but following a couple of years' layoff from pulling due to an elbow injury, I suddenly started "dipping, gripping, and ripping." It just felt right, now that I did not have much meat in my glutes and quads. Marty Gallagher, who had handled me at a couple of meets, pointed out to me that explosiveness was my trump card, so I went with it.

John McKean is a whiz with bands.
Photo courtesy John McKean

Although I have not succeeded in pulling PRs with this plan, I had the easiest time ever keeping my "no-no-no" pull at 500 with so little, so easy work that it felt like cheating. And four wheels were going up so fast, you would have sworn it was 135. That is what makes it a perfect QIII strength regimen, in my book.

McKean explains:

> *From my past four years or more of "lighter" bar work, but with bands over the bar, I'm really convinced this is the way to go and feel YOU will enjoy your training much more! . . .*
>
> *I'd usually run downstairs, where it was set up and do five singles, emphasizing a strong "normal" initial pull, then try to accelerate the higher the lift got. Did this three or four times per week. . . . The big change, and the toughest for a long-time lifter, is to lower the poundage to train speed! The MAX you should train, ever, is 350 pounds (the magic 70% which all my experiments prove is ideal!) for a 500 deadlift. However, with a meet approaching, it is advised you go lower to 60% (and even 50% during the final few workouts). Also, don't go crazy with bands—one purple one over the bar will do. I usually just use one or two "mini-monsters" over my bars. Load the bar, step through one loop of the band after getting your stance, throw the band over the deadlift bar, and step on the end section so there's tension from the band at the start. It's that simple. . . .*
>
> *Take around 350 for five singles against a purple band three to four times weekly, and you'll be ready for well over 500 at the meet. (Just don't start there at the contest! I always take my first "warm-up" single out on the platform to set up a good mental framework. Beyond that, I don't warm up with the lift itself!!)*
>
> *Especially for us "master" lifters, this band/ballistic approach has proven to me as the only safe, sensible way to train. Knocking our heads at that brick wall known as "limit weights" can only lead to injury—the one thing that's guaranteed to ruin a competitive mindset! Band/bars will not only train a relatively underworked but important component (speed), but they can actually revive the body from injury (as I found at last weekend at the Nationals!). Good luck on your training & let 'er RIP!!*

I started with 315, not because it was some special 63% but for the sake of simplicity. Stupidly, I did not listen to John in my first workout and did 10 singles plus a few heavier ones. As McKean had predicted, my most explosive single was number 5, so from then on, I listened. Armed forces powerlifting champ Jack Reape also admonished me to stop when I was not getting any faster, so I decided not to be a knucklehead. From then on, I limited myself to 5 or 6 singles per practice, starting with 315, sometimes staying with it, sometimes going up to 335 or 355 (63, 67, and 71%, if you insist, but I was just throwing dimes on and not thinking about percentages). I did this three to four times a week, as John had recommended. If 355 felt as fast as 315, I occasionally would follow it up with 1 or 2 singles without bands with 455–475. The rest of my very QIII training consisted of 5 singles of weighted pistols, a couple handstand push-ups, and Captains of Crush® grip work—again, very low rep and low volume (e.g., 2 sets of 5 or 3 triples with the #2, only occasionally going up to a single with the #3 in a parallel set, and never on the day when I pulled heavy).

I felt strong and fresh, as one should after a QIII strength practice.

Justa's Singles is another effective EES deadlift program. The original plan goes like this: Pull daily. Do no other work for the involved muscles, although you may carry on with your regular lifting for the rest of your body. On Monday, do 3 singles with 70% 1 RM and 1 to 2 minutes of rest in between. Use compensatory acceleration. Add 2 sets of 1 daily. Five singles with the same poundage on Tuesday. Seven on Wednesday. Nine on Thursday. Eleven on Friday. Thirteen on Saturday, and 15 on Sunday. 3-5-7-9-11-13-15. On Monday, add 5 or 10 pounds, and repeat the cycle. Once a month, test your max and recalculate your 70%.

Steve Justa explains his Even Easier Strength wisdom in *Rock, Iron, Steel: The Book of Strength*:

> *The great thing about this type of training is that you will build great strength without really ever making yourself tired because the body is adjusting naturally and rhythmically....*
>
> *The target zone should be between 70% and 80% of your maximum effort....This is the zone you must stay in when training to get stronger the fastest. I believe the 70% range is better than the 80% of the max range.*
>
> *There cannot be enough said about staying in this zone to develop super strength. With me, even after 15 years of training, I still catch myself trying to jump out of the zone and constantly have to monitor my ambition of wanting to lift too heavy too fast. Nothing will stop your progress in your quest for strength faster than when you try to lift too heavy too fast.*

It is interesting that Sheyko analyzed the training loads of top Russian powerlifters and discovered that the average intensity most effective for strength gains was 70%, plus or minus 3%. He warned not to interpret this data as a recommendation to train with 70% weights exclusively:

> *Extrapolation is the ability of the nervous system to ... solve new motor tasks based on existing experience. Thanks to it, the athlete's organism, learning different skills while lifting barbells of different weights acquires the ability to correctly perform the exercise with a greater weight. One should know that monotonous repetition of a movement, for example continually training with the same barbell weight, narrows the extrapolation ability while varied repetition enhances it.*

This does not mean you should change Justa's plan, though. Just don't stay on it forever. Keep cycling it in and out of your training. I would suggest staying on Justa for as long as you are improving the first time around and later for eight weeks.

Justa's plan has been tested in the trenches by many. Writes Paul McIlroy, RKC, fighter, and world junior WDFPF deadlift champion:

> *I began powerlifting at the age of 22 after nearly 10 years on and off as a boxer. I started lifting weights at 17 years old to improve on my natural punching power for boxing. I then decided to take a break from boxing for 1 year to give powerlifting a serious push. Within 18 months I was fortunate enough to win regional, national, international and world titles in 3 different organizations simultaneously.*

Out of the three lifts my body always favored the deadlift with a first pull of 352 lbs raw and beltless at 140 lbs of body weight. Goofing around got me to 420 lbs quite quickly but I hit a brick wall soon after and even regressed a little bit! It was then that I picked up a copy of Muscle Media *magazine and seen that Charles Poliquin's* Question of Strength *column had been invaded by a Russian with an unpronounceable surname! In the bottom right hand corner of that issue Pavel wrote about a strength routine entirely based around singles, he spoke of how it wasn't uncommon to go from lifting 400 lbs to lifting 500 lbs in a year "without breaking a sweat" on this routine.*

One ***BIG*** *promise!! But immediately, from looking at the structure of the routine and how it played out, I could see how this kind of effortless perpetual progress could indeed be possible. I've wasted my fair share of time on other routines but the only program that has consistently worked for me has been the original Justa singles format. It brought my deadlift up from 420 lbs at 143 lbs body weight to about 550 lbs at 155–158 lbs body weight, raw, no belt, drug free. Furthermore . . . it's* ***EASY!*** *The Justa singles routine is one of the fastest, easy to recover from sub-maximal delights you're ever likely to come across in the powerlifting world.*

Paul McIlroy, RKC is happy to pull big. Photo by Eddie Robinson courtesy Paul McIlroy

This is why Justa's plan is a great choice for an athlete who is not a lifter. The hard Irishman understands why the plan delivers:

The reason it works so well is because the intensity (Eastern European definition, i.e., percentage of 1 RM, not Western, i.e., percentage of preserved momentary effort) is low enough to make the initial volume quickly adaptable but not too low to have a training effect on the CNS. The fact that

sub-maximal weights are used in single rep fashion allows you to really focus on your workouts as a strength skill-set practice instead of a life and death adrenaline fest guaranteed to wear down your resolve eventually. This coupled with the frequency of practice and small incremental progressions make Steve Justa's original plan a groove greasing dynamo!

Paul McIlroy proceeded to form a powerlifting club and coach a number of guys to powerlifting titles, or at least impressive strength:

So what was the total impact of the Justa singles routine on the deadlifts of my athletes? Well, I'd say about 10 to 12 guys put an average of about 100 lbs on their deadlift in about 6–9 months with some doing WAY better than that!! Ninety percent also stayed roughly the same weight, only the heavyweights gaining mass due primarily to differences in squat/bench routines and dietary habits.

Damien McErlean went from being a skinny fat kid to pulling five wheels and winning the Northern Ireland Deadlift Championships in the junior 181s category. Eighteen-year-old 132-pounder Stephen McKee took his DL from 230 to 400 (triple bodyweight) in six months and became the teen national champ in the Irish Drug-Free Powerlifting Association. Paul added a wrinkle to Stephen's routine:

For the second cycle I kept the starting weights exactly the same as the first cycle. Only this time I had Stephen stand on a 3-inch block thus extending the ROM, making the exercise more difficult. Once he had again made his way from 70% to 80% I would recycle the program, this time adding 5% to 10% to the starting weight but lifting from the floor once more. Even though the weight was up the decreased ROM made progression possible again. For the next cycle I'd keep the weights the same and add the block again, and so on and so forth.

Ben Loughrey is about to stand up with 661 pounds. Photo courtesy Paul McIlroy

Note that like Baccari and other smart trainers, McIlroy changed only one variable at a time. He did not try to increase both the weight and the ROM at the same time. Consider this variation for your training.

Paul made another intelligent adjustment for another athlete of his by reducing the training frequency to three times a week:

This drags the cycle out, making it easier to adapt to, and should be given serious consideration once you've successfully completed a couple of cycles of the original format as a means of "milking" or prolonging progress from the routine.

Three times a week is a probably the most optimal frequency for the Justa DL routine, if you have another sport to train for. Following this plan, Peter Van Merkom took his pull from 352 at 165 to 75 reps in two weeks with close to 500 pounds. He never maxed, but he has to be good for at least the high fives.

Paul offers a few useful tips for Justa DL success:

- *In the beginning of the routine I never had my athletes or myself take anything close to the full 1–2 minutes' suggested rest. It was SO easy, I felt this was excessive. I usually had them take between 5–10 seconds to start with and increased this as I seen they needed it. In the end, 1–2 minutes were taken. I felt this fast-paced (almost nonstop) start was important, as it built a kind of special endurance that made the longer rest periods to come seem like a joy ride. This in effect was an "organic" approach to cycling the rest periods, as well as the volume and intensity. I feel it extended the cycle and produced greater results.*

- *Don't go over 80% on any of the DL variations as a top end weight! I've tried this, burned out. Potential injury comes fast—don't risk it. The only way this can be done successfully is in the WSB variation Ben Loughrey used. This is made possible due to the vastly reduced frequency.*

- *Don't do any other assistance work for your lower back or hamstrings. Waist work is OK, but keep the resistance high and the volume low.*

Damien McEarlean.
Photo courtesy Paul McIlroy

A smart coach who knows that one size does not fit all, McIlroy put another one of his athletes on the vintage Westside Barbell singles cycle, which calls for pulling only once a week:

Week 1:	70% x 1/15 (reps/sets), 1 minute rest between sets
Week 2:	75% x 1/12, 1 minute
Week 3:	80% x 1/8–10, 1.5 minutes
Week 4:	80% x 1/8
Week 5:	90% x 1/1–3, 2 minutes
Week 6:	Max or recycle with 70%

A few comments on the Westside DL cycle, above, and the cycles below: Louie Simmons designed them to be used in conjunction with a lot of other exercises—heavy squats, good mornings, and so on. Doing them will build a bigger deadlift but not leave the athlete whose sport is not powerlifting much energy to do anything else.

I suggest that you do the following: Increase the frequency to three times in two weeks—Monday, Friday, next week's Wednesday—and do no other deadlift/squat/good morning-type exercises. Do not max after the first cycle, which will last a month. For the second cycle, add 10 to 20 pounds to all workouts, and finish with "sort of maxing." Then switch to an altogether different ES or EES regimen.

Explains Ozolin: "The principle of novelty and variety denies the possibility of repetition of one large cycle with the same training contents. Experience shows that such repetition, in the best-case scenario, is possible only twice. Then work capacity and results decrease." While one can hardly call the above a "large cycle," the advice is still valid. After two, you will be hitting the point of diminishing returns.

Following is another WSB DL cycle for you to consider:

Week 1: 65% x 1/15, 30–40 seconds rest between sets in all workouts
Week 2: 79% x 1/15
Week 3: 75% x 1/2
Week 4: 80% x 1/8
Week 5: 85% x 1/6
Week 6: Max or recycle

And here is one more for the SQ and the BP. I would do this twice a week and skip the DL for a cycle or two. Or alternate SQ/BP and BP/DL every other day.

Week 1: 70% x 3/8, 2 minutes rest between sets
Week 2: 75% x 3/8, 2 minutes
Week 3: 80% x 2/6, 2 minutes
Week 4: 85% x 2/5, 3 minutes
Week 5: 80% x 2, 85% x 2, 90% x 2, 5 minutes
Week 6: Max or recycle

Readers familiar with WSB training will rub their heads and point out that the above cycle has not been used at Westside since the time of the George Bush Sr. administration. Now, WSB uses lighter weights to emphasize power, rather than absolute strength. This may be true, but without this cycle, you will not develop absolute strength and will have to add some heavy lifting (as they do at WSB on "max-effort days"). That is fine, but you will have to complicate your programming.

If you have the knowledge, go for it. Contemporary WSB dynamic effort cycles happen to be popular with some Russian full-contact fighters. Andrey Kochergin is a fan of benching with 50% to 55% for 5 to 7 triples, with 1 minute of rest and with an emphasis on explosion. But that is pure dynamic effort, not meant to build strength. With moderately heavy weights, as in the old Westside cycles, you will be building strength as well as power. Efficiency.

Another effective QIII deadlift plan was designed by powerlifter Bob Gaynor. This 63-year-old gent pulls high 600s in the 198-pound class, and his plan is a rare PL routine adaptable to almost any power athlete. According to the author, this program "can be continually used and is designed in a way to change enough to prevent mental fatigue and still make progress":

- DL every five days. This is a DL specialist plan that has no squats. Three times in two weeks—Monday, Friday, next week's Wednesday—may be a more user-friendly frequency.

Weeks 1–4

- 3 x 3. Start "with a weight you can do without too much trouble." Add 10 to 15 pounds a week.

Weeks 5–8

- 3 x 3 starting with the weight from week 2.

Weeks 9–12 (Optional)

- 3 x 3 starting with the weight from week 6

The second cycle is identical to the first except for one detail: You will be pulling from a 2.5- to 3-inch deficit, standing on a block or with smaller plates. Start lighter—for example, 450 if used 500 in week 1.

An option: Jump 10 pounds a week while jumping 15 in the previous cycle. Do this for 4 to 8 weeks. (Powerlifters, compete at the end of the fourth, eighth, or twelfth week.)

Now, you have 12 to 20 weeks of heavy pulling under your belt. The third cycle is off the floor with red or purple half-inch bands. Do 3 x 3 for four weeks and a single with bands in week 5.

The fourth cycle is with the deficit and bands. Do four or five weeks only, perhaps only singles.

"What have we done?" asks Bob Gaynor. "We have trained for six or eight months and should be much stronger. What we have not done is burn out."

Bob Gaynor shows 680 who is the boss (below and next page). Photos courtesy Bob Gaynor

The 40-Day Workout might be an excellent way to progress through any diet strategy that involves a set number of weeks. After ending the 28 days or six weeks of the diet, your strength will take off as you ease off the strict nutritional efforts.

Of course, now where do you go? Well, let's just take one example: the full-body explosive movement. Do each of the following for just one 40-Day Workout:

- One-handed swings (DARC)
- One-handed swings
- Two-handed swings
- Overhead throws for height with a med ball
- Overhead throws for distance with a med ball
- Forward throws for distance with a med ball
- Overhead throws for height with a shot
- Overhead throws for distance with a shot
- Forward throws for distance with shot
- Power snatch off a high box
- Power snatch off a low box
- Power snatch from the hang
- Power snatch from the floor
- Power clean off a high box
- Power clean off a low box
- Power clean from the hang
- Power clean from the floor
- Clean grip snatch off a high box
- Clean grip snatch off a low box
- Clean grip snatch from the hang
- Clean grip snatch from the floor

Honestly, it's just as easy to do this with push and pull variations, but the deadlift and ab moves might not get you up to 20 variations.

See *Power to the People Professional* for exotic variations of the deadlift, like the Russian deadlift from the edge, or use very simple same-but-different variations. Using 45-, 35-, and 25-pound plates gives you three variations. Add sumo and conventional to the above, and you have six. Charles Poliquin uses three grips: clean, snatch, and one in between. Here are another three: Deadlifting standing on a soft mat to increase the leg drive is a cool Westside DL. A Russian favorite half-deadlift, from the platform to the knees and back, is another good one. Fill in the rest with lockouts.

Your training sessions should focus on quality. Please don't invent work force production numbers and vectors and timed weight ratios to make 5 crappy push-ups sound impressive. Quality has always been king in both fitness and performance. And the key to quality is repetition schemes.

Important point: Like Pavel said at the RKC, we can design a workout to destroy you. Hey, here you go: Get up right now and do 1,000 swings. You will be trashed. So what? Never confuse working out with training. I'm a sinner, too, on this principle, and I have the scars and surgeries to prove it. So, yes, there are times to work out, to train to limits, and to exceed limits, but most of the time, focus on quality.

So, what is the key to quality? I have a simple answer for most people: Control your repetitions. No, what you are about to read is not always exact and perfect for your needs at this time or that time. But consider carefully the three principles I have discovered with repetition selection.

Principle 1: The Whole-Body Movements and the "Rule of 10"

(snatch, clean and jerk, deadlift, and squat variations for elite athletes)

Pavel spoke in detail earlier about the "rule of 10," so I won't repeat it here. Basically, I discovered, as many have, that around 10 reps is the right number for whole-body lifts—for an experienced lifter—in a workout.

The longer I read programs from advanced lifters, like Hossein Rezazadeh and his 6 to 8 singles ONLY in a workout (and that's spread over three lifts), the more I think that I have been right for a while. Much of my insight comes from personal experience and an article by Dr. Randall Strossen in *Milo*, where the superheavyweight Olympic champion's training was outlined.

Working out twice a day, six times a week, he has a lighter morning workout:

Power Snatch

70 x 3 singles
120 x 3 singles
170 x 3 singles
(These are all in kilos, but many readers might not be able to do them in pounds.)

Power Clean and Jerks

Singles with 120, 170, and 220 (!)

Front Squats

220 x 2
270 x 2
300 or 320 x 1

Here's his afternoon workout:

Snatch

Singles with 70, 120, 170, 200

Clean and Jerk

Singles with 120, 170, 220, and either 250 or 260

Back Squats

Singles with 270, 320, and 370

Readers, feel free to go heavier, if you like.

Basically, then, the rule of 10 means that you have probably 10 real reps in a workout with a big lift like the deadlift, the snatch, or the clean and jerk. If you're doing PTTP, it fits perfectly. The workouts are simple:

- 3 sets of 5
- 2 sets of 5
- 5 reps, 3 reps, 2 reps (one of my favorite workouts)
- 6 singles (yes 6, not 10—10 ten serious singles will really tap you out)
- 1 set of 10 (a "tonic" workout that will really make you feel better)

You see, these are all around 10 reps, and the experience of many lifters reflects this reality.

Here is a two-week example of how I do this for my older, advanced athletes:

	Monday	Tuesday	Wednesday	Friday	Saturday
Snatch	2 x 5	5-3-2	2 x 5	6 x 1	2 x 5
Clean and jerk	6 x 1	5-3-2	2 x 5	6 x 1	2 x 5
Front squat	2 x 5	5-3-2	2 x 5	6 x 1	3 x 3

If necessary, add a "tonic" session when you're not up to your best. Certainly, it can get more complex than this, but you don't really need to make it that way. Honestly, complexity rarely trumps the basics when it comes to training.

While I was working on this chapter, an elite American thrower contacted me. For the record, this wasn't necessarily unusual, because I'm beginning to see a pattern in the athletes who contact me:

- These athletes have "been there, done that." Often, they seem to realize that they have one more Olympiad or one more set of trials in the tank.
- These athletes have tried just about everything and more to improve.
- These athletes have large bruises on their foreheads from slamming their heads against the wall.
- These athletes have come across this notion that Pavel and I discuss to death: *Quality trumps quantity.*
- These athletes admit to both "Knowing what to do" and "Having no idea what to do" in the same sentence.

So, I give them this advice:

We need to remember we are throwers that lift, not lifters that throw.

In fact, this advice is valuable for anyone from QII, QIII, or QIV.

Recently, I had a thrower tell me that he simply does this training with a basic traditional deadlift, the bench press, and the ab wheel (just get in reps—don't make it an act of war), and the results are illuminating. As Dr. Tom Fahey noted to me many years ago that once you are strong, the only thing you need to work on is absolute strength (the DL and BP fit nicely). Everything else will stay in place.

Principle 2: Grinding Lifts and "Three Ladders and Three Rungs"

(kettlebell presses, bent presses, two-hands anyhow, and the myriad of slow grinding movements)

For those of you too cheap to buy *Enter the Kettlbebell!* this is basically the rite-of-passage program. But one small thing: I have found that somewhere between 15 and 25 reps is the right range for working the grinds. From my recent experiences, the basic moves, including nearly all the presses, are best done in this range.

For one thing, it is a reasonable workout. Three sets of 5, for example, is what most people actually end up doing on the 5 x 5 workouts and variations. That's a lot of serious front squats, if you aren't counting warm-ups. In the kettlebell world, that would be 3 ladders:

1-2-3
1-2-3
1-2-3

That is 18 quality reps. Sure, we have all done more, but one of the issues I want you to consider is *repeatable* workouts. I think I have made my career on simply continually coming back to the gym and track and getting the work in.

Steve Shafley wrote an article about his experience with ladders in Dan's online magazine a couple of years ago. A drug-free powerlifter with typical shoulder dings, in the beginning of the program, Steve had a 335 close-grip max. He started doing (1, 2, 3) x 3 ladders three times a week—occasionally, two days in a row—with the starting weight of 275, which happened to be is 5 RM (a good call). He would add 5 or 10 pounds to the bar if he made all three ladders, and if he did not, he stayed with the same weight until he did. The first four weeks of his training looked like this:

Week 1
Day 1: 275 x (1, 2, 3) x 3
Day 2: 285 x (1, 2, 3), (1, 2)
Day 3: 285 x (1, 2, 3) x 2

Week 2
Day 1: 285 x (1, 2, 3) x 3
Day 2: 290 x (1, 2, 3) x 2
Day 3: 290 x (1, 2, 3) x 3

Week 3
Day 1: 295 x (1, 2) x 3
Day 2: 295 x (1, 2, 3) x 3
Day 3: 305 x (1, 2, 3) x 2

Week 4
Day 1: 305 x (1, 2, 3) x 3
Day 2: 315 x (1, 2, 2), (1, 2), 1
Day 3: 315 x (1, 2, 3), (1, 2)

In week 5, the lifter tested his CGBP max and got 365—a whopping 30-pound improvement. His training partner made similar gains.

Shafley has made some useful observations on using ladders in what we call the easy strength format:

> *It's about staying fresh and crisp. It's not about grinding them out and gritting your teeth. Let the volume do the work. The ladder technique, in my opinion, is a powerful yet underused tool. The concept of lots of practice; moderate, progressively heavier weights; and low fatigue really works well for many people. The emphasis really is on managing fatigue. The RPE becomes valuable when performing ladders. I've found that the last rep in a ladder should be of "medium" to "hard" difficulty. If you are doing ladders for the same movement multiple times a week, it should be closer to "medium." If you are only doing ladders once a week, then you can move into the "hard" or even "very hard" category, as long as the repetitions are being performed in an OK or preferably crisp fashion.... Note for a moment that using a ladder style of sets and reps can very easily be dropped into almost any existing framework.*

The whole issue of volume always needs to be addressed. Certainly, we have all done those contests where you bench 100 pounds 100 times just to one-up a friend. But that isn't really a training program, that is just fun. Keep having fun, but plan things occasionally, too.

Principle 3: The Explosive Lifts and the "Fast 10 and 20"

One of the great insights, among many, that I picked up at the RKC is the idea of doing 20 swings with one kettlebell and 10 swings with two kettlebells. After doing literally hundreds of swings a day, I noted that my technique held up fine in that 10 and 20 range. It is the basic teaching of sports: Don't let quantity influence quality. In other words, 10 good reps is far better than dozens of crappy reps. If you want more volume, just do more sets.

Others have noted the same issue. If I can do 100 snatches with the 24 or 16, what additional good will come from doing 120? Yes, I know: In competition, this is the key. But to a non-GS athlete, 100 snatches is probably way above the level necessary for improvement. If you can get what you need in 20 snappy swings, why add more reps at the expense of technique?

There are absolutely times when you should do more than 20. There are times when you want to do all kinds of things. There are times, though—known as "most of the time"—when you should just keep moving ahead. I usually call these the "punch the clock" workouts, and I think doing them is the key to staying in the game.

So, you may ask, is this enough? Let's look at a sample workout:

- **Deadlift:** 5-3-2 with a heavy final double
- **Kettlebell press left and kettlebell press right:** 1-2-3/1-2-3 . . . 1-2-3/1-2-3 . . . 1-2-3/1-2-3
- **Double kettlebell swings:** 10/10/10/10/10

That's the key, I think. It is repeatable. Should I say it again?

With kettlebells, I really often have up to three choices—sometimes, only one—for an exercise. The 53 is the perfect choice for snatches, but I *could* use a 70. That is a 17-pound *could!!!* So, I have to back off the reps, tighten my butt—well, you know the drill. I have to take a lot of energy to rethink and reassess the movement. I need to think about the grip, check my feet ("claw the ground"), load up, and snap. You might get away with a lazy finish with the 35, but the 70 will punish you for your momentary lapse of will.

Less choice means less mental RAM going out the door. The more you choose, the less you have left over to push the workout. Those leg "innie" and "outie" machines can convince you that you are working your legs. You're not, but you can use your brain to convince you that you are. Double kettlebell front squats are too light? Move up a size—that's about a 32- to 34-pound jump! This is an increase in weight—a commitment! That 34-pound "fact" is going to make you reconsider jumping—or just maybe it won't.

I think there is value in training extremely mixed groups. I have cheerleaders, Division I football prospects, elite throwers, skateboarders, and guys who will one day take care of your taxes for you. With such a mixed group, you have to be insightful about how you train the big moves, like the clean, the squat, and the deadlift. Pavel still seems amazed at how I coax huge deadlifts from my athletes. (Four hundred is more the norm than the exception for my boys, and remember—most of them are too young to drive.) So, let's review my secret "easy easy deadlift protocol."

I think the first key (always!) in thinking about any lift, movement, supplement, or idea before adding it to a program is this: What's the least I can do to utilize this new thing? In other words, avoid the problem most people have with any new groovy idea: If a little helps, a lot will be better.

When creatine first snuck out of the quiet confines of some track and field guys and hit the greater world, I was astounded to find out how many guys got massive cramps and diarrhea from using it. I then found out that guys would triple (and more) the recommended serving. The same is true for fat-loss supplements. Some people have had to check themselves into the hospital to slow down a raging heartbeat.

Please don't ask me to repeat what Dr. Brunetti told me about a patient who got some Viagra and took four times the right dose. Don't make me even think about it again—please! So, I think that the deadlift is a crucial human movement. I believe it is part of a typical strength athlete's program. In fact, I think everyone can benefit from some pulling from the floor.

Now, before you ask about the Viagra overdose, think about the deadlift overdose: It's a great lift, it does wonders—now stop it. Don't go there. And where is *there? There* is this idea, this notion, that if a little is good, then a massive amount is better.

Back to the premise: The deadlift is a basic human movement and deserves to be in everyone's training regimen.

But now you may well ask, Why do your athletes deadlift so much? So much *what?* Are we talking volume, intensity, or load? We do a lot of deadlifts, but we never go heavy—except every so often!

You may still ask, Why do your athletes deadlift so much? Ah, you mean the numbers on the wall. You are referring to those staggering max numbers that amaze some people and scare some parents. You are discussing the deadlift max.

I need to be clear about the deadlift max: I don't think one necessarily EVER has to attempt it. I never have—not even one time! In junior college, the Pacifica Barbell Club record in my weight class for the deadlift was 550. So, one day, Dick Notmeyer and I decided to break it. I went to 555 and made the lift, and I owned the record. A year or so later, Bob Arello challenged me to deadlift 600. In the gym, we didn't have many small plates (they break easily under lots of use), so I pulled 605. A few years later, in the wee hours of the morning (3 a.m.), I was the last guy deadlifting at a contest and just told the guy to add 5 pounds (2.5 kilos, actually) to the amount the guy just missed. I pulled a 628 deadlift.

Today, my students follow my exact plan!

I can see some hands going up, so let me save you some energy: What plan?

You can drive your deadlift up to amazing numbers by NEVER deadlifting heavy. In fact, I sometimes think it is actually counterproductive to pull heavy deadlifts. But you need to hear this: *You need to lift hard in a wide range of movements to have a massive deadlift without deadlifting.*

My athletes front squat every workout. They do lots of hip mobility work. They snatch and clean and jerk all the time. They swing, snatch, and move kettlebells every session. They deadlift, clean curl (power curl), and do pull-ups as part of their normal day. Most of my athletes train at 50% of their max deadlift BUT mix them with other lifts and keep the reps fairly high on the movement. And then, just a few times a year—and for many, just once a year—they go after a number.

Personally, I see no value in adding 10 pounds to your max deadlift. If you pull 400, I would love to see you attack your quicklifts, grind out some squats, do some hurdle work, jump on a few boxes, pull some sleds, carry some farmer's bars, and swing some kettlebells for a long time before you max again. And when you do, I'd love to see you jump right up to 450 or 500, instead of tossing on a few puny plates. Attack your max!

Have a friendly competition or enter a meet, but don't just wander in by yourself, load the bar, and say "Ooooh, that FEELS heavy." Pretend your kid is under the plates, and wedge it off him. If you don't have kids, pretend it's Pavel!

So, here is a typical training circuit. It is called "On the Minute", and it works well with large groups. To me, a large group is 30 to 80 athletes at once. We set up our stations so at on the minute, the athletes perform the reps—let's say 3 in this example. Athlete 1 goes first and his partner spots, and then they switch. You can get up to four athletes a station, but it gets crowded.

Then, we add some weight. It takes a time or two to nail down the weight increases to manage the number of sets. I have found that in large groups, 8 sets is ideal. Many will argue with me on that large number, but the first sets are light warm-ups, and the speed of the rest period keeps the load down.

On the Minute: 8 Sets of 3

- Front squats
- Bench press
- Hurdle walkovers: Flight of 10 hurdles—The group just marches over them each minute; it's a hip mobility drill and a bit of a rest.
- Backward sled pulls: In this case, a 20-meter sled pull; hand the reins over to your partner, and just do 1 a minute.
- Deadlifts

In big groups, athletes will start at every lift and move to the next exercise after finishing the 8 sets. (Logically, this should take 8 minutes, but it will really take more like 10 with transitions.)

For 8 sets of 3 on the minute for deadlifts, a strong athlete will still start with just 135 and probably not even sneak up on much past 255 for the workout. With all the movements, this is not the time to crank up a big pull. But the lifter will be "greasing" the movement with 24 repetitions all done under the extra load of time, partner issues, and the aggregate work down through the workout. (This is true for all the movements.) Moreover, the lifter is also stressing the body in so many ways that supercompensation is just around the corner with some rest and food.

When it is time to max, be sure you have nothing crucial to do for about three weeks. In other words, don't max deadlift the day before the Olympic trials. You are simply trying to get a measure of your absolute strength. Honestly, a couple of standing long jumps a few times a year would be as good, but I have the same issue: I like to move heavy iron.

For the record, I have no interest in what you "could have" made. Please, no failures on max deadlifts. Just make the lifts! For whatever reason, max DLs seem to take a ton out of your CNS, and it doesn't come back easily. Max DL misses seem to take even more out of the body. So again, make the damn lifts!

I don't suggest more than 2 max attempts, and most people are only good for 6 DLs in a heavy workout. So, I consider that warm-up with 135 for a single part of the 6. If you don't know how to deadlift perfectly or at least properly, don't use a max as a teaching unit. Please, know what you are doing when you grip the bar, and leave it all on the table for these few attempts.

Does it work? Oh, absolutely. I love to tease men who are using an exaggerated vocabulary about some minute fitness detail and tell them that they are almost as strong as my homecoming queen with a 355 deadlift. So, save those max efforts for max efforts!

Can a powerlifter use this approach? Well, there are a few issues:

1. It's not so much the grip, but I worry about the skin of the hands. Maximal DLs tend to rip the hands in a way that is honestly hard to mimic. The hand toughness needed to yank a huge weight off the ground is hard to train outside yanking huge plates off the ground.

2. Second, there is a need for rooting, wedging, and synchronizing everything that is hard to practice outside of deadlifts.

But for pure absolute strength gains, I think it is still possible to harvest benefits from nondeadlifting activities. I think a good deadlift coach probably has a number of arrows in his deadlifting quiver and can pick and choose elements to focus on—and to ignore—over the course of a career. Some athletes will flourish on more pure deadlift work, and others will just step up to the bar at a meet and pull the bar off the floor. So, let me be completely clear: A powerlifter's deadlift training should come under the heading "It depends!"

There are a few drills that I think all athletes should use to increase their deadlift. But they are so simple, that few will consider them!

- **Thick-bar deadlifts:** If you don't have a thick bar, wrap some towels around a normal bar to thicken it up. Use the C grip (also called the "raptor grip" by me), and arrange it so you can't get your fingers and thumbs to meet. Now, deadlift away. Try as hard as you can to jerk the bar off the ground by shoving your hips straight to the sky. Go ahead—try! You will see that you can't. The thick-bar deadlift insists on perfect technique without an ounce of teaching from me!

- **10-rep deadlifts:** Another secret that will challenge your thinking. How many times do you have to do something to master it? In discus throwing, we say 10,000 moves a year. While maybe you don't need to do that many DLs, you need to do some, right?

A few years ago, I rediscovered that heavy deadlifts really beat up athletes. They are so competitive, and their "never say no" mentality makes them tired, beat-up people. So, I began working with really light reps. If a female athlete can pull 315, I have her do 135 for tens. It is tonic, in the older sense of the word. The athlete can work on technique without any CNS hit, and the lower back stays happy. It works. I don't know why, but it does.

So, when programming with these ideas, stay at the lower end of training sessions. Two deadlift sessions a week is about right for most people. Certainly, the deadlift is a basic human movement, and everything that is done in athletics, life, and the weight room will be elbowing your interest in increasing your deadlift. My solution is to keep the actual deadlift sessions low but to acknowledge that there will be a lot of work done on the movement in training and life.

It is better to have three tonic sessions and a thick-bar session over two weeks and keep you and your athletes fresh than to risk the condition that can only be called "deadlift burnout." If you have gone to the well too many times in the DL, you will recognize it. Certainly, doing this will have a value for a time, but overall, the risks outweigh the rewards. Don't ignore the value of these easy days, as they seem to put a lot of power behind the big attempts.

Years ago, my friend Dr. Jim Wright said something that got burned into my brain: "Consistency and moderation over intensity." Not nearly as sexy as "Do or die!" or some other juvenile T-shirt slogan, but you could not think of a better set of directions for durable performance.

You are about to meet a man who has done just that. He is a military special operator whose name I will withhold due to the nature of his duty. Let us call him "Victor." I met this quiet professional at one of our RKC military courses. He was capable of a strict pull-up with 160 pounds of extra weight at a bodyweight of 195 pounds (and one-arm chins, naturally). He could close Iron Mind's #2.5 Captains of Crush® gripper, 237.5 pounds strong, for 3 reps without a set. And he had run over 10 ultramarathons, from 50 to 100 miles! Any of these feats is an accomplishment, but combining either the first or second feat with the third is unheard of—especially if one considers that this man is not a pampered professional athlete but a warrior with many combat deployments under his belt.

I had to know more. Victor graciously described his training:

- ***Low mileage.*** *I only ran 30 miles per week in preparation for the 100-miler. The most important training event for ultramarathons is the weekly long run. I kept my heart rate low and breathed through my nose during training runs, and I think that this helped to minimize muscle damage. I can run 20 miles on a Sunday and still perform strength exercises on Monday. The key is having the LOW INTENSITY. I use a heart rate monitor, and I stay at 60% to 65% of my MHR. This means that I am often walking on the hills. If I ran 20 miles at 70% to 75% MHR, my recovery time would be much longer. I would do high-intensity track or hill intervals on one day during the week, but the interval workout never lasted longer than 30 minutes. I keep the intervals pretty intense though.*

- ***Fueling.*** *I am religious about using proper fueling for all long distance events....*

- ***Prior experience.*** *I did my first 50-mile race 11 years ago, and I have completed over 10 ultramarathons since then. I know how my body will react after long distances, and this experience helps with the mental side of the sport. I have also completed many similar types of endurance events in my military training. Having this experience is very beneficial. I know that I can walk out the door anytime/anywhere and run a marathon pretty easily.*

- ***The hand strength and COC stuff is just fun to do.*** *I train them "grease the groove" style. Of course, it helps that I have been doing literally 100s of pull-ups per week (on average) for the last 14 years. I also have done a lot of rock climbing in my past, which really helps with grip strength.*

- ***Variety.*** *I have enough variety in my training (yoga, running, biking, kettlebells, clubs, calisthenics) to help keep me injury free. I try to get 1 or 2 days of yoga per week. Sometimes I go to a class, and sometimes on my own. I work the basic poses and focus on releasing some of* *the tension that comes from lots of running and strength training. The yoga has been great for injury prevention. I also do not lift any other weights besides my single 53-lb. kettlebell and my two 25-lb. clubs. The only 1 RM training that I do is with the COC. I used to do presses and deadlifts after reading your* Power to the People! *but I felt my ego pushing me harder and faster than my body wanted to go. So I decided to limit myself to one kettlebell and two clubs and just focus on adding repetitions and intensity. Staying injury free has helped me to maintain consistent progress for the last 10 years.*

- ***I rarely train for more than 30 minutes per day.*** *The only exception to this would be a weekly long run (3+ hours) and a weekly trail run (50 minutes). I have always done lots of trail running, and I find that the trails are much easier on the legs. The steep trails keep things fun and help to prevent overuse injuries. I also keep my exercise selection pretty minimal: push-ups, pull-ups, swings, TGUs, club mills/swipes, windmill, goblet squat. That is pretty much it.*

I attribute most of my success to consistency. I have been training almost daily since I was 14 years old, and I am also fortunate to have a job that requires me to stay in shape. I also don't think that there is any reason why strength and endurance have to be mutually exclusive.

The concept of "easy endurance" fits perfectly with "easy strength".

In the mid-1990s, a curious book came out in the States: *Body, Mind, and Sport,* by John Douillard. Given its focus on endurance sports, apparent dislike of hard training and beef, and heavy doses of New Age discussions of Ayurveda, it is not likely that many of our readers have read it. At least one did, though: Victor.

The book was dedicated to improving one's performance by reducing the effort to 50%, enjoying the process, and not focusing on the result. The author cited a University of Texas at Austin study of goal-oriented and process-oriented people in the workplace. Unexpectedly, it was not the hypercompetitive Type A's who were doing more for the company, making more money, and getting more raises and promotions. It was the folks who were enjoying their jobs.

Ironically, not getting wrapped up in the results may deliver higher gains. I had heard that before. One of the best pistol shooters in the Russian armed forces made a breakthrough in his accuracy when a coach told him, "You know, you have the right to miss."

One of Douillard's techniques was practicing a competitive sport without keeping score. In his words: "Focusing on the score attaches you to the result. Focusing on the process lets you access your greatest skill and increases your fun." That rang true.

When I was working on my running in preparation for my military service, at least once a week, I would leave my watch at home and go as far as I could while staying totally relaxed. I would draw out my breaths as far as comfortably possible, taking a series of partial inhalations, one per step, and then partial exhalations, one per step again. It took several steps—say, six—to complete one breathing cycle. Regularly, I scanned my body for hidden tension and released it by "breathing out" through the tight muscles and by shaking them off. I would keep my mouth closed, but not tightly, as a relaxed jaw is essential to effortless running. Even after weeks when I did no other kind of running—no hard runs, no hills, no intervals, no running with weight—I could race any distance up to 10K very fast, if I chose to. All I had to do was add some "gas" to the relaxation, and I flew.

Nose-only breathing was later stressed in my unit. They sometimes had us run with a mouthful of water—a brilliant self-limiting exercise in the best Gray Cook tradition. Some Russian marathoners hold a handkerchief in their teeth for the same purpose of preventing panicky and inefficient mouth breathing.

Not surprisingly, nose-only breathing and keeping the heart rate low were key components of the *Body, Mind, and Sport* program. The inventive author figured out a way to "make it a competitive endeavor. For example, . . . run around the track and the winner be the one who not only finishes first, but has the slowest breath rate and heart rate." Here is how he scored the winners: "Finish time + heart rate + (breath rate x 3). The lowest score wins. I multiply the breath by 3 to emphasize its importance."

Victor stresses, "The low HR and nose breathing are essential. After a few months of consistent practice, nose-breathing should be used for the tempo run as well. Nose breathing teaches breath control, and also acts as a 'governor' that helps to prevent overtraining." This is especially important to an athlete for whom running endurance is not the number-one priority.

Endurance or strength? Bondarchuk makes a stunning revelation that the harder you push the body, the more stubbornly it refuses to change:

> *In our practice, with each year we have become more convinced that the stronger our desires to significantly increase the level of achievement, . . . the less the effect. . . . This is explained by the fact that the stronger the complex of training effects, then the more harmony there is in the defense functions in the body. . . . This in every way possible creates barriers or prevents a new level of adaptation, where in the process of restructuring it is necessary to expend a significant amount of energy resources. . . .*
>
> *The defense function of the body systems in high level athletes is more "trained" than in low level athletes. From here a very "bold" conclusion follows, that the process of increasing sports mastery takes place at the same level as the process of developing defense functions. In the end result, the defense functions prevail over most of the time of sports development. . . . Up to this time, all of this is a "superbold" hypothesis, giving food for very "fantastic" propositions, but there is something in all of this. . . . Today it is only sufficiently clear that in the process of sports improvement, the body always defends itself against the irritants acting upon it.*

The ability to differentiate between laziness and doing just the right amount to get the job done is a mark of a winner. Recalls AAU American bench press record holder Jack Reape: "I spent the first half of my training career learning to work harder and never miss workouts, and the second half learning when to sometimes go easier and when to back off." Let us hope this book will provide you with a shortcut to this process.

CHAPTER 4

Plyometrics—Demystified. Heavy Lifting—Acquitted.

Necessity is the mother of invention. In the late 1950s, Yuri Verkhoshansky was coaching high-jumpers at the Moscow Aviation Institute. The young coach was frustrated by the absence of winter track and field facilities at the school, and he "was looking for something better to do than skiing." He found a rusty barbell and plates under the stairs and became the first Soviet coach to implement this now-common tool into track athletes' training.

Verkhoshansky's jumpers were doing full squats with 120 kilograms and the establishment scoffed, sounding like a Pilates commercial: "Jumpers and sprinters need deers' muscles, not bulls' muscles!" Then came the spring, and the results the coach's charges posted raised a lot of eyebrows. Suddenly, the young specialist was no longer mocked but copied.

Getting stronger made the athletes fly higher, but eventually, they hit the wall. Lanky jumpers, with their birdlike bones, started complaining about sore backs. The solution came by accident. In the process of doing biomechanical analysis, Verkhoshansky learned that the jumpers experience forces around 300 kilograms during the push-off. The young coach knew that his athletes could not squat anywhere near that poundage. He decided to take advantage of dynamic eccentric loading to allow them to generate such forces. Depth jumps were born. The rest is history.

If I may, Pavel, this history needs to be studied. When the plyometrics boom hit the States (even though Pat Matzdorf used them in the 1960s to break the world record in the high jump), the movement exploded. It was the newest "answer" in the coach's arsenal. Sadly, many elite athletes' careers ended far too early from the tremendous injuries caused by plyos. Moreover, many coaches forgot the basic techniques and tactis and had their athletes leaping and bounding—surely, expecting their athletes to improve by leaps and bounds.

Let us talk about depth jumps, or "plyometrics," and then revisit absolute strength and heavy lifting.

When famous Soviet javelin thrower Yanis Lusis went overboard by depth jumping off 1.5 meters (5 feet), he experienced such a sharp increase in his speed-strength qualities that it affected his sprinting rhythm. He had no time to adapt his technique to his new strength before the Tokyo Olympics, and this cost him the supposedly certain gold. "The training effect of depth jumps on development of explosive strength is extremely high. In this they have no equal among other means of strength preparation. It has been confirmed by a series of studies," stated Professor Verkhoshansky, also citing a laundry list of studies.

As explained by the impact method's inventor:

> *A muscle pre-stretch takes place in a number of strength exercises with weights—for instance, squats or jumps with a barbell held on the shoulders. However, it is not as intense as when the velocity is braked after a free fall, where the pre-stretch has an impact nature. This is why the method of muscle stimulation by absorbing the kinetic energy of the fall was called "impact."*

To do a depth jump, step off an elevation—don't jump off!—fall straight down, hit the deck, and immediately rebound up or up and forward. Land on the balls of your feet, your legs tensed and nearly straight. Do not squat deep. Rebound as soon as possible and as forcefully as possible, with a vigorous arm swing. Verkhoshansky recommended motivating yourself for a more powerful jump by aiming for a certain mark on the ground, if you jump for distance, or for a suspended object—no low-hanging fruit, Comrade!—if you go for height.

Another Russian expert, A. Falameev, offers an excellent description of a perfect depth jump:

> *The step-down is done in such a way that assures that the body falls strictly vertically. Step of a pommel horse or another gymnastic apparatus with, say, your left foot while slightly leaning forward. The right foot joins the left as the fall begins. Lay dense rubber on the floor to soften the impact... . Land on slightly bent legs. First the balls of both feet make contact with the rubber, then the heels. You should not allow deep knee bending after the landing. A deep semi-squat will interfere with the following push-off and the performance of a quick jump. However, an excessively shallow squat depth is not desirable either. Not only does the force of the impact increase, but it becomes difficult to push off effectively.... Don't allow a stop after the landing; you should immediately make a powerful jump.... The athlete should interpret ... the landing and the following ... take-off as one single movement.*

Verkhoshansky and Siff add an important subtlety:

Breath should be held and never released during the contact phase or any other phase where maximal effort is to be produced. Exhalation during any landing phase reduces overall stability and increases the loading on the spine during depth-jumping.

Siff adds:

> *It is vital that the athlete holds the breath during the amortization and early propulsion phase to stabilize the body, offer pneumatic shock absorption and to increase the rebound force. Forced exhalation should accompany the remainder of the propulsion phase. Footwear or the floor covering should not be very soft or excessively shock absorbent, since this may impair ankle stability, diminish the storage of elastic energy in the tendons (and other connective tissues) and delay the triggering of the positive support reaction [a strength-boosting reflex explained in* Power to the People!*—P.T.] of the foot contacting the floor.*

Falameev recommends starting the depth-jump practice with joint-mobility drills followed by easy jumps—for example, depth jumps from 1 foot. He offers the following height guidelines: 0.3 to 0.7 meters (approximately 1 to 2 1/3 feet) for regular-sized athletes and a maximum of 0.5 to 0.6 meters (approximately 1 2/3 to 2 feet) for those over 220 pounds.

Verkhoshansky suggests a more aggressive depth range for the best results: 0.75 to 1.15 meters (approximately 2-1/3 to 3-3/4 feet). He explains that at greater heights, the transition from the eccentric to concentric work is too long. Naturally, he does not advise to jump into (no pun intended) these heights from the get-go but to start low and gradually progress to the recommended heights. Verkhoshansky and Siff stress that if the momentum forces your heels to the ground, the depth jump height is excessive.

The scientists warn that you have to pay your dues by performing max-strength exercises—such as the Olympic lifts and their variations, back and front squats, and the like—before tackling depth jumps. Siff stresses the need for eccentric strength.

That is the most overlooked aspect of all of this, Pavel. This is advanced stuff, and all too often, people just start leaping without first looking.

But even a high level of absolute strength is not enough. Learn to jump before you depth jump. The *Supertraining* authors suggest jumping rope—not for endurance but for speed—as a good preparatory exercise for depth jumps, along with easier jump exercises, such standing broad jumps and standing vertical jumps.

So, a QI coach could probably help an athlete prepare for this fairly simply and help that young athlete transition to the elite level.

The scientists emphasize the need for exercises like clean pulls to teach one how to maintain the proper back alignment and extend the body properly. In my opinion, kettlebell swings rule in this department.

When depth jumps are done by themselves, rather than in a complex, experienced athletes should not exceed 4 x 10 (sets x reps), and 2 or 3 x 5 to 8 is enough for less-prepared athletes. Rest for a full 10 minutes between series, and practice relaxation exercises. Depth jumps feel deceptively easy, but they are a very strong medicine and you must rest! Don't lollygag between the jumps in a set, though.

Do them once or twice a week in your strength workout. The Russian professor cautions that the only other exercises you may do in this workout are localized exercises for other muscle groups and easy GPP drills. Another option for experienced athletes is do them three times a week for 2 x 10 after the skill portion of their sport practice.

Verkhoshansky warns that you have no business depth jumping if you have achy or simply tired muscles or injuries that have not completely healed.

This point breaks my heart: How can the coach of a team with 100 athletes know if some are sore, injured, or tired? Doing plyos is NOT a group warm-up, even if that is exactly what you see in many high schools. It is wrong, wrong, wrong!

Depth jumps have a great tonic effect on the nervous system, which is why you should not schedule your sport skill practice earlier than three or four days afterward. The best type of a training session the next day is a low-volume GPP workout.

Falameev recommends doing depth jumps for three or four weeks two or three times a year and reducing the leg training during the depth-jump period. Verkhoshansky points out that depth jumps belong primarily in the second half of the preparatory period, although they may be used in the competition period for maintenance. Do them every 10 to 14 days, but make sure to discontinue them no later than 10 days before the competition.

It bears repeating: *The training effect of depth jumps in developing explosive strength is extremely high. They have no equal.* Power to you!

Just don't forget another admonition of Professor Verkhoshansky: "More often than not, plyometric enthusiasts do not consider the possibility that the athlete's sport alone may offer all or most of the plyometric training that is necessary and that adding more of this type of loading may be excessive or unwarranted." As one of Steve Baccari's charges, an amateur national boxing champion, colorfully quipped, "I do them plyometrics in the ring."

It's funny to think that the same exact thing is said in the discus, shot put, and hammer.

I shall wrap up the plyometric section by repeating the point that you must have a base of absolute strength before going explosive. And those levels are quite high. The Russian admonition not to start intense plyometric training until you can back squat a barbell equal to 150% to 200% of your bodyweight should give you a clue. "One should start developing [explosive strength] only after increasing one's maximum strength abilities," warns Verkhoshansky. Jumping is a fun dessert, but don't forget the steak and potatoes of heavy strength training.

I'm convinced that few have read the research here. This warning NOT to do intense plyos is so often ignored. A decade or so ago, I coached the finest high school thrower in the United States. A coworker who had some experience as a track coach in another state asked me if we did plyos. "No," I replied. That person went on to explain that at the other school, every practice began with a long session of team plyometrics. He was convinced that this was the key. I asked if anyone in the program threw as far as my athletes. "Well, no," he said, "but plyos are really important."

And that is the lesson, folks: Plyometrics are really important once you squat double bodyweight and have achieved a high technical level and . . . In other words, if you haven't built the foundation, don't paint the ceiling.

And when you have reached high levels of maximum strength, don't forget to at least maintain it. Dyachkov confirms that eliminating strength exercises quickly leads to a decrease not only in strength but also in speed-strength of the athletes and their athletic results.

What is the relationship between strength and power? Power is strength compressed in time, so to get powerful, you must get strong. A good example is the muscle-out on a straight bar—basically, a quick pull-up immediately followed by a dip. If you are not moving fast by the time you have completed the pull-up, there is no way you will be able to finish the movement. It should be obvious that one has to have respectable pull-up strength—in the pure 1 RM sense, rather than the explosive—before he hopes to pull fast. If you can only eke out 5 pull-ups, you just don't have the 1 RM strength reserve to move fast.

"Enhance maximal strength," insists Professor Vladimir Zatsiorsky, one of the premier Soviet sports scientists. "It is impossible for athletes to generate a large force in a fast movement if they cannot develop similar or even greater force values in a slow motion."

So in order to get explosive, you must first get strong. Grind those deadlifts, Comrade. You know the drill.

Increasing your absolute strength will make you more explosive—but only up to a point. Zatsiorsky continues:

> *But don't overemphasize the role of maximal strength in power production [either]. To be a strong athlete does not mean to be a power athlete. It is true that all elite power athletes are very strong people. On the other hand, not all strong individuals can execute movement powerfully when combining large force and high velocity.*

The capacity for fast force production initially increases in response to heavy strength training but may decrease afterward, according to Häkkinen. Polish émigré coach and author Thomas Kurz writes:

> *Slow squats with huge weights will increase the athlete's maximal strength but they will not develop explosive strength. (For someone with insufficient maximal strength slow squats may increase explosive strength but then the weight will not be huge.)*

Well-placed sarcasm.

It is not great strength per se that compromises explosiveness. It is the training required to achieve such strength. We know what is the best way to build brute strength—powerlifting. We should all powerlift—but not exactly the way competitive lifters do it. Andrey Kochergin, a karate master and a big fan of powerlifting-based GSP, explains:

> *Different goals prevent us from full-blown powerlifting practice. I don't need to tell you how much time and effort one has to give to achieve real results in a lift; we just physically can't take this time away from out main event—karate. That does not prevent us from pulling, squatting, and benching twice a week.*

Does an extremely high level of strength have to slow one down? There certainly have been plenty of brutally strong individuals who were also very explosive. Stanley Floyd, a one-time US champion in the 100-meter sprint, squatted 675 weighing less than a buck-eighty. Dr. Fred Hatfield, a powerlifting champion with a 1,000-plus squat, had a vertical jump of nearly 40 inches. They could be exceptions to the rule, however.

If I may, it's rare to find someone whom we would all call "brutally strong" who isn't also explosive. Avoid getting into fights with people who have 400-pound power cleans!

Our colleague Chad Waterbury speculates why powerlifting elite-level strength may be counterproductive to a power athlete:

Superheavy training can be tough on the joints, no doubt. And the nervous system senses trouble (i.e., joint degradation) before we do. If a guy wakes up with a painful shoulder, he usually blames it on his previous workout, or maybe he slept on it wrong. However, we know that pain is often the last step in the injury process. Months can pass before our brain gets the pain signal. We also know that strength training can make the joints stronger and healthier in the early stages. Could it be that a [very heavy] squat/deadlift causes joint degradation that we can't feel but the nervous system senses? Therefore, it diminishes neural output to the muscles as a way of protecting us from further damage?

Ed Coan was invincible. Photo courtesy *Powerlifting USA*

Indeed, joint injuries will inhibit fast movements. Does one have to be injured lifting world-class poundages? There have been specimens, like Ed Coan, who have competed at the highest level for decades with hardly a ding. Yet most world-class athletes—not just powerlifters—are injured.

Rif's famous corollary number 3 reads: "If you seek your limits, you will find them." The closer you get to your genetic ceiling in any endeavor—be it strength, endurance, or anything else—the narrower your margin of error becomes. The world's premier spine biomechanist, Professor Stuart McGill, points out the similarity between his two types of patients: elite athletes and people with back injuries the medical establishment has given up on. Both have a razor-thin area in which they can train safely.

Don't confuse *elite* sports with *health*. They have nothing to do with each other. There is a famous recommendation to health seekers in Russia: Don't aim to become an elite athlete in one sport, but get low to intermediate rankings in multiple events. The jack-of-all-trades is healthier than the master of one (unless the former "seeks his limits" in his many events).

For life, that is great advice. Life rewards the person who can do a lot of things and adapt quickly. But sport, sadly, is not life.

Another one of Rif's hard-earned pieces of wisdom is "Glory is temporary. Pain is forever." If you will go to the top—any top—you will hurt. The least you can do is hurt less—by pushing your limits only in your event and moderating your supplemental training.

Mark Reifkind, Master RKC, sums up:

> *A fitness enthusiast or competitor from another sport would not benefit much at all from using hard-core powerlifting techniques to the extreme. . . . Too much soreness in the muscles and the joints, severe CNS loading, and the overall weight loads on a human frame that can only recover from a limited amount would not play out well. . . . Athletes can learn many things by reverse engineering powerlifting mechanics, periodization cycles, special exercises, and methods of increasing strength/tension. They just should not train as a powerlifter, in my opinion.*

Rif adds that the extreme tension levels present in elite powerlifters may be counterproductive to other athletes. Recall that according to the principles of ratios, there is an optimal ratio of different qualities for different sports. Relaxation, while rarely mentioned as a quality, is a critical one.

Professor McGill has valuable insights on the subject:

> *I agree . . . that optimal expressions of athleticism (like jumping) require a tuned balance of variables: strength, speed of contraction and relaxation, direction and precision of force application, tuning of stability/stiffness at some joints with compliance/mobility at others, etc. . . .*
>
> *When muscles contract, they create both force (influencing strength) and stiffness (influencing speed). Stiffness slows motion. Hence, the paradox and the topic of the MMA article we wrote for* the Strength and Conditioning Journal. *Power production and the jump require speed and strength, but these two variables compete with one another. Strength is needed to propel, but to enable the strength to convert to speed, relaxation is needed to mitigate the associated stiffness. Thus, the jump is actually a measure of the ability to "pulse" and will be defined or bounded by both the rate of muscle activation and relaxation. Strength without rapid pulsing will never create an impressive jump. Of course, rate of muscle dynamics is bounded by physiological processes but also neural and biomechanical.*

It is this author's belief that a speed-strength athlete should powerlift following the 80% approach described by Patagonia founder Yvon Chouinard in *Let My People Go Surfing*:

> *I've always thought of myself as an 80 percenter. I like to throw myself passionately into a sport or activity until I reach about an 80 percent efficiency level. To go beyond that requires a level of obsession and degree of specialization that doesn't appeal to me. Once I reach that 80 percent level I like to go off and do something totally different.*

The second half of this statement needs to be qualified for the needs of an athlete aiming to become elite. The "obsession and . . . specialization" is not appropriate for him—not because he is bored but because he already has his own obsession and specialization. Beyond a certain point, increasing strength demands severe powerlifting-type regimens. The organism's limited adaptive capacity gets channelled to absolute strength and is taken away from other qualities.

"Going off and doing something totally different" after reaching 80% does not mean changing sports but changing the quality one needs to prioritize. Perhaps you could put strength on "cruise control" and focus on your rate of force development. Once increasing one psychophysical quality (or its particular manifestation) no longer yields an improvement in performance in your sport, you should switch to maintaining it at the reached level (which is very easy) and switch your physical preparation priorities.

Let us set admittedly arbitrary numbers in the raw powerlifts for a male power athlete—numbers that can be achieved without PL specialization training, numbers that are challenging without pushing one's genetic limits:

Squat	x 2 bodyweight
Bench press	x 1.5 bodyweight
Deadlift	x 2.5 bodyweight

We believe the above point of diminishing-returns lifts should be achieved and maintained with "punch the clock"-type easy strength workouts throughout most of the year. If strength is the priority, add a couple of concentrated six-week strength blocks a year.

But the biggest reason to scale back on your strength development at some point is something called the *explosive strength deficit* (ESD). It is the fault of ESD that a powerlifter friend of mine, who has squatted 900 pounds without a Monolift, cannot hit a golf ball as far as his 100-pound wife. Because the golf club is so light, it moves very fast—so fast, that Big Fred has no time to put his muscle behind it.

Zatsiorsky explains that while it takes 0.3 to 0.4 seconds and even longer to crank up one's force production to the max, most athletic movements are a lot faster—a 0.11- to 0.12-second long jump, for instance. Thus, the ESD measures the difference between the force you could have generated if time was no object and the one you did manage to uncork in a rush.

The professor offers a helpful shot put example: An elite athlete produces 50 to 60 kilograms of force throwing a shot 21 meters. The same athlete is capable of benching 220 to 240 kilograms, or 110 to 120 kilograms per arm. Therefore, he uses only 50% of his max strength during the throw. Zatsiorsky continues:

> *In principle, there are two ways to increase the force output in explosive motion—to increase the [maximal force] or decrease ESD. The first method brings good results in the beginning of sport preparation. If a young shot-putter improves [his] bench press from 50 to 150 kg and also pays proper attention to the development of other muscle groups, this athlete has a very strong basis for better sport performance in shot putting. This is not necessarily valid, however, for a bench press gain from 200 to 300 kg. In spite of efforts devoted to making such a tremendous increase, the shot-putting result may no improve. The reason for this is the very short duration of the delivery phase. The athlete simply has no time to develop maximal force. In such a situation, the second factor, explosive strength, not the athlete's maximal strength, is the critical factor. By definition,* explosive strength *is the ability to exert maximal forces in minimum time.*

The heavier the athletic implement, the more power gains an athlete can squeeze out of more strength and vice versa. A javelin thrower will hit his point of diminishing strength returns sooner than a shot putter, and a weightlifter will never hit his. But good luck finding an event in which strength is not needed. German scientists Jürgen Hartmann and Harold Tünneman stress:

> *It should be noted that movements of negligible resistance are a rare occurrence in sports. Body mass must be overcome explosively by sprinters and swimmers on starting, by fencers at flèche, and by volleyball players when jumping at the net. Boxers, fencers, and javelin throwers must be able to develop considerable strength to accelerate their equipment in addition to the resistance of the mass of their arms (approximately 5% of their body mass).*

An advanced athlete needs to get stronger in the *time-deficit zone*. One way to do this is what Zatsiorsky termed the *dynamic effort* (DE) method, back in the 1960s. According to him, this method "is used not for increasing maximal strength but only to improve the rate of force development and explosive strength." The parameters for DE training offered by Professor Verkhoshansky are 5 to 10 RM weights lifted for sets of 3 to 4 reps and with the focus on the maximum rate of force development.

Fred Hatfield pioneered the use of DE as a combined modality for developing both explosive and absolute strength: *compensatory acceleration training* (CAT), or maximally accelerating a moderate weight throughout the concentric range of motion. His recommended protocol is 60% to 85% for 5 x 5 of squats or other big and long movements with 5 minutes of rest. Dr. Squat assures:

> *Powerlifters who are using this technique have never failed to add well over 100 pounds to their squat ... in three months or less. Many football players I have trained claim that they are coming off the mark far more explosively than they had ever done before, and basketball players are jumping as much as five or six inches higher than before.... This technique requires very concentrated effort on your part. You must concentrate! Concentrate on exploding every inch of the way through the movement—not just initially or at the top, but all the way.*

Dr. Hatfield's book *Power: A Scientific Approach* may be over 20 years old, but it is still a must-read for strength professionals.

Here is the recommended CAT technique: "Squeeze off" and accelerate the deadlift. Drive! The nervous system is naturally economical and needs to be retrained to give it all, especially when the load is submaximal. CAT is a form of feed-forward training. In the squat and bench, control the descent. Then, before blasting off, you have two choices: One is to let the bar drop the last inch or so to elicit the stretch reflex, and the other is to pause for 1 to 3 seconds. Use both, alternating them every several weeks.

It is this author's conviction that one should not attempt CAT until he has mastered the skill of "tightness." When the emphasis is on acceleration, inexperienced athletes tend to lose their midsection brace, shoulder packing, and so forth. Get tight before getting fast. And even if you have tightness down pat, you should alternate cycles of touch-and-go and paused squats and bench presses in order not to lose it.

Kirk Karwosk's IPF squat world record, 1,003 @ 275, is still untouchable fourteen years later. Photo courtesy *Powerlifting USA*

I have had the privilege of watching Marty Gallagher coach. In one bench press session, I observed a lifter lower the bar in a very loose style, bounce it a little off his chest (not enough to risk cracking the ribs), then push-press it with his whole body, starting with his legs. When the lifter left, I asked the coach of Coan and Karwoski why had he allowed such a loose style. According to Marty, this allowed the athlete to handle near-maximal weights for reps, thus building confidence and raising the plank.

I also could not help noticing a great coordination between different muscles, truly making the bench a full-body lift. I asked, "But won't the lifter end up getting sloppier and sloppier as the time goes by?" "No," replied Marty. This was only for a few weeks. Then, the lifter would switch to superstrict paused benches. Looseness and tightness were strategically alternated in the great coach's plan. He was getting the best of both worlds.

This experience reminded me of the squat cycle by Rickey Dale Crain I had done some years back. The first exercise was the squat to a high box—2 or 3 inches above parallel. The weight was heavy—eventually, above the parallel squat 1 RM—and you did 10 nonstop reps with it. "In order to handle the heavy weight needed, . . . you must get in the groove on your sets," warned RDC. "Do not stop, . . . or you may not be able to get up and get started again." This set was followed by a set of 5 competition-style squats and chased with another fiver with 3-second pauses—RDC's way of not getting used to the "sloppy" technique. Note the difference in reps. One does not spend as much time under load during a "cheating" rep. Therefore, more reps are usually in order.

RDC's repetition high box squats are evil.
Photo courtesy Rickey Dale Crain

Finally, here is the last reason serious strength training tends to negatively affect speed and power. Following is an excerpt from *Supertraining*, with my emphasis:

> *Kotz has shown that prolonged, heavy workloads [***In Russian texts "heavy workloads" usually refer to high volume, not intensity.***—P.T] slow the contraction speed of trained muscles. More specifically, Filimonov has established that excessively heavy strength loads diminish the force and speed of boxers' punches, while Deniskin (1976) has found that prolonged use of high volume strength loads diminishes the power and speed of weightlifters, high jumpers and triple jumpers. . . .*
>
> *Excessive maximum strength training can impair speed-strength and technical skill in boxers (Verkhoshansky, 1977). It can also lead to a deterioration of several months' duration in the technique of weightlifters and javelin throwers. Other studies have shown that heavy training loads reduce one's ability to control movements, primarily of their most complex technical phases. . . .*
>
> *Concentrated strength loading . . . leads to a brief but consistent decrease in speed-strength, which diminishes the athlete's special work-capacity and complicates the task of improving technical skills and speed of movement. . . . [Antonova (1982)] found that in the months with the largest training volumes, there was a noticeable decrease in the special-strength preparedness and sporting results. However, the same qualities rose during the subsequent months of reduced loading. . . . [Levchenko (1980), in a study of sprinters,] found that an increase in the volume of special-strength training means results in increased muscle stiffness and decreased explosive force. Unfavorable conditions were thus created for improving technique and running speed and the likelihood of injury increased significantly.*
>
> *Thus, it is apparent that voluminous strength loading creates adverse conditions for improving skill and speed. Considerable research has established that voluminous strength loading is detrimental to the technique of the weightlifting movements (Khlystov, 1976; Vorobyev et al, 1978), javelin throwing (Ruvinsky, 1980) and punching speed in boxing (Filimonov, 1979).*

See a pattern?

Now please consider the state-of-the-art, month-long strength block from Verkhoshansky's twelve-week "program to develop explosive strength and reactive ability of the leg muscles."

Verkhoshansky's 12-Week Program

Barbell back squats are trained twice a week.

Workout 1

1. 90% x 5/2–4 (reps/sets), 4–5 minutes rest between sets
2. 6–8 minutes rest
3. 80% x 10–12/2–3, 2 minutes

Workout 2

1. 93%–95% x 3/2–4, 4–5 minutes
2. 6–8 minutes rest
3. 80% x 8–10/3–5, 2–3 minutes

Workout 3

1. 93%–95% x 2–3/3–5, 4–6 minutes
2. 6–8 minutes rest
3. 85% x (8, 2–3)/2 ("After completion of the last repetition in the squat, . . . do 2–3 additional repetitions.") Rest as long as you wish between sets.

Workout 4

1. (80% x 10, 90% x 5, 90%–95% x 2) x 2–3
2. Rest between sets 4–5 minutes and between series 6–8 minutes.

Workout 5

1. 93%–95% x 2–3/3–5, 4–6 minutes
4. 6–8 minutes rest
5. 80% x 8–10/3–5, 2–3 minutes

Workout 6

1. (70% x 12, 80% x 10, 85% x 7) x 2–3
2. Rest between sets 5–6 minutes and between series 8–10 minutes.

Workout 7

1. Barbell squat jumps are introduced.

Workout 8

1. 85%–90% x 1–3/4–5, rest-pause. As the sets progress, "the number of repetitions decreases and the duration of the rest pauses increases. For example, in the first set of 3 repetitions the rest pause is 30–40 seconds; in the second set of 2–3 repetitions the rest pause is 40–60 seconds; in the third set consisting of 1–2 repetitions, the rest pause is 60–90 seconds; and in the fourth set there is one repetition."

Workout 9

1. Barbell squat jumps.

Workout 10

1. 95% x 1–3/4–5, rest-pause, as in workout 8.

Any clues yet?

This is an absolute killer for fast-twitch athletes. Powerlifters would have to lower the specified percentages, because they generally add a rep for every 5% stripped off their max (100% x 1, 95% x 2, 90% x 3, 85% x 4, 80% x 5, etc., based on Bobrov). Marathoners—who, according to the same author, typically add 3 reps per step (95% x 4, 90% x 7, 85% x 11, 80% x 13, etc.)—would do OK, but this program was not meant for them.

Given the triple whammy of volume, heaviness, and proximity to failure, you will be one sore puppy and should not be surprised that your SVJ will be suffering. So will your walking, getting up from a chair, and even rolling over in bed.

Professor Verkhoshansky's solution to the problem of the stiffness, soreness, and fatigue produced by serious strength training was intelligent periodization. Specialize in strength for some time. Then unload and crank up the speed and power. You can have it all, just not at the same time.

The bottom line on the strength and power relationship:

- Both heavy training and explosive training are needed to excel in power sports.

- Power cannot be maximally expressed during a period of heavy, high-volume strength training. One must unload first.

- Get strong by gym standards, not powerlifting standards.
- The simplest formula is to do low-rep, low-volume powerlifts plus overspeed eccentric kettlebell swings and snatches.

- Compensatory acceleration training with the powerlifts should be added in QII or QIII. Reducing the barbell weight and attaching Jump Stretch™ bands to the bar is an option.

- Everything else is the individual choice of an experienced coach who is clear about the place of his event on the force-velocity curve and who is on a first-name basis with *Supertraining*. Power has many aspects: starting strength, reactive ability, and so on, and so does speed. In this book, we purposefully keep things simple and use generic terms like "power" and "explosiveness". A serious coach or athlete needs to study specialist texts to learn the classification and understand the exact needs of his sport. This will help in selecting the appropriate explosive training modes.

- To quote Schmidtbleicher: "We can conclude that maximal strength and power are not distinct entities; they have a hierarchal relationship to one another. Maximal strength is a basic quality that influences power performance."

CHAPTER 5

Armor Building, or the "Elephant in the Room"

"Quick guys get tired. Big guys don't shrink."
—Marv Harshman, University of Washington basketball coach, explaining why he favors size over speed

Pardon me, but we seem to have an elephant in the room. Perhaps we can call it by its other name: the 800-pound gorilla in the room.

If you are not up on your delightful English idioms, both expressions are used to identify an obvious problem that no one wants to address. But if you want to be a strength coach, you had better come to grips with this issue.

The issue? Bodybuilding. Body culture. Muscle spinning. Pumping the guns. Pumping iron. Blasting, blitzing, and bombing your pecs.

Something nefarious has been happening in strength coaching for a long time, and it has taken on many guises and disguises. Honestly, have a group of young athletes do any serious movement that involves peak concentration, perfection of technique, well-maintained equipment, and developed skills, and one of these fine young people will ask, "What muscle does it build?" Shake your head, shake your hand to the sky in rage and wrath, or come to grips with all of this stuff.

For the record, we have two standard answers to "What muscle does it build?" when the athlete is snatching, cleaning, or swinging:

1. "You know when you leap up in the end zone and snag the ball between two defenders and win the state championship? Yes? Well, it's **THAT** muscle."

2. "Let's just keep doing snatches for another hour, and we'll ask you tomorrow as a pop quiz."

Both answers are excellent, but the second one is really more fun for the coach.

The role of hypertrophy remains the boogeyman in the field of strength and conditioning. Most strength coaches are tormented by the image of the Grim Reaper standing in the hallway outside every weight room—dressed in a black Speedo and a "doo rag"—screaming "It's all you, Bro" and demanding supersets of skull crushers. It would be hard to find a strength coach or a sport coach who hasn't had to deal with an athlete arguing that "Mr. Greater Galaxy does this, so I should, too!"

In the past 50 years, bodybuilding has gone from being an underground activity, to literally defining the barbell sports, to its odd role today as the starting point for most people's understanding of how to train with weights. Hypertrophy—or simply, gaining muscle mass—is doubtless an important part of training for many athletes. The key is discerning how much and how often in the training mix. Moreover, the role of hypertrophy training changes as the athlete moves through life and is a key to the longevity of the active or retired competitor.

Bodybuilding focuses on two qualities: hypertrophy and fat loss. The artistic elements of symmetry and stage performance that are the keys to superior placing in a bodybuilding contest are beyond the scope of this work. And it is important to take a moment to note that excellent lighting, intelligent use of tanning and coloring, AND selective altering of photos on a computer can do wonders for a subject's body. A good tan in the right lighting can completely change the perception of one's body in seconds. The composition of the body won't change, of course—just the look.

"I knew we were in trouble when we got there and their cheerleaders were bigger than us," admitted Matt McDonagh, a 13-year-old ball player.

Seriously, before bodybuilding branched out from the iron sports tree into a specialized activity (I can't make myself call it a "sport"), it was a worthwhile pursuit. The French name for bodybuilding, *culturisme*, refers to the physical culture.

Bodybuilders of the past paid their dues to the different aspects of the physical culture—not just the mirror. They were all-around athletes. Arnold and Franco were powerlifting champs in Europe, with 700-pound deadlifts to their names. Clarence Bass was a successful weightlifting competitor, and Dave Draper, although he did not compete, could bench 440 in a T-shirt. The guys who came before them did not boast such impressive benches but were skilled in gymnastics and acrobatics. If I had been born earlier and moved to Santa Monica, California, in the 1950s, I could see myself getting into bodybuilding of that vintage.

In the Soviet Union, bodybuilding and powerlifting were Siamese twins, impossible to separate. This was explained partly by the old-school respect for strength and partly by the need to downplay the pursuit of looking good in a country where such things were frowned on. The bodybuilding-powerlifting hybrid was called "athletic gymnastics" and "athletism." Competitions were run in multiple stages. First, you were tested in the standing broad jump and pull-ups. This was the elimination round. If you failed to reach the specified norms (regardless of your bodyweight), you were out. The competitors who had made it were weighed in and proceeded to powerlift.

Posing was referred to as the "freestyle program" and included gymnastic and kettlebell moves, which were worth a certain number of points: handstands, splits, back flips, the kettlebell cross with 24s for athletes under 75 kilograms (165 pounds) and 32s for those over 75. Pure "beauty queens" did not stand a chance. You had to be an all-around athlete to win.

I would love to see a modern-day bodybuilder do a handstand—or even put up a respectable weight in the powerlifts. I have met strong bodybuilders like Mike O'Hearn, who pulls seven wheels, but he is a rare exception, not the rule.

It's odd for me to talk to some people about strength training. I want to talk about correct posture during a quality repetition, and the other person wants to talk about one-legged snatches off a Swiss ball. I would love to discuss the role of the swing in the throwing arts, but everybody seems to want to talk about loading creatine into an espresso.

For the record, I'm pretty much done with it. I'm tired of hearing about the incredible number of pull-ups or Hindu push-ups people have done for three months while inexplicably failing to gain any appreciable muscle. Worse yet, these fine people e-mail me, asking what they're doing wrong.

Of course, you know my only question: What are your goals?

The answer, almost universally, is lose fat or gain muscle. Occasionally—and this makes me salivate—I hear "I want to be the world champion!" So, why, I think to myself, are you doing a half-baked high school PE regimen based on a boot-camp program from World War II? It's one thing to train a Depression-era farm boy into an infantryman or a marine, but it was never the drill sergeant's goal to prepare you for a photo shoot on the beach.

Marines need strength as much as anyone else, if not more, given the weight of the kit in modern wars. A Force Recon friend of mine was on a mission in Afghanistan. Every member of his team was loaded with 120 pounds of gear, and they had a donkey equally loaded to the gills. When they were climbing a particularly steep pass, the donkey had a heart attack, collapsed, and rolled down the mountain. The jarheads had to climb down, retrieve the gear from the dead animal, load it on top of their already ridiculously heavy kits, and continue the mission.

Thanks to Aaron's exceptional physical preparation, he retired in one piece after two decades of service and many combat deployments. And his PT was not all conditioning, I can assure you. To give you an idea, several years before, he had worked up to a bodyweight barbell clean and press when deployed in Iraq following the 5 x 5 x 5 routine from *Beyond Bodybuilding.*

The problem with this boot-camp approach is that it's been keyholed into what appears to be a modern and scientific approach for elite training. When you read that the Soviets or East Germans developed these secret techniques in some secret facility in some secret location, hell, I get all 007, too.

Sadly, for most of us, it's just not working.

Let's look at this approach and let me offer the great insight of this program: the development of *qualities.*

What are the *qualities?* You can come up with your own list, but here are the basics:

- **Strength**—the ability to move a load
- **Power**—the ability to move a load pretty quickly
- **Flexibility** and/or joint mobility
- **Endurance**—whatever that means anymore
- **Fat loss**—if applicable to your sport or goals
- **Hypertrophy**—if applicable to your sport or goals

The Russian classification is mind-bogglingly complex—with qualities like *parastatic strength, strength-skill,* and *active flexibility endurance*—but we will not go there.

Obviously, skill shows up in much of any training. Something as simple as speed training can involve lots of deadlifts and squats, but there's also a need for smooth and efficient technique, too. (However, I'd argue that genetics is where we start when it comes to elite sprinting.)

Here's the issue: For most of us, what qualities are we addressing?

Recently, a bodybuilding magazine stated something along these lines: "We don't want to BE strong; we just want to LOOK strong." After I vomited a little in my mouth, I thought about it. It's true. Guys who tell me "I just want to look good naked" (and I pray they aren't thinking of doing that with me) are probably thinking along these lines.

Of course—and I love to point this out—most guys who train to look good naked nearly have to be naked before you can tell they even train. In street clothes, they look like members of the high school band, which is probably why most of them wear T-shirts three sizes too small and love to cut the sleeves off most of their clothes.

In other words, the two qualities that the bulk of us wish to achieve nearly all of the time are fat loss and hypertrophy (more muscle mass or size but with an eye to symmetry).

Fat Loss

Dieting works. But it is hard, and it can be brutal. My friends who have competed on the platform in bodybuilding can barely form sentences the week before an event.

Josh Hillis gave me the life-changing insight that ALL diets work IF the person follows the plan. He maintains that simply demanding a food journal will help the fitness coach far more than trying to learn the ins and outs of every new diet craze. And that leads us to THE problem.

The problem with both these two qualities—fat loss and hypertrophy—is that so much has been written on them that most people have lost sight of what's important. In many cases, when people think of fat loss, their first thought is that they have to do massive amounts of crunches, which one world famous bodybuilder told me is the key to having back surgery at some point in your future.

The answer, then, to meeting most people's goals is to go on a diet. As always, I'm fine with whatever serious approach you take—whether the Atkins induction or the Warrior diet or whatever. But fat loss is diet. Sorry! The truth may set you free, but you will crave doughnuts.

Folks, a tough diet will find your six-pack. Mine is under a nice padding of insulation.

Hypertrophy

As a strength coach, I field a lot of questions about hypertrophy. Actually, against all public opinion to the contrary, hypertrophy is an important part of the game for many sports.

Mike Ditka, a great American football coach, noted on the radio show *Mike and Mike in the Morning*, "Some guys look good in the shower but can't play." I always say, "Looks like Tarzan, plays like Jane." So, you do have to be careful with the balance of things.

This is a common story with some fighters who take up lifting. They go for the Rocky look, and before you know it, they get gassed, get beaten, and quit fighting to take up bodybuilding. WBA Heavyweight Boxing World Champ Nikolay Valuev warns: "For us the barbell is an auxiliary tool.... When I see a very 'pumped up' boxer with large muscles, I immediately know that he will quickly get tired during the fight." In addition to decreased performance, the Russian champ warns about the unhealthy stress the extra weight places on the heart, claiming that this is what happened to Evander Holyfield. Valuev himself once fell for the siren song of Tarzan building, gained 42 pounds, and had a very difficult time fighting. Since then, he has taken iron in moderation.

Then there is the other extreme: hard-core traditionalists who refuse to touch iron. But on average, as my dad would say, "They are where they need to be." "The average temperature in the hospital is normal: half of the patients have fever and the other half have assumed the room temperature."

One way I address this issue is to change the term "hypertrophy" or "bodybuilding" to "armor building". Yep, **ARMOR.**

I played varsity football for South City High back in the glory days (key Bruce Springsteen), and all my games were at night except my last game. It was played early in the morning on Thanksgiving. Hours after the game, when I normally would've been asleep, I ate Thanksgiving dinner. I was simply amazed at how much pain my upper arms felt from the banging of a game. Since that time, I've bought into the idea of armor building for football.

There's no question that the more time one spends under load, the more hypertrophy that will result. Note that I never give absolutes here. I had an athlete ask me about soreness, and I found myself speechless, because I've never found any credible evidence that soreness is an indicator of anything. Like soreness, any and all methods of training seem to work across the spectrum, but few of us have ever found the answer that works for everybody, every time.

So, how do we increase the amount of time under load?

Recently, I discussed the idea of *complexes*. Like the circuit-training programs of the 1960s—especially Bob Gajda's "Peripheral Heart Action", in which you combined lifts to drive your heart rate through the roof—the reality for most people is simply this: *If the two qualities you want to address are fat loss and hypertrophy, then why are you doing all that other nonsense?*

I'll say it again: Fat loss is diet. Although you shouldn't ignore exercise, focus on the diet side for fat loss.

For many of the people I've worked with on hypertrophy, basic strength needs to be addressed before we move the program into something complex. Try the 40-Day Workout, and drive your basic lifts up. But for most of us, we will reach our goals far more quickly and relatively easier by following a focused diet and a simplified lifting program.

Hypertrophy and fat loss are qualities that can have an impact in sports. In contact sports, hypertrophy can provide two qualities worthy of discussion:

1. **Armor.** In fact, an appropriate title for the hypertrophy phase of an athlete is "Armor Building." In American football, a bigger forearm is a weapon. Larger arms can protect the ball better (my athletes argue), and basic overall size is a tool late in a game. As the saying goes, "I've seen athletes slow down in a game, but I've never seen one get smaller." In the fourth quarter, the accumulated toll of banging against a larger, heavier team adds up.

2. **Confidence.** There is a wonderful term called "peacocking". Love it or hate it, athletes like to look good. For those who take this to the extreme, we also have my wonderful phrase: "Looks like Tarzan, plays like Jane." There's nothing harder for a young coach to recognize than the error of judging an athlete by how he looks physically. "You can't judge a book by its cover" is absolutely true when it comes to determining competitive performance. Having said this, athletes will always stay a few extra minutes, no matter how difficult the training, to work the "show" muscles of biceps, pecs, and abs. Of course, these body parts tend to be "all show and no go!"

Big muscles were not all created equal, which becomes obvious when you see a male bodybuilder lift weights lighter than a female RKC. A cocky 18-year-old boy made the mistake of jokingly challenging Delaine Ross, RKC Team Leader and figure competitor, to an arm-wrestling match. Predictably, she whooped him. I doubt he will ever recover—but I digress.

Professor Evgeniy Ilyin explains the two types of muscular hypertrophy: *sarcoplasmic* and *myofibrillar.* The former is the result of an increase in the volume of the sarcoplasm, or the noncontractile part of the muscle fibers. The latter increases the size of the fibers' contractile apparatus, or myofibrils. Sarcoplasmic hypertrophy is characterized by an increase in the muscle's energy stores—glycogen, creatine phosphate, myoglobin—and an increase in the capillary number. The Russian scientist stresses that these processes increase the muscle's size and endurance but not its strength: "Which type of the working hypertrophy is going to develop depends on the nature of training. Prolonged dynamic efforts with a small load lead to the first type of hypertrophy, large muscle tensions in isometric regime—to the hypertrophy of the second type."

Delaine Ross, RKC Team Leader, is not interested in sarcoplasmic hypertrophy, only strength. Photo by Gordon Smith courtesy Delaine Ross

Although the quality of *weight loss* has been discussed for perhaps two centuries, *fat loss* is the quality to impress on athletes. Certainly, there are weight categories for competing in the combat sports and weightlifting, and there are dozens of methods of rapid weight loss that vary from practical to deadly. Fat loss continues to mystify everyone who can't understand these four words: *Eat less, move more.*

This is an oversimplification, without a doubt, but it follows the same basic logic as "Buy low, sell high." No one can deny that many of the programs in the weight-loss industry are quick-fix gimmicks. Years ago, Harvard nutritionist Jean Mayer said, "To attribute obesity to 'overeating' is as meaningful as to account for alcoholism by ascribing it to 'overdrinking.'"

True fat loss can improve a wide range of physical performance results, varying from jumping and sprinting measurements to flexibility standards. In fact, if there was a single magic wand to wave that would instantly improve performance in most sports, it would make fat disappear. The challenge, of course, is to maintain the dietary rigor to force fat loss while training the other qualities needed in performance.

And that is the key. The reason bodybuilders can go on extremely difficult fat-loss regimes is that they deal with only two qualities. Bodybuilders are probably in quadrant IV, but wrong-thinking people keep trying to train football players like bodybuilders. Tanning or skin coloring is not the same as mastering an opponent's offensive schemes. Once a bodybuilder shifts from pure hypertrophy work to final preparations for a contest, his single concern is fat loss. Any other athlete in any other sport MUST juggle multiple qualities.

This brings us back to the wonderful quote by Art DeVany that seemed to upset some people. In response to the question "What's the best way to lose fat?" DeVany answered, "Don't get fat in the first place." Given the advice that came out back in the 1970s—that, to overstate the case, "all carbs are bad"—it's a wonder that only one-quarter of the US population is obese, as I write this sentence.

For the modern athlete, "Don't get fat" means going against a lot of cultural norms, over a long period of time. High-fat school lunches, combined with a lack of required physical education plus the proliferation of every sugary substance imaginable at every athletic practice and event for the kid involved in club activities, make it very difficult for even a well-informed child to stay lean. Add today's lack of honest play. and we have the recipe for obesity.

America, I don't understand your situation. When I was growing up, there were hardly any fat kids. And what we considered "fat" would pass as svelte in US high schools these days. In 1968, Tanno and Sorokin—whose book *Athletism* was still the muscleheads' bible in the 1980s, when I was a teenager—exclaimed how horrible it was when a person who does not lift iron grows to be 180 or even—gasp!—200 pounds. Laugh or cry, your choice.

Healthy food definitely did not explain our low body fat. I was fortunate to grow up in a well-off (by Soviet standards) family of a senior army officer, and I ate well. But my situation was far from normal. Most families made do on a diet of potatoes, low-grade pasta, bread, and other starches. These staples were complemented by pig lard. Fruits and vegetables rarely made it to the table, and meat, even less so.

But we did not sit on our rumps playing video games or watching TV. A blessing in disguise, there were no video games and the TV had but a couple of channels, usually filled with coverage of the latest Congress of the Communist Party or reports on agricultural production. We were outside, and we moved. Hours-long skiing trips in the winter and games in the summer kept the preteen busy. When we got a little older, we would spend hours each evening "greasing the groove" with various gymnastic moves on the playground behind our high school. You could argue that the smokes taken between sets helped the kids to stay lean, but don't go there.

"Back in the USSR": at my high school playground. There was no shortage of gymnastic and obstacle course type equipment—note 15-foot or so tall climbing poles in the background. Tires, monkey bars (also very high) and a lot of other fun stuff did not make it in to the shot. The feeble word "liability" was not known.

School at every level, from elementary to university, had several hours of physical education a week, and the tests were much tougher than in the armed forces of many Western countries. To graduate from high school, a boy had to bang out 8 strict dead-hang palms-over pull-ups. That barely got him a grade equivalent to the American C. You had to do 12 to get an A, and no one applauded. It took at least 18 or 20 to sort of impress your peers.

For all the luxuries available to today's American children, in their nerdy bike helmets, I pity them. Without knowing "muscle joy" (a wonderful expression by weightlifting great and accomplished writer Yuri Vlasov), they will immediately settle into middle age. They have been done in by a combination of zero physical education at school, the sedentary distractions of technology, and overbearing protectiveness by their parents and school. If the United States went into a big war today and there was a draft, my septuagenarian father and father-in-law (retired Soviet Army officer and US Marine, respectively) would be much better equipped—physically and psychologically—to handle the rigors of infantry life than a typical 18-year-old of today's generation. I am dead serious.

But I have digressed again. We were on the topic of fat loss. My wife has made a good point: If you sit or lie down for 23 hours and move only for 1, even if you "work out," which demand will your body more readily adapt to?

So, the athlete needs a long-term perspective when dealing with fat loss. Certainly, over a 10-year period, there can be an honest commitment not to "get fat in the first place." However, a good strength and conditioning coach also needs some built-in programs to deal with the athlete who has let his or her overall condition slide.

Addressing body composition needs to be done with some compassion and probably an eye toward not leading the athlete into the area of eating disorders. This is a balancing act that not every one has the skills to accomplish. And let's add one more issue: Losing fat may have little effect on performance. True, maybe (or maybe not) a leaner athlete will be healthier, but sports rewards those who do a task the best. Shave off your body hair, dye the hair on your head, and wear as much glitter as you want, but sports is a cruel mistress: It rewards the one who performs the best, not the one who looks the best.

And this has been the problem for decades: What is the proper role and impact of hypertrophy and fat loss on performance? The answer actually comes from studying master athletes—those men and women who are at least beyond 35 years of age but often continue to compete at a high level well into their 70s, 80s, and 90s. Years ago, master hammer thrower George Matthews noted the issue of massive muscle loss that seems to affect master athletes, usually after 55 years of age. Many of them are empty-nesters and have enough financial resources to train and travel extensively. Sadly, it seems, their muscles just vanish overnight.

Assuming an understanding of efficient techniques in the sport of choice, the master athlete probably needs to move back to the basic rules of hypertrophy training: getting as much reps under load in as little time as possible. The master athlete reminds us of the critical need for hypertrophy for athletes far away from the posing dais. So, there is a place for hypertrophy, and it follows a very clear path.

I call Henry Duval "the last man on Muscle Beach." He is pushing 80—and he is still pushing over 200 pounds overhead and doing Good Mornings with 400. The youngsters doing curls around him have a snowball's chance in hell of making these lifts.

Henry has been lifting for over 50 years. But this does not mean you have to build muscle in your youth in order to have it later. My father, although a lifetime athlete, had not touched iron until just a couple of years ago. Then, the deadlift bug bit him. In a year, he pulled an American record for his age group (374 at 181, USPF DL only, 70–74 years old). When Professor Stuart McGill examined him, he commented that he had never seen such a muscular back on a 70-year-old. And Dr. Franco Columbu said my father had the muscle tone of a 40-year-old.

Why give up being a man, just because you have reached some arbitrary age?

I am proud of my old man.
Photos courtesy Venicepaparazzi.com

Early in the training career, simply doing push-ups, pull-ups, and general exercises seems to lead to some muscle gain. For young athletes—especially those enjoying the growths spurts of adolescence—practically any training program will work wonders, in terms of bodybuilding. Anyone coming into weight training seems to enjoy this early growth spurt, and any exposure seems to work. For a coach dealing with athletes from the basic levels of training, you can't go wrong with practically any kind of program—from basic boot camp training to exposure to traditional lifting sports (Olympic, power, or kettlebell lifting). Machine training might also be a perfect option here, as there is a very low level of technical training and large groups can be herded through in a relatively short amount of time.

Hypertrophy, then, follows the same path as the athlete in the early training curve. Hypertrophy will climb the same gentle slope of basic technical training and all the other qualities of either a specific sport or simple exposure to sports. As the skill level grows, the athlete will literally grow along with it. For most athletes, hypertrophy needs will rise along with the level of sport until the athlete completes his career—usually, in the late teenage years.

That's why basic bodybuilding can be so useful for a high school football program. It meets the immediate needs of nearly every member of the program. Without a doubt, it is also the reason that probably any training program can support wins and losses in team sports. Many parents spend a lot of money on paraprofessional coaching programs that promise improvements in agility, acceleration, and other qualities that would improve just as quickly, in all likelihood, by doing a few circuits on the rusting Universal gym at the local YMCA. There seems to be about a four- to six-year period when pure hypertrophy work, with simple exposure to explosive training, might be all the athlete needs to succeed.

Especially in the area of armor building, a certain honest assessment needs to be made: If the athlete isn't ready for professional or elite performance by, at the very latest, 22 years, it's safe to assume he will never be ready. If a 23-year-old football player or basketball player is still working on basic skills, the game will have passed him by. There may be exceptions in individual sports, but it would be fun to name the athletes who have attained elite status by making enormous gains after age 23. I will wait.

After the initial "hill" of hypertrophy, approximately four to six years into training, the importance of this quality quickly drops down for the next few years of elite performance. It certainly doesn't disappear, but the importance of other qualities must take over.

An important warning: This discussion is about the role of hypertrophy, so don't read or understand this in a vacuum. Hypertrophy or bodybuilding is the "elephant in the room" in sport training: It is an obvious issue that no one wants to talk about very much. Its role is not nearly as important as that of technique, game preparation, tactics, injury prevention, recruiting, or perhaps any of a dozen other qualities. But bodybuilding is sitting in the weight room and has to be discussed.

The elite athlete who is still worried about modeling for photo shoots probably only has a season or two left in the game.

Just a few years ago, a professional football player in a speed position became obsessed with bodybuilding. As he got larger and larger, his game skills evaporated, because he was simply too big to make efficient movements on the field. After he appeared on the cover on a bodybuilding magazine, his skills continued to diminish until he was out of the league in a year. His increase in bodyweight, although laudable for the "look," ended his playing career.

Bill Walsh, the late-great football coach who led the San Francisco 49ers to several Super Bowls, was often credited with purposely not recruiting athletes that just looked good. He looked for players with a winning competitive mindset and seemed, according to some observers, to avoid athletes with any tendency toward narcissism. The elite athlete in the prime of his career needs to focus nearly blindly on achieving the goal and avoid working too hard on looking good in the part.

For a few years, the role of hypertrophy has little importance. Toward the end of a career, there probably will be a rise in the role, especially in sports that have a long life, such as the throwing sports. After retirement, it would be wise to transition for a few years with basic bodybuilding in the truest sense of the word: repairing the sport-related injuries and adjusting and adapting the body from all the overwork caused by specific training.

Literally, as one ages, he begins the fight for life. There is no truer indication of actual age than the amount of lean body mass. An undermuscled and overfat body is not only unappealing, but it's unhealthy. As one moves into the last decades of life, time spent in the gym might improve the quality of life exponentially.

The role of hypertrophy follows a reverse, fallen-down S curve. It starts up a gradual curve, comes back down (but not to zero!), and then continues to be important until death, quite literally. Keeping lean body mass as long as one can is the true fountain of youth.

The problem with standard hypertrophy programs—besides their built-in boredom (at least, for the strength or power athlete)—is their inability to jack up intensity. We tend to let accumulated fatigue, which is good in the case of high-rep squats, to limit the load. By breaking apart the sets just a little bit, you can add more weight to the bar and actually cut rest periods between what we traditionally called sets. For example, I have shared an interesting way to do the German volume training: the 10 sets of 10 workouts. Rather than let reps 60 through 100 dictate the load, we play with this rep scheme: 2-3-5-10. We use the same weight each set, and rep and strive to do a total of 5 of these clusters. It adds up to 100 reps, with only 5 sets being that rep-reducing, tough set of 10. What is amazing about this program is that you often find that you put the bar down or in the rack and almost immediately do the double, because that set of 10 was hard but "anybody" can do 2. Oddly, the triple is done quite quickly, and, as I often think, "I might as well do the 5, too." So, between those hellacious 10s, you nail 10 more reps with surprising little rest. If hypertrophy is honestly "time under load" or "time under tension," it logically follows that more load (because you are NOT doing 10 sets of 10 and roasting yourself in the process) in less time will lead to greater muscle mass. Now, you don't have to do 100 reps. Oddly, I have found that doing 3 clusters (2-3-5-10-2-3-5-10-2-3-5-10) seems to be enough for any athlete. It is better to leave a little in the tank, especially for a drug-free athlete, than to go to the edge with this magic 100-rep barrier.

What is actually more exciting is a very interesting variation on the 5 x 5 workout. The reps simply drop out the last set of 10, so we have 2-3-5. There are two very innovative changes that seem to really work well in the big lifts: the bench press, the military press, the squat (all its variations), and the deadlift. As I noted in other settings, writings and workshops about "5 sets of 5," the big issue is, of course, what do YOU mean by 5 x 5? Since writing an article about 5 sets of 5, I'm even more confused about the dozens of variations of what I used to consider the simplest workout for bulk and power. Here are the two innovations: First, stick with one weight throughout the workout. Of course, you know that, but with this rep scheme of 2-3-5-2-3-5-2-3, you can handle far more load than the traditional 5 sets of 5. You are not held back by that heavy last set of 5 that often forces one to take a lighter first 4 sets.

The ladder is an extremely powerful program design tool. It is one of the cornerstone beliefs in modern Russian sports science that the greatest performance gains can be achieved only when periods of hard training are alternated with periods of easier training—and not only during months and weeks but also during individual workouts.

The Russian ladder format fulfills this requirement. It refers to multiple sets of an exercise where one variable (reps, weight, or rest periods) gets progressively harder. The ladder starts out very easy, gets progressively harder and harder, and then starts all over from the bottom. The built-in recovery periods enable the athlete to tolerate a very high volume of loading without burning out.

Another benefit is technique enhancement. Without any concerns about making the lift, one can be very mindful of the technique subtleties on the "lower rungs" and let the adrenaline take over later, when the groove is set. Gray Cook's statement is worth repeating: "The body will always compromise quality for quantity." When you are gunning for more reps or more weight, subconsciously, you will be tempted to cut corners to make that goal. If you always train with your pedal to the metal, your technique will progressively deteriorate. You will just keep thinking of making the target number, at any cost.

A colleague pointed out to me that people who always train all out live in a startle reflex—with their shoulders hunched up and forward and their necks "turtled." No wonder! Their bodies do not ever get a chance to enjoy exercise and see it as nothing but a threat. I will make a blanket statement: Those who always train all out have the worst exercise technique. Fortunately, not for long. As Jack Reape put it, "Show me somebody who goes hard all the time, and I will show you a career about to end."

There are several types of ladder. The *rep ladder* is the most common. Add reps without changing the weight—for example:

1-2-3-4-5
2-3-5
5-7-8-10

Note that in a classic Russian ladder, once you have reached the top rung, you start over on the bottom rung instead of pyramiding down. In other words, do 2-3-5-10, 2-3-5-10, rather than 2-3-5-10-10-5-3-2.

If you are going for muscle mass, doing an occasional pyramid is a good call. Just remember that it significantly slows down the recovery, so plan accordingly. Powerlifting Team IPF Russia members use the following pyramids, nicknamed "marathons," once a week or once in two weeks in the squat and the bench press during the preparatory period, when hypertrophy is one of the main goals:

50% x 5, 60% x 5, 70% x 4, 6, 8, 9, 7, 5, 3 (52 lifts)
50% x 5, 60% x 5, 70% x 3, 5, 7, 9, 8, 6, 4, 2 (44 lifts)

They also employ special ladders that Boris Sheyko calls "jerky":

50% x 5, 60% x 5, 70% x 3, 6, 4, 8, 2, 7, 3, 5 (38 lifts)
50% x 5, 60% x 5, 70% x 4, 8, 3, 7, 2, 9, 4, 10, 5 (52 lifts)

The team coach explains: "The number of reps changes sharply: After each set with a large number of reps follows a set with a low number of reps. This variation ... is easier physically and psychologically."

Unless you really know your way around the barbell and have solid technique, don't even think about this advanced hypertrophy program. The reps climb too high to be safe.

In the *weight ladder*—or the "chain," as old-time strongman Hermann Goerner called it—the reps stay the same while the weight climbs. In the Soviet military, many guys built big shoulders, arms, and strength unwittingly following DeLorme's 50-75-100 percentages. (Although DeLorme is referenced in many Russian textbooks, these knuckleheads definitely did not read these books.) Russian kettlebells come in three standard sizes: 16, 24, and 32 kilograms (or 35, 53, and 70 pounds). So, soldiers would do weight ladders pressing the 16 five times, then immediately do the same with the 24 and then the 32. After a brief rest, they started over with the 16. It worked like a charm, in spite of malnutrition, stress, and sleep deprivation.

There are also *time ladders* and *breathing ladders*, but they are more appropriate for conditioning with kettlebells than muscle building with barbells.

Following is a field-tested, DeLorme-inspired muscle-building plan from Beyond Bodybuilding.

DeLorme Method Inspired Six-Week Hypertrophy Cycle

From *Beyond Bodybuilding*

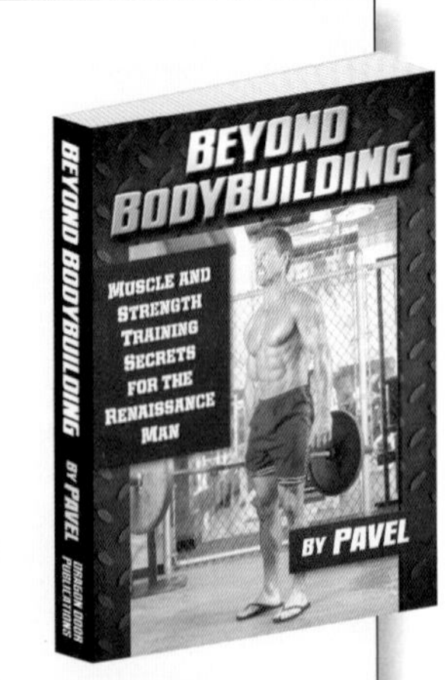

Monday (50% 10 RM x 5, 75% 10 RM x 5, 100% 10 RM x 5) x max
Wednesday (50% 10 RM x 5) x number of series performed on Monday
Friday (50% 10 RM x 5, 75% 10 RM x 5) x number of series performed on Monday

- Do two exercises—bench presses and deadlifts, in that order—and no other exercises.
- Perform all your sets at a medium to slow tempo, with a 1-second pause on the bottom. Don't relax with the bar on your chest.
- Rest for approximately 1 minute or as long as it takes to adjust the poundage between sets. Rest for 3 minutes between series.
- On Monday, perform as many series as possible in good form. When you have successfully completed 5 series, add 5 pounds to the bench press and 10 pounds to the deadlift 10 RM, and recalculate the 50% and 75%.

Assuming that your 10 RM in the deadlift is 200 pounds—a rough estimate will suffice—on Monday, you will perform the (100 x 5, 150 x 5, 200 x 5) series as many times as you can. You should stop when you can barely make 200 x 5. The only rest you will get between sets is whatever it takes you to add plates. Rest for 3 minutes between series. Walk around and loosen up your limbs, as if you are shaking off water.

Assuming you have completed four series on Monday, on Wednesday, you will do only (100 x 5) x 4. This light session will aid recovery and painlessly increase your weekly tonnage.

Friday, you will another 4 series—this time with (100 x 5, 150 x 5). This medium day is building back up to a tough Monday workout.

On Monday, you will hopefully make five full-size series of (100 x 5, 150 x 5, 200 x 5). When you have made 5 series, it is time to add weight to the 10 RM you have used in planning your workouts. The deadlift calls for a 10-pound jump, unless your 10 RM is higher than 400 pounds or lower than 100 pounds (200 + 10 = 210). Recalculate your 50% and 75% sets based on the new top set poundage (105 and 160 in the 210 example), and keep on plugging away. Add only 5 pounds to your bench press.

The souped-up DeLorme workout calls for up to 75 reps per exercise, and most trainees will be totally unprepared for such a manly workload. That is why before tackling the real thing, you should do a 2-week long introductory cycle that gently builds up the tonnage.

Introductory Cycle

Week 1

Monday	(50% 10 RM x 5, 75% 10 RM x 5) x 3
Wednesday	(50% 10 RM x 5, 75% 10 RM x 5) x 4
Friday	(50% 10 RM x 5, 75% 10 RM x 5) x 5

Week 2

Monday	(50% 10 RM x 5, 75% 10 RM x 5, 100% 10 RM x 5) x 2
Wednesday	(50% 10 RM x 5, 75% 10 RM x 5) x 7
Friday	(50% 10 RM x 5, 75% 10 RM x 5) x 5

Speaking of the original DeLorme workout with 10s, I had a 40-some-year-old friend of mine alternate it with working up to a heavy single in the DL every other week. Mike progressed from barely being able to pick up his toddler without pain to pulling 475.

Certainly, some of the options—like the "Wave"—have value, but this has been an issue for many of us for years. Yes, I realize that someone is going to comment by saying something like "I thought 5 x 5 was obvious" and then add a whole new variation that no one has ever seen before. With this the first option, the lifter only has to deal with 2 big sets of 5. So, try to find a weight that forces you to give it all on that second set of 5. (Obvious note: Get a good spotter on the bench and squat.) And once again, since you have nothing better to do, that triple often happens when you're out of breath. I suggest timing only the whole duration of this variation and seeing how fast all 25 reps are finished. Honestly, it goes fast, even with a serious load.

Small reminder: This is not a powerlifting workout! It is intended for those in our audience interested in a nice mix of power and bulk. Again, if you have more plates on the bar and the workout finishes faster, isn't that hypertrophy training?

A simple way to program a hypertrophy program: Get a pump with a heavy weight.

The second option is really opening my athletes' eyes. It is so simple of an adjustment that many will dismiss it and note "I've been there, done that." Well, good for you. Let's review the second option.

First cluster: 2-3-5
Now, **ADD** weight!

Second cluster: 2-3-5
Add more weight.

Third cluster: 2-3-5
Add more weight.

Challenge cluster: 2-3-5

You can use the first cluster as a warm-up of sorts. What is funny is that this program begins to resemble one of the earliest recognized programs in lifting: the DeLorme Workout.

This second variation can reflect those numbers, except that we focus on the 5-rep max (a number in many people's experience that rewards bodybuilding training more than higher reps). Try this variation in a simple workout after any kind of intelligent workout.

I have been training my athletes with the second variation (40 total reps, three plate changes) with the front squat, bench press, and power clean (or power curl, a cur-grip clean using the legs) mixed with some hurdle walkovers and some farmer's bar walks. This is not a fancy workout, but the load really impacts the athletes. If you can do some kind of hurdle walkover or hip mobility work during a training session that has a squat and deadlift or clean variation, I strongly recommend it. I also like to finish this workout with a Farmer's Walk, but keep it within reason.

Return of the Kettlebell offered a very simple program for building hypertrophy with two kettlebells. But the simplicity can kill!

If you want to build armor, not just simply a little more muscle for the beach season, focus on two things. First, always emphasize the muscles that "people only see when you are walking away." Fear the athlete with big glutes, big calves, big hamstrings, big spinal erectors, big traps, and big delts. This athlete is built to win. Biceps and pecs might make good photos, or as strength coach Casey Sutera chants about these muscles, "If you Tri to get Bi, you'll get Trapped by these guns." (Triceps, biceps, trapezius, and a most muscular shot!)

The exercises that seem to build armor the best are the following:

With a Barbell

- Zercher squats
- Suitcase deadlifts
- Snatch-grip deadlifts
- Bench press
- Curls (Try doing them with a thick bar!)

The kettlebell can surprise you. For armor building, the Zercher squat is an appropriate barbell lift. A better choice might be the double kettlebell clean and front squat. This exercise is best worked in ladders:

- 1 clean and 1 front squat
- 2 cleans and 2 front squats
- 3 cleans and 3 front squat

Doing this ladder up to 5 times is an excellent way to understand the intensity needed for hypertrophy. A fun test is to do this up to 10 reps (55 front squats without putting the weights down), but that might be a once-in-a-lifetime training test. The next day, enjoy finding your rhomboids, traps, obliques, thighs, and abs. (Then you can ask what muscle this series builds!)

In fact, I'm a fairly good example of actual bulking. In a four-month period, without steroids (always a caveat), I put on 40 pounds, going from 162 to 202. What's interesting about my four-month, 40-pound gain was what I was doing before I started to gain size. Why? Well, it's probably what most people, especially athletes, are doing now.

At a bodyweight of 162 pounds, I benched heavy and hard nearly every day. At a bodyweight of 162 pounds, I did lat pulldowns, a variety of curls, and lots of ab work, and I moved from machine to machine quickly. Then I met Dick Notmeyer, and the scale began to move.

At Dick's place, there was a bar on the floor and a squat rack. Three days a week, I walked over to the bar on the floor and moved it overhead a bunch of different ways. Two days a week, I squatted the bar. Soon, I was always hungry—so much so that I famously ate sandwiches just before dinner so I wouldn't be hungry while I was eating. Dick had me weigh in every day, and it was shocking to watch the numbers go up. I came home one day after working out and my brother, who hadn't seen me in a few weeks, looked up from the table and said, "Holy shit!" In case you are wondering, that is a bulking program. If you miss seeing someone for a few weeks and they don't recognize you, well, you have dialed it in. If, in two months, you find yourself smaller than when you started, welcome to the club.

Most people who want to bulk fail. Why?

1. Because they do too much of the things that get them tired, but not big

2. Because they do too little of the things that get them big and really tired

Let me explain:

1. You must get stronger, but you can get there with any intelligent, basic program. Recently, many people have fallen in love with Jim Wendler's 5/3/1 program because, well, it works. I have had great experiences with easy strength through the 40-Day Workout. Certainly, doing *Power to the People!* with the deadlifts and presses is going to work miracles for most people, too. You need to do two things to get stronger: Add weight, and do more reps. The answer has never been Lift light weights for high reps" or "Lift heavy weights for few reps." The answer remains "Lift heavy weights for high reps." It bears repeating. Copy it and hang it on your wall.

2. The other part of the formula is as old as the rack: You need to do some serious squatting. In the March 1980 edition of *Ironman*, Jack Kirwan offered a short article, "A Seminar by Tom Platz." Platz's honesty and candor has always been his hallmark, along with, if you didn't notice, the size of his thighs. His answer to small arms, small chest, or whatever was simply to load the body up by squatting.

To repeat: *The answer is squatting.*

3. Finally, you literally need to spend more time on the bar. The single-best way I know to get more time with a bar in your hands is to use complexes.

Complexes involve cycling through a series of exercises without putting the bar down, performing all the reps on one exercise before moving to the next. It's tough. You'll whimper. But then you'll want to do it again (though not right away). In my other works, I have given credit to Bob Gajda and Istan "Steve" Javorek for their clarity on complexes, but I also need to give a nod to those old Universal machine charts hanging on the walls of my high school. We did circuit training up to five days a week and got in pretty good shape doing simply those rotations with little rest.

A small note: Designing a complex takes a lot of thought. You need to think through the movement of the bar and your head, as well as connect the movements.

The magic in a bulk-building program is putting these three elements together and surviving the workouts.

If you decide to take on kettlebell complexes, do yourself a favor and get *Kettlebell Muscle*, a book by Master RKC Geoff Neupert.

First, let me say this: The ideal way to get ready for a bulking program is to lean out first. Although that seems counterintuitive, in my experience, the athletes who've made the best gains have just come out of something that ate huge amounts of resources and time and energy and calories. The body adapted to that load and was primed to gain size—to adapt to any future crisis. That is why football players in December and wrestlers in March tend to put on 10 to 20 pounds seemingly overnight.

Leaning out can be done in a variety of ways, but I think low carb is the way to go. Moreover, the great lesson of my experience on various diets is that I didn't take in enough protein previously. I also agree with Chris Shugart's basic contention that the really important changes are psychological. If you don't want to think too hard, simply remove all your carbs from your diet. Atkins was right. Now, I understand that few people will take my advice about leaning out first. But if you ever get a chance to actually try this sequence—leaning out followed by bulking up—you'll be amazed at the difference.

So, how do you put the workouts together? Like this:

Element 1: The Basic Strength Program

We (and I'm including all of us) come into hypertrophy programs too weak. So, when most people begin doing complexes or circuits or whatever, the weights are too light.

There, I said it. To build muscle, most of us need to build strength. So to get stronger, I'd like you to consider doing four basic strength movements. Jim Wendler recommends the back squat, the military press, the deadlift, and the bench press. Use a low-volume approach, with one serious set of "as many" on the last set.

During the week, I've tweaked the program like this for my athletes:

Day 1: Front squat and bench press. We do front squats in the strength part of the workout. The back squats are for high reps.

Day 2: Deadlift and military press. It takes 15 minutes or so for the athletes to get in some light warm-ups and then do 3 serious sets of each exercise. The last set is "as many," and that's the only number we record. If your reps are moving up on a weight, then you're getting stronger (the word *duh* can be used now), but for whatever reason, people miss this simple point.

If you're doing something else (and there are dozens of basic strength programs), that's fine, but double-check the amount of time you're spending to get the work done. Basic movements and basic training can be done much more efficiently. I had great success years ago training only two days a week with simple movements.

Element 2: The High-Rep Back Squat

Now, during the bulking phase, the next exercise is the high-rep back squat. Tom Platz recommends this program:

Monday

135 x 10
225 x 10
275 x 6
325 x 3
345 x 3
345 x 3
275 to exhaustion

Friday

135 x 10
225 x 10
275 x 5
325 x 5 325 x 5
325 x 5

For my athletes, I allow a two-week breaking in period. Why? Because if you're coming in from a sport, anything you do the first two weeks will increase the number on the scale at the weigh-in.

Here's exactly what we do:

Week 1

Day 1: 1 set of 30 with 95 pounds
Day 2: 2 sets of 30 with 95 pounds

Week 2

Day 1: 1 set of 30 with 95 pounds, and 1 set of 30 with 115 pounds

Day 2: 3 sets of 25 with 115 pounds During the week 2 workouts, the ash-colored faces of my athletes on indicate that something good is happening! From there, we strive for one back squat workout a week, with a heavier and heavier weight, and the other workout strives for more reps.

So, it could be something as simple as this:

Week 1

Day 1:
Warm-up
185 x 10 205 x 10
225 x 10
275 x 5
315 x 5

Day 2:
Warm-up
185 x 5
205 x 5
225 x 20
225 x 15

Week 2

Day 1:
Warm-up
185 x 10 225 x 10
275 x 5 315 x 5
335 x 3

Day 2:
Warm-up
185 x 5
205 x 5
225 x 25
225 x 20

So, there's no secret to bulking. You have to load the iron and squat down. Then, come back up.

Give yourself about four weeks after the break-in period to focus on the high-rep squats. Then, stop. For clarity, two weeks to break in, four weeks to push up the weights and the reps, and then move on.

Element 3: The Complexes

I've had great success with my athletes using complexes to really increase the time under load. If you're unfamiliar with them, try something this simple:

1. Clean the weight 8 times.
2. Do 8 military presses after the last clean.
3. Lower the bar to the back of your neck, and do 8 back squats.
4. Pop the bar over your head, and do 8 front squats.
5. Lower the weight, and do 8 deadlifts.

Here's a great hypertrophy complex: With two kettlebells, clean and press the weight overhead. This is the starting position. Then do this:

1. Press the kettlebells 8 times.
2. Clean the kettlebells 8 times.
3. Double front squat the kettlebells 8 times.
4. Deadlift them 8 times.

Important point: I suggest that you use complexes as your general warm-up two days a week. For example:

Day 1

Complex D
Upright row
Clean-grip snatch
Back squat Behind-the-neck press
Good Mornings
Row
Do this complex for 3 sets of 8 with a light weight.

"Big 2"
Front squat
Bench press
Utilize the 5/3/1 program
High-rep back squat

Do 1set of 30 with 95 pounds.

Consume food.

Day 2

Complex A
Row
Clean
Front squat
Military press
Back squat
Good Mornings

Again, do 3 sets of 8.

"Big Two"
Deadlift
Military press
Utilize the 5/3/1 program
High-rep back squat program

Do 2 sets of 30 with 95 pounds.
Consume food.

This would be a nice break-in workout.

Bonus Day

I'd also strongly suggest one additional day a week. On this day, warm up and do 5 sets of 3 with any of the standard complexes, striving to add weight each set.

Then, do any of the things you feel you missed—curls or whatever. Get in a good workout, and then go home. No, I'm not going to spell it out for you. If you choose not to do it, that is fine, too.

Nutrition and Other Factors

1. Eat three meals a day. Snack three or four times a day. I'd prefer each meal to be a meat, egg, fish, or poultry-based meal with black, pinto, white, or navy beans and veggies. But you get a little wiggle room on a bulking program. Snacks? Well, you can get away with dietary murder on a bulking program. Yes, peanut butter and jelly sandwiches work for putting on weight. (No, I can't believe I wrote that, either.)

2. If you really want to shock yourself, take fish oil. Now, here's an odd secret that I use for my extremely motivated athletes: Continue to increase the amount of fish oil capsules you take until you get a bit "runny." (If you don't know what I mean, then you've never taken too many fish oil capsules.) From that number, back off one or two, and that's the amount of capsules you need a day.

3. Recovery is important. You must sleep. It's OK to watch movies and television on a bulking program. I never recommend that bulking programs last too long, so it's okay to become like a typical American for a few months. Also, I really don't want you to play basketball or train for a marathon or learn a new sport. Later, yes, of course, but not now.

4. Do not try to perform your sport at an elite level! Focus on something else for now. You may even find your skills eroding. That's fine temporarily, as you're focusing on adding mass.

And pay attention to what Russian sports scientist Dr. Issurin has to say:

> *Workouts for muscle hypertrophy impose very special demands when planning consecutive sessions within the period of restoration. Use of high workloads during this period adversely affects the anabolic phase of muscle restoration and eliminates the hypertrophy process. Thus, to obtain the anabolic effect it is necessary to substantially reduce workloads for at least 20 hours and to utilize appropriate means of restoration.*

Bulking is basic. Remember that. If you try to do too much or get too clever during the six weeks, you're not going to make the kind of progress that I've typically seen.

Honestly, you can expect a surge during the first two weeks that'll convince you that the simple combination of strength training, high-rep squats, and complexes actually works better than something more exotic and sexy.

Remember, I didn't say it was easy—just simple.

Then there are times when the last thing an athlete wants is adding any weight, even muscular. He still has to be strong, though. The solution, according to Russian specialists, is avoiding slow movements, avoiding training to failure, and focusing on quick movements with maximal and near maximal efforts.

CHAPTER 6

Specificity Demystified

"I need specialization to get strong and variety to keep me sane."
—Rob Lawrence

Of course, as John Jerome wrote years ago, "Specificity works, but at a price." The price for me has been, at best, a lot of limping and, at worst, a lot of surgeries.

If there has been an overused image in life and sports in the last 50 years, it has to be the yin-yang symbol. Even so, it is hard to find a more poetic image to represent the complementary notion of seeming opposites in union. Joseph Campbell did a marvelous job discussing how the Garden of Eden represents the cleaving of opposites and how we strive to reunite.

You can run down the list: black-white, day-night, male-female, and so on. These are among the many pairs of concepts that seem polar opposites yet strive for union. A joke that I have beaten to death in my teaching career sums this up well, I think (though you might not agree): "I tried to get in touch with my feminine side, but it slapped me."

Sometimes, making something SO simple leads to problems. I think I may have done that in teaching people that general conditioning and technical training live in a yin-yang world. Oh, it works well! But that's not the problem. The problem lies in its application. You can do wonderful work in the field of sports training by simply looking at yin-yang and thinking, "Fine, I will spend half my time at the gym or track 'working out' and half my time working on my sport."

You know, that's not bad. I know many people who spend nine months getting in shape for a season of sport and then continue to "work out" all through the season but rarely focus on technique, tactics, and strategy. I would even argue that this is the norm for many overachievers. Others just "play" year-round and seem to do fine, although they may be missing something.

I was working with a young coach who couldn't figure out why his athletes weren't getting stronger, since they were following an "elite" lifting program. His young teens were squatting once a week and not making progress on the program, based on percentages. (He had never read my work.) I told him simply this: "If you were a basketball coach, would you work on free throws only every Monday?" "No," he told me. "That's something you have to do **EVERY DAY!**"

The same principle applies to everyone low on the learning curve. You need to practice your sport a lot. How much? In discus throwing, we insist on 10,000 throws a year. Several recent books, including *The Talent Code*, have argued that 10,000 hours of training—no matter what the field—is the ticket to success. Those kids just playing their sport are on to something.

But they could be better. That something missing from year-round play becomes very evident at the highest levels. Just look at pictures of female tennis players from the 1960s and compare them to Serena Williams. Truly, we live in a time when athletes are faster, larger, stronger, and leaner than ever before. Golfers ignored lifting for a long time, except for a few names here and there. That's no longer the case, however. They were all chased into the weight room by a Tiger.

So, that's the issue: Do you spend half your time in sport and half your time in the weight room? Well, no. What most coaches forget—and I'm raising my hand along with all the rest of you—is that training in sport IS perfect conditioning for the sport! However, the weight room, the track, and even the beach can offer some qualities that athletes can no longer ignore.

Two economists are having a conversation:

Economist 1: Do you understand what is going on?
Economist 2: Let me explain it to you . . .
Economist 1: I can explain everything myself. Do you understand what is going on or not?

Whoever tells you that he understands specificity is kidding himself. We are not going to get dragged down into the fray between the proponents of the generalist, specific, and holistic theories of training transfer. In this volume, our goal is only to pragmatically present a few strategies that have been proven to work without dwelling on partisan academic theories.

We believe the following:

- There is no clear division between GPP and SPP; they fall along a continuum.

- Physical preparation should become progressively more specific in an athlete's career. If one can make progress with general exercises early on, why not save the ace of trumps of high-specificity SPP until nothing else works?

- General strength should be prioritized in QI and QII and at least maintained in QIII.

- "Same-but-different" special exercises, as well as the conditions of their performance, are the bread and butter of QIII and QIV athletes. Such exercises should be changed every three or four weeks.

- Hardstyle kettlebell exercises should be used extensively in all quadrants due to their "What the hell?" effect.

Making QI and QII athletes improve is ridiculously simple: GPP plus practicing the skills of one's sport. A newbie gets impressive positive carryover from almost anything. As he climbs the competition ladder, the means of physical preparation (strength, speed, etc.) have to become progressively more specific to his sport if he is to keep improving.

This is where he runs into the conflict between the demand for specificity and novelty. On one hand, the exercises have to be the same as the athletic event. On the other hand, since the nervous system eventually stops responding to monotonous stimulation, they have to be different. The "same-but-different" dilemma is solved through so-called special exercises and changes under the conditions of performance.

Train "Same but Different"

Explains Ozolin:

> *Special exercises are used for developing physical qualities and willpower, as they strictly apply to the chosen sport. These exercises are set up and selected according to the greatest correspondence of the coordination structure and the character of performance, kinematic and dynamic characteristics, and also psychological manifestations to the chosen sport or its part. Exercises performed in easier or harder conditions belong to the class of special exercises as well.*

There are three subclasses of special exercises:

1. For development of qualities very specific to the chosen sport.
2. For teaching—These can be elements of technique or imitation exercises, like shadow boxing.
3. For development of willpower, decisiveness, courage, and the like, "similar in the character of concentration and manifestation of psychological qualities."

Given the strength emphasis of this book, let us focus on the first category.

Borrowing heavily from Ozolin's writings, here is a summary of the Russian philosophy of "same-but-different" exercise. Special exercises can be performed under different conditions: *loaded, unloaded,* and *complicated:*

> *Unloaded, loaded, and complicated training conditions play an especially important role ... in performance of an exercise and its parts. They allow one to exceed the level of the required quality (or a complex of qualities) in multiple repetitions, get established on this level, and see a considerable transfer to the competition exercise performed in standard conditions.*

Training under loaded conditions is familiar to most Western coaches: throwing heavier than regulation weights, running wearing a weight vest, and so forth. A standard method is to do three to five attempts with the load, followed by a record attempt without it. Russian coaches like to say that "heavy" exercises develop the sense of lightness.

Loaded special exercises can be further subdivided into *simulation* and *accentuation* types. The former simply load the movement, as in the above three examples. On second thought, scratch out the word *simply.*

Simulation is not for amateurs. Load the movement excessively or in a wrong manner, and you will ruin the athlete's technique. A boxer may have heard that his Russian counterparts practice punching with dumbbells. So he grabs a pair of 5-pounders and starts swinging them in the air. Before you know it, he is tensing his shoulders to support the bells from dropping, and his punch, instead of gaining power, loses it. And his elbows hurt. Someone forgot to tell him that Russians use dumbbells weighing as much as a roll of quarters.

When simulating the main event, it is important to remember that each skilled movement is characterized by its *invariances,* or fundamental and unchangeable features, and *surface features,* which are adjusted to accommodate immediate needs without changing the nature of the movement. To use an analogy, your height and shoe size are invariances, whereas your haircut is a surface feature. A wise coach knows to leave the invariances alone and to play with the surface features only.

Louie Simmons does just that when he has his lifters squat with every imaginable type of a bar or deadlift in different stances. The Westside Barbell Club (WSB) mastermind stresses the simulation nature of such exercises: "Remember, when doing the Good Morning, in your brain, you must duplicate the action of the deadlift precisely. It is not so important to raise your Good Morning as to raise your deadlift by performing the Good Morning.... Remember to use the same body mechanics as you do in the deadlift."

Simmons's advice is not an idle admonition. Another way an amateur coach can mess up an athlete's technique is by prescribing exercises similar to the main event in kinematic characteristics yet different in neuromuscular coordination.

Consider the deadlifting styles of two of the world's best pullers: Andy Bolton and Konstantin Konstantinov. I have been fascinated with Andy's style since I saw him pull at the Arnold Expo years ago because of its similarity to the Hardstyle kettlebell swing we teach at the RKC. I finally checked with him: "Correct me if I am wrong, but it seems that you try to keep your shins vertical, don't think about t h e leg drive, and snap your hips forward right from the start?" The deadlift master replied: "Yes, you got it; that's the way I pull. The hips go forward as soon as possible and as fast as possible, and I don't really think too much about the legs. They do their stuff without me thinking." The Brit's squats have the same "box squat" look and support his deadlift well.

Andy Bolton broke the impossible 1,000 deadlift barrier. Photo courtesy AndyBoltonStrength.org

Konstantinov starts his pulls with a lot of ankle dorsiflexion and quad drive. He "leg presses" the platform away and spreads it apart. Not surprisingly, the Russian squats narrow with his toes out and uses pure leg drive to get a carryover to his deadlift.

I would venture a guess that if Bolton did some leg press–style deadlifts as a special exercise and Konstantinov did some swing-style pulls, two of the world's greatest deadlifters would lose their statuses as kings of the hill. Motor-learning confusion is no joke.

Even more effective than simulation is a class of special exercises based on *accentuation.* In these exercises, some element of the competitive movement is singled out and hammered hard.

Konstantin Konstantinov is closing in on the grand. Photo courtesy *Powerlifting USA*

Going back to WSB, board presses accentuate strength building in a particular range of motion. And here are two examples of special exercises accentuating a critical component of the competitive event from Russian track and field (T&F): shot putters initiating the leap while standing on a 20- to 30-centimeter (8- to 12-inch) elevation, and sprinters running downhill to increase their stride rate.

Issurin comments on a subclass of accentuation exercises:

> *Positive skill transfer* **[and qualities' transfer, I might add—P.T.]** *is achieved by any kind of movement facilitators that artificially simplify, but do not distort technique. The "Concept" rowing machine, for instance, allows [rowers] to develop sport-specific muscle endurance when the motor task is substantially simplified (no interaction with water, standard work conditions) with the same coordination.*

An example of such simplified-yet-not distorted exercise is the power clean in weightlifting. It takes away the finesse and the stress of going into a full squat without altering the fundamental skill. Ozolin adds one more reason to practice such exercises: "Very often the number of repetitions of competition exercises cannot be made sufficiently large, primarily because of large loads and high nervous strain. That is why the lacking training volume is made up with tens of thousands of repetitions of special exercises."

According to Verkhoshansky and Siff, "The competitive action executed with maximal physical exertion represents the most specific of all the special training means." Regardless, it is extremely stressful to the athlete. Indeed, full squat cleans get old in a hurry. A boxer cannot train just by full contact sparring; he will be destroyed by such specificity.

The Russians did a poll of boxers, asking them whether boxing causes brain damage. One-third of the respondents answered "Yes," one-third answered "No," and one-third did not understand the question. (Yes, it was a joke.) This is why boxers do focus mitt work, heavy bag work, light sparring, prearranged combinations, and so on.

High nervous strain is not exclusive to athletes who get hit and requires elaboration. Godik singles out three characteristics of a training load:

1. Specificity
2. Intensity
3. Volume

It is telling that specificity appears before intensity and volume in a list of load variables. That is why Russian weightlifters perform 90% of all maximal lifts on special exercises, which are a lot easier on the adrenals than the competition lifts. The closer an exercise is to the competitive event, the more effective—and stressful—the practice. For instance, the competition-style squat or deadlift is a lot harder on a powerlifter's nervous system than a Good Morning—and not just because the latter requires less weight. The man is defined by his SQ and his DL. No one compares his Good Morning to that of the other guy.

Another benefit of a Good Morning to a lifter of either persuasion is the fact that it works the key pulling and squatting muscles harder while reducing the systemic strain. (This is a sneaky way of saying the muscles are more isolated.) Dr. Fred "Squat" Hatfield understood this clearly when he trained high-bar squats in the off-season to hammer his quads while using less weight.

Ozolin continues:

> *Adaptive capacities of the organism are large but not unlimited. They are greater when the load acts locally or on particular organs or systems, and then the resources of the whole organism promote more effective adaptive reactions. This underlines the especially important role of special exercises. Adaptive capacities are smaller when the demands are made on the whole organism and almost all of its adaptive resources are called up.*

Isometric special exercises illustrate this point beautifully. Say that your goal is a strict, neck-to-the-bar tactical pull-up with a 48-kg kettlebell—a Beast Challenge event. You already can do a pull-up with 40 kg. Chances are, you will have no problem with the bottom and the middle of the movement. It will be the lock-off that kicks your butt.

You could approach the challenge with the QI and II approach of building a broader foundation of volume: 5 x 5 or *Enter the Kettlebell!* rite-of-passage ladders with 32 kg. This will undoubtedly work, but it will take time and consume a lot of your energy—which you could have spent on training the other two Beast Challenge events, the pistol and the press.

The three events of the Beast Challenge with a 106-pound kettlebell.
Jeff Steinberg, RKC tamed the Beast at the June 2007 Certification.

The answer familiar to rock climbers is the "lock-off," using a lighter weight (perhaps a 24), pulling to the top, and holding the position for several (up to 10) seconds. And not just holding but intending to pull one's neck or upper chest through the bar, leaving a red welt from the bar on the skin. In doing so, the organism's limited adaptive resources are focused on the exact muscles, nerve cells, and pathways involved in the pull-up finish.

This is an example of *functional isometric training* (FIC), which was the rage in the sixties. Why isn't it today? Because its practitioners were not aware that FIC is a top-of-the-food-chain special exercise, the ultimate ace of trumps up the athlete's sleeve. Once you have used up your ace—in six to eight weeks, at the most—you will have nothing left.

Professor Verkhoshansky wrote extensively about the need to sequence different training means in a training cycle from less effective to more effective. In other words, play your junior cards first. And this applies to an athletic career, QI to a higher quadrant, just as much as it does to a month-long preparation for a competition.

To get back to our aspiring Beast Tamer, he could start a competition cycle with four to six weeks of volume with fives in different kinds of pull-ups. Then for the next three weeks, he could reduce the reps to doubles and triples and add some intense specialized variety drills, like weighted rope, monkey bar, and Bachar climbs. Finally, he could finish with two weeks of lock-offs mixed with some fives for the sake of keeping muscle mass. (Isometrics are notorious for their "wiry strength.") Once he has conquered the Beast, our Comrade—whose "sport" is the 1 RM tactical pull-up—will take a week off training and then spend some time with exercises other than pull-ups to sensitize his system to future pull-ups. Then he will return to ladders and sets of five …

And if our guy can put up only 24 kg or even less, he should forget about lock-offs until stronger times. Otherwise, he will make quick progress (to 32 kg perhaps) and stall. Patience.

Another word from Ozolin:

> *It is very important that although repetition of the same training … work of moderate power for weeks and months does not deliver a high level of sports results, it significantly fortifies and stabilizes skills, creates a more perfect coordination of functions of organs and systems, and strengthens them and the whole organism through positive structural and morphological changes. This is how the so-called special foundation is built.*

At a very high level, in QIV, there may even come the time for isolation-type exercises. Again, quoting Ozolin: "One must know that in exercises where efforts in speed and strength are expressed at the limit of the athlete's abilities, even the smallest reserve in the leading [quality] acquired through local special exercises, immediately gives an increase in the sports result."

Although I deadlift raw, Louie Simmons suggested that I train in groove briefs. (A note for nonpowerlifters: Imagine unbelievably tight Levi's cutoffs, artificial hip extensors.) "This will make your hips temporarily stronger," he told me. "You will be able to pull more and thus strengthen your back more." If I ever make it to QIV, I will definitely listen.

Here is what Jack Reape, who gets to train with a powerlifting star, told me:

Jesse Kellum uses the Smith machine bar across the athletes back to hang chains on when doing push-ups. We used to do them with hands elevated up on aerobics steps—the only use of either item that adds value. He adds bands to the Smith machine for both speed benches and speed squats. (His are done with a much narrower squat stance and done dive bomb, Shane Hamman style, not to a box.)

In the days when the Olympic press was a competition event, Russian weightlifters and Paul Anderson used the handstand push-up with the feet against the wall as a special exercise. One of its benefits was a greater stress on the shoulders and triceps, thanks to not having to precisely groove the bar. Besides, you can really grind this exercise. Your body might come to a complete stop, yet a couple of seconds of enduring effort will likely get you moving again, ever so slowly. This special *grinding endurance* is an essential quality for a powerlifter or another static or parastatic strength athlete.

Marty Gallagher has coached me to use the vertical leg press to improve my deadlift leg drive. It is logical that if we can challenge the stabilizers by purposefully decreasing stability (remember the Swiss ball?), we should be able to do the opposite and challenge the prime movers by increasing stability. An experienced lifter's stabilizers and groove are extremely developed, so there is no reason to fear detraining. Not only does such muscle isolation benefit the QIV athlete's muscles, but it greatly spares his nervous system, which is of paramount importance at this level.

Of course, this approach is damaging for an up-and-coming athlete. His back will be challenged plenty without artificially boosting his hips with groove briefs. He does not yet know how to set his back for pulls, and the last thing he needs is the leg press, which will make his legs too strong for his weak and uncoordinated torso. And pressing without the balance challenge will not help him develop control and groove, though it might set him up for an injury, as his prime movers get way out of his stabilizers' league.

Machines—at least some—can be useful. Ironically, they belong in QIV, not QI.

Of course even in QIV, isolation should not be abused. Barry Ross warns:

It seems as if we are moving toward the time when each finger should be exercised individually in order to assure that the needs of the thrower and the catcher are perfectly matched to the skill required by each one. Nothing could be further from the truth. Nothing more complicated and nothing could extend workouts to extreme lengths faster.

Finished with the loaded conditions—on to the unloaded.

Ozolin explains the logic for special exercises in lightened conditions:

Any athlete can throw a lighter implement considerably father than the standard weight implement. Therefore, the neuro-psychological apparatus of the athlete is capable of creating such a high starting strength. So what prevents the thrower from creating the same (or slightly lower) speed when throwing the regular implement? Supposedly one needs to increase the muscles' strength, their elasticity. That is correct! Yet these new strength needs to be complemented by the sensations and the numbers of super record speed. Therefore [one must train] with the lighter implement until the new sensations become habitual.

Russian specialists recommend two or three months of throwing lighter implements in conjunction with serious strength training. For instance, leading javelin thrower Yanis Lusis threw only the women's javelin (600 grams as opposed to the men's 800) for three months. He totaled 700 maximal throws, typically exceeding his best result with the men's javelin by 6 meters or more. Two weeks after completion of the experiment, he set a new USSR record. I. Ippolitov's method of having bicyclists follow a motorcycle is another example of the lightened method.

Jack Reape has a few things to add:

The lighter javelin or implement concept is a powerful one. When my son's bat speed drops in baseball, we check the training load (very common in the off-season for bat speed to be down on week 3 of 4-week cycle) and use a lighter bat in practice, and the speed comes back up quickly. Metal bats come in standard weights of drop 3 (3 ounces lighter than bat length in inches), drop 8, and drop 10. Speed is a skill and can be retaught and/or reclaimed in often 5 to 8 lighter practice reps, whether in the DL or box squat or baseball swing. The above speed work has been a great recovery tool for me.

Finally, there are complicated conditions. They challenge the reaction time, tactics, and so on. Playing ping-pong with two balls simultaneously and playing soccer on a smaller-than-regulation-size field or with fewer players are examples. Tennis players play on wooden courts, where the ball bounces faster, to speed up the game tempo and on grass courts, where the ball may bounce in an unpredictable direction. Sometimes, Russian coaches like E. Korbut even have them play with a ball colored the same as the court to increase the challenge by making it less visible. Wearing blindfolds when weightlifting, as pioneered by R. Roman, is another fine example. Changing the rules of the game fits into this category, as well. For instance, full fighters might spar under the conditions of a simulated injury (e.g., use the left leg only). A single-attempt powerlifting meet is a beautiful example.

The concept of "same but different" goes beyond the variety of exercises. Changing the conditions in which the exercises are performed also gives the coach a great many possibilities. Speaks Ozolin:

A change of environments adds variety into the athletes' preparation and lowers the psychological strain: train in the woods, on a clearing, in a park, on different stadiums and fields, with and without spectators, with and without music.

The professor has a lot to say on the topic of music:

The majority of sports preparation means can be enhanced with music. . . . Light, rhythmical music promotes work capacity, quickness of movement, and endurance, restoration processes. . . . You may use music before a practice or competition or during practice, as well as in the intervals when switching from large loads to a new type of work. In addition, music can be useful after practice. In the course of the day, it will help acquire alertness in the morning, increase the tonus before leaving for the practice, and give relaxation after competition or before night's sleep. . . .

Music is not supposed to be on all the time.... In any situation, the volume of music must not exceed the level of normal hearing.... One must avoid repetition of the same music in a series of practices, unless there is a special requirement for it, such as in figure skating. Music to which one is accustomed to and sometimes tired of may become ineffective and vice versa. If the athlete has found music especially effective for resting before competition or for mentally gearing up for it, it should be used less frequently, keeping it in store for the most important competition....

Music significantly helps development of endurance. It has been known for a long time that the sounds of a drum, and especially of a military orchestra, make tired soldiers pick up the pace, withstand a long march. It is explained by music's emotional influence and a person's obeying a clearly sounding rhythm....There are quite a few long-distance runners and skiers who sing to themselves a melody fitting the rhythm of the event and liked by them.

You must bring your music if you deadlift at a public gym. Even if you do not need Judas Priest to get jacked up, you need it to block out Lady Gaga.

A lot of variables may be changed in an athlete's training without losing sport specificity. For example, you can vary the speed or the power. Steve Baccari has his fighters alternate speed punching and power punching for 30 seconds each twice for three to four rounds. The possibilities are endless—just remember to make the variety relevant to your sport. Do not do anything just for the hell of it.

It pays to have a healthy, middle-of-the-road attitude toward specificity. If you take the idea of SAID too literally, you will never squat 500 because you will never have practiced squatting 500. This is a vicious cycle, where you can never do something that you have never done. On the other hand, if you go in with the "everything works" attitude, you will have nothing but "great workouts" to show for your efforts.

Keep your exercises "same but different." Change them every three or four weeks, and keep getting better.

The "What the Hell?" Effect

My first experience with the wonderful "what the hell?" effect happened as I was prepping for the Nationals in the Weight Pentathlon. I was pretty good, except for one thing: the javelin. So, year in and year out, I would battle with everyone in the shot put, discus, hammer, and weight and then give away the competition in the javelin. It was time for a change.

A couple of years ago, the synergy of the Internet started changing the way a lot of my co-conspirators trained in the arts of throwing. Before 1998, we trained like this:

- **Three days a week:** Bench, clean, squat
- **Four days a week:** Throw

Any questions?

You know, it worked. Oh sure, we had some little nagging issues, like surgery, burnout, obesity, and boredom. But how important are they compared to throwing the same distance, year in and year out, for decades?

Odd things started popping up on Internet training forums. Odd things? Yeah, like odd lifts and odd objects. I thought it was all silly. I mean, really, who could tell me how to throw farther? Certainly not these lunatics in Converse shoes with their asphalt bodies, also known as "kettlebellers." I was wrong. OK, I said it: WRONG!

Let's discuss the number-one thing that I was wrong about: kettlebells. Let's look at my first impression: "Are you kidding?" You see, my experience has taught me a lot. If it's new, it's wrong. If it looks good in the ad, it doesn't work. If "everybody" is doing it, I won't.

My first experience with the kettlebell was at the Seattle Super Heavyweight Meet. That's the day that we throw the 35-pound weight, the 56-pound weight, the 98-pound weight, the 200-pound weight, and the 300-pound weight. I was promised that we would be done by noon for the BBQ, and I had plans to spend the evening with friends on one of the rivers.

Ah, plans . . .

The organizers made some changes. By noon, I still hadn't taken a throw, and by six that evening, I still had throws to make. The next morning, I got there at eight and warmed up. (What was I thinking?) Then ten hours later, I noticed the tell-tale signs of stiffness.

What to do?

Dan Mohegan had turned up to support me as part of the infamous "Old School" ground crew. I said, "Jeepers, I have noticed the onset of stiffness due to the cold, lack of nutrition, and long day." Actually, I may have said something else, but Dan offered this advice: "Here, do swings with this kettlebell."

Ten swings per side later, and my back was flushed with a warm glow. Also, my breath had left me, because obviously, when you come from nearly a mile high to sea level, you breathe harder because YOU HAVE TOO MUCH OXYGEN!

When I got home, I got my first kettlebells.

The next winter, Pavel kindly offered to let me speak at the first Kettlebell Convention. I had literally stumbled on a new way to train athletes. It's this simple:

Bring one or more kettlebells to practice with you. Do your event. Do a kettlebell movement. Repeat—a lot.

Among my core group of throwers, we began to see some odd changes. Certainly, my athletes were getting leaner with better grip strength (the two most notable improvements with the kettlebell). But we were also observing an interesting side effect: We were throwing further.

Why? I don't know. That's why it's called the WTH effect. You perform better, but you can't get a handle on why.

After Steve Maxwell's talk, I asked him a very simple and pointed question: What are the three best kettlebell drills for loosening and warming up? He answered without hesitation:

1. **Halo drills:** Two-handed kettlebell circles around the head.
2. **Squat cradling a kettlebell:** At the bottom, let it "roll" down to your extended arms. Push your hips up into the start of the straight-leg deadlift. Roll the hips down and recover back into the squat. Repeat.
3. **Windmills:** C'mon, you know them.

My job as Chief of Research for the Murray Institute for Lifelong Fitness is to be the "crash test dummy" for all new information. So, what did I do? For the next few months, I focused on improving my weakest competitive event.

For me, it's the javelin throw: the nightmare of my weight pentathlons. I blew my rotator cuff apart throwing the javelin in junior college, and I never recovered. Generally, I throw 90 feet and coil in pain after.

So, I tested the kettlebell using an event that hurts me physically, that I can't stand, and that I'm not good at. Sure, that sounds fair. Five days a week, I did my "Steve M. Three": the halo, the boot-strapper squat, and the windmill. Then, I followed the instructions given me by Bill Witt, my coach: a nice bouncy run-up (like Tigger!), leap into the Y position, wrap the X, and ruin your shoes in the C. That all makes sense to us, but the efforts were all easy and striving for "no pain."

It was time to compete! I headed off to Dallas for the Nationals. After a terrible discus throw, I walked in the humid Dallas heat about a mile to the javelin area. I was hot, sweaty, and depressed after a bad day so far. Yet at the top of the runway, I reviewed my technique, and all the time, I did my "Steve M. Three" and my "YX-C." I drove down the runway, Tigger style, threw the spear, and heard the crowd yell "Whoa!" I recovered and looked up to what appeared to be the flight of a really good javelin throw. Knowing I was the only thrower meant that I had thrown that! I added, at age 48, 6 meters to my personal best in less than five months. My throw ended up being just under 160 feet.

Three lessons are crucial here:

1. I trusted the experts. I listened and followed Steve and Bill's advice and didn't let the perceived ease of the training bug me. I can't think of better advice: Trust the experts—those who have been on the road before.

2. The kind of dynamic flexibility you need for athletics won't come from touching your toes or tossing your leg up on a barre. You need to challenge, shape, stretch, tug, pull, groove, and move all at the same time—every day and in every way. My "Steve M. Three" training was perfect. In fact, I have some cross-country runners doing it, and they just discovered that they have hamstrings.

3. I realized, finally, that the formula for success is generally right. Having said that, you also need to have the courage and confidence to explore other ways of getting beyond what you or others think is possible. Watching that javelin fly, a thought came through my head: "What the . . .?!!"

For the first time in my four-decade athletic career, I think I got it right.

Let us talk about the kettlebell WTH effect. One aspect of it is the Hardstyle kettlebell exercises' hidden specificity to a lot of power movements in sports. Consider that sprint training helps a speed skater's speed. Although the two sport movements' structures are different, there is a positive transfer because of the similarity of the deciding movement—a maximally quick hip and knee extension—according to the Russians. Ditto in throwing, skiing, and weightlifting.

D. Markov recommends short sprints, especially group starts, for throwers to promote the final extension phase in throwing. A. Vorobyev recommends the same to weightlifters. The patented hip snap of the Hardstyle kettlebell swing must have a similar effect on performance in a variety of speed-strength sports.

One of the kettlebell's many benefits is the unique way in which Hardstyle swings tend to match the dynamics of strikes and other athletic movements. Specifically, it is the ability to initiate a technique with a brief burst of effort, to relax while the strike is in flight to allow maximum speed and endurance, and to finish with a powerful *kime* or focus, locking all the muscles of the body into a statue to deliver a devastating impact.

Tension and relaxation are the yin and yang of martial power. Tension is strength, but it is also slowness. Relaxation is speed and endurance, but it is also weakness. The expert strike of a full-contact fighter rapidly alternates between tension and relaxation to get the best of both worlds. According to *Supertraining*:

> *Muscle relaxation time markedly decreases as the athlete's skill improves (Verkhoshansky, 1996). In some sprinters improvement in performance is largely a consequence of strength increase while the ability to relax the muscle remains the same, whereas some talented sprinters improve more because of an increase in their capacity for efficient muscle relaxation.*

(If you have not been practicing your *Fast & Loose* drills, the time to start is now.)

I will stress the importance of lifting your kettlebells powerfully if your sport demands power. Professor Verkhoshansky was once asked, "Can you increase max strength and starting strength using kettlebells?" He replied, "Yes, if you use the kettlebell exercises in a correct muscle work regime."

Mastery of relaxation is a hallmark of an elite athlete. Professor Leonid Matveyev observed that the higher the athlete's level, the quicker he can relax his muscles. The Soviet scientist observed an 800% difference between novices and Olympic-level sportsmen! That is why Russians—from grade-schoolers in a PE class to elite forces and Olympic athletes—practice special dynamic relaxation exercises in every athletic practice.

Explains Mark Reifkind:

> *The ballistic loading of the kettlebell swing also creates an alternating cycle of muscular tension and relaxation. The inability to relax the muscles creates too much tension for high-speed movement. Kettlebell ballistics train this cycle into the muscles in a way no other weight tool does. This also teaches trainees to learn to create very big forces and then really relax immediately after.*

Like punches, kettlebell ballistics rely on a rapid-fire sequence of high tension and relaxation. Tense-loose-tense.

Rif's hunch was proven correct by the lab of Professor Stuart McGill, at the University of Waterloo in Canada. The professor wrote to me after I visited his lab: "Your punching and kicking data was very interesting for us. You created a nice double peak, which is an excellent example of skilled contraction and the very important high rate of relaxation for speed and then hitting power."

A *double peak* means the muscular activity jumped sharply as I "threw away" the leg, dropped when the leg was in flight, and peaked on impact, as shown in the chart.

"I collected some interesting data on some UFC fighters, and they showed to different extents the double peak you showed in your kicks," continued the scientist. "The trick is to hit harder and faster by optimizing the pulses."

What makes this especially interesting is that unlike St. Pierre and other UFC fighters tested by the researcher, I had not practiced martial arts for over a decade. The timing of my kicks was the result of my kettlebell practice. Note the same double peak in the EMG of the Hardstyle kettlebell swing. Tense-loose-tense.

In boxing, the rate of movement is directly related to breathing rhythm and the boxer's ability to control this rhythm, according to Verkhoshansky. Another apparent WTH effect of Hardstyle kettlebell swings is the way they develop the skills of *power breathing* and *matching the breath with the force.*

Fifty-two-year-old David Zaharik, Canadian Kyokushin full-contact karate champion in the 1980s, took up kettlebells recently and wrote in our magazine *Hardstyle*:

One of the amazing things about training with kettlebells is that after not training in my martial art for over two years, I have actually increased the speed of my strikes and the power and speed of my kicks! I go and grapple with my old buddies who train this stuff everyday and I hold my own very well. And I getting comments back like ..."man you are strong".... Oh, by the way, these guys are 20–25 years younger than me.

David Zaharik (left) at the 1984 Kyokushin World Tournament in Tokyo, Japan and today (below).
Photos courtesy David Zaharik

Specific Training for Characteristics of Movement

Verkhoshansky lists 10 characteristics of a movement that should be trained specifically:

- Type of muscular contraction
- Movement pattern
- Region of movement
- Velocity of movement
- Force of contraction
- Muscle fiber recruitment
- Metabolism
- Biomechanical adaptation
- Flexibility
- Fatigue

Let us see how the Hardstyle kettlebell swing stacks up in each different sport.

• *Type of muscular contraction*

Ballistic concentric and eccentric. Rapid alternation of tension and relaxation. Think sprinting, jumping. Ballistic concentric only—striking, throwing. That covers most of T&F and contact sports.

The contraction type of the kettlebell swing is radically different from that found in swimming and bicycling. Yet for some mysterious reason, athletes from both sports see remarkable results from it. I have seen a photo of Lance Armstrong doing a perfect Hardstyle swing. Kenneth Jay has had remarkable success with Danish Olympic swimmers. This is no longer specificity. This is pure WTH?!

• *Movement pattern*

The late Charles Francis criticized sprint coaches who trained the hamstrings as knee flexors, rather than hip extensors. I think he would have liked the kettlebell swing.

The jump-like hip loading and extension is present in many sports. And because the Hardstyle swing ends with a complete and powerful hip extension—something many athletes do not know they are missing—it often improves the technique and power in many athletic movements. For instance, throwers add more "pop" to their throws and martial artists to their crosses, front, and back kicks.

• *Region of movement*

• *Flexibility*

Again, the ROM of the swing is highly specific to jumping. It is a little short in the hip extension department for a sprinter—because the swing is bilateral. But it still appears to get the job done, given the intent for a full hip "pop" and the hip-flexor stretch, which reinforces this intent. Front kicks suddenly gain a few extra inches of reach. This goes "beyond specificity."

• *Velocity of movement*

Check.

• *Force of contraction*

When Brandon Hetzler, an RKC from Missouri State University, came to one of our certs with a force plate, a couple of our instructors topped 500 pounds swinging a 53-pound bell, making it 10 times "heavier." Check.

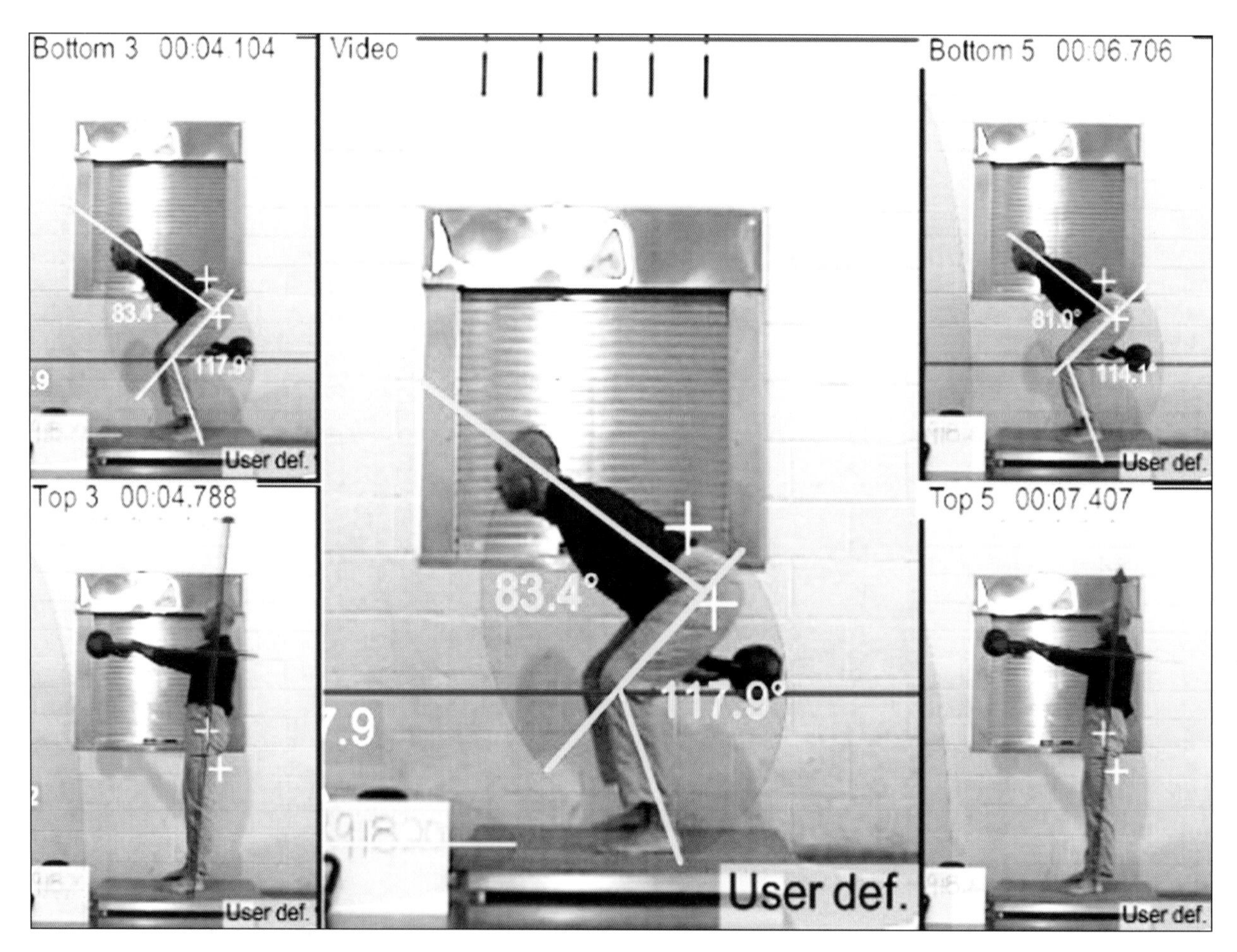

Over 500 pounds of force—and almost 10G of acceleration—were generated in this set of Hardstyle swings with a 53-pound kettlebell. Courtesy Brandon Hetzler

• *Muscle fiber recruitment*

• *Fatigue*

• *Metabolism*

• *Biomechanical adaptation*

Fast twitch, Comrade, which is critical not only for power but also for special endurance. Many fighters make the mistake of developing muscular endurance with exercises like high-rep bodyweight squats and push-ups. This does nothing for the FT glycolytic fibers engaged in striking, and it recruits and develops slower fibers instead. Even worse, it slows the fighters down and builds some useless tissue. The swing, on the other hand, is perfect for developing power endurance.

The swing is highly adaptable to the metabolic needs of power athletes, team sport athletes, track athletes, and athletes from contact sports. An MMA fighter would alternate swings and shadow boxing for 5 minutes, a thrower might do a few sets of 5 to 10 with a lot of rest, and so on.

As Dan has colorfully put it, "The swing is a fat-burning athlete builder."

Breon Hole was struggling with her kettlebell swing. Josh Vert asked me to help out, as Breon's lower back screamed after doing a few repetitions of the swing. After she did just 2 reps, I stopped her.

It's funny, because years ago, a young man told me, "Squats hurt my knees." I asked him to demonstrate his squat. He did and I said, "Squats don't hurt your knees. Whatever you are doing there hurts your knees." So, I told Breon, "Swings don't hurt your back. Whatever the hell you are doing hurts your back."

Ah, great coaching again! I knew something was wrong and stated the obvious. Breon then asked the million-dollar question: "Well, then, what am I doing wrong?"

Thank you, Breon. In fact, I could SEE the problem, but I had no ability to fix it. Oh, I knew drills, and I could have pushed, pulled, and prodded her to a better movement, but I knew that I knew that I didn't know what to do. Like that famous exchange in *Mystery Men* (and, yes, I think it's the greatest film of all time):

> **Captain Amazing:** I knew you couldn't change.
> **Casanova Frankenstein:** I knew you'd know that.
> **Captain Amazing:** Oh, I know that. AND I knew you'd know I'd know you knew.
> **Casanova Frankenstein:** But I didn't. I only knew that you'd know that I knew. Did you know THAT?
> **Captain Amazing:** Of course.

So, I knew that Breon was swinging wrong, but I didn't know much else. For a few minutes, we waved our hands around, did some drills, and actually fixed her swing. But I still didn't know something. Did you know THAT?

Breon was bending her knees too much, which let the bell go too low, which tossed all the forces on her lower back. It's sometimes called the "squatting swing."

When I said that out loud, my little world of lifting had absolute clarity. You see:

The swing is not a squat, and the squat is not a swing.

Dan and the hip displacement continuum.

To this, you may reply "So?"

Well, this was the greatest insight of my teaching career. We went to a whiteboard and began talking about this notion. It soon became known as the *hip displacement continuum*. Within a few minutes, I had posted this first tickler on the idea at my forum at **davedraper.com**. (The picture comes from a later discussion, when I decided the SWING is the king of the hip moves. Live with it!):

> *Breon and Josh Vert asked a good question and I already called Mark Twight, but somebody else will claim it later. . . . Breon was taught to do swings from a "deep squat" and "you are cheating if you don't deep squat." Well, no. . . . Put this on a "rainbow" curve or continuum. On the far left: vertical jump, standing long jump, swings (all variations), Romanian deadlifts (tackling in football would go here); in the middle: bootstrapper squat; in a narrow beam: snatches and cleans and DLs; back squats, front squats, overhead squats; on the far right: goblet squats.*

The most powerful movements the human body can achieve are from this swing position or, as it has been called more recently, the hinge movement. If you are walking and a rattlesnake crosses your path, your leap away will be more on the left side of the continuum. If you first wish to kiss the rattler, that movement will be a squat. You decide, as I have no question about what I would do.

Bad jumpers start with a lot of knee bend and diminish the pop of the hinging hips. Bad squatters bend their knees a lot and ignore the hip movement. The continuum clarified this thinking for me—forever. This discovery marks one of the few times that some mental effort has actually improved physical performance.

As a test, we added a series of standing long jump tests. First, we encouraged the athlete to use a lot of knee bend and to "really use your legs." We tested three jumps. Then, we asked for nearly no knee bend but a snappy hip movement. Most athletes are within 3 inches of their best with this style, and many actually do better. Finally, we allowed some additional knee bend but emphasized the explosive hip. The athletes made a few more attempts. More often than not, athletes reach personal records with this style.

Pavel recently added much to this concept at the HKC presentation in St. Paul. Hinge movements, like the swing, are movements with deep hip movement and minimal knee bend. Squat movements have both deep movements in the hip and the knee.

So, to memorize the following:

- **Hinge the hips (swings, jumps):** Deep hip movement, minimal knee movement
- **Squats:** Deep hip movement, deep knee movement

As you move across the continuum, you might note that the knees bend more and more but never **NEVER**. During any movement, there must always be a slight bend in the knees. Pavel calls the stiff-legged swing the "tipping bird," named for the plastic bird dipping up and down into a glass that used to be a standard feature in old bars. One of the great errors of beginning squatters is to lock out the knees at the start or top of the movement. No need to jack up your knees for life, my friend. Keep a slight bend.

It is interesting to think about the popularity of leg extension and leg curl machines in the 1970s and 80s. Both movements technically have no hip movement and deep knee movements. Since that era, some research has indicated that these movements are terrible for the knees. Mother Nature seems to know best when it comes to training.

When someone complains that swings hurt the back, it is often because they have turned the movement into a "squatting swing." Always keep the bell above the knees, "attack the zipper," hinge the hips, make the hips fold—or whatever clue is going to help you. When someone complains that squats hurt the knees, take a moment to clue the hips.

Once you understand the hip movement continuum, teaching the body to move powerfully becomes much simpler, safer, and sounder.

I hope the following letter from Timm MacDonell, of Calvary Chapel Murrieta, inspires you to get serious about your kettlebells:

I have served as strength and conditioning coach, football coach and track and field coach for the past 10 years at a small private high school in Southern California. I have certified through NSCA and USA Weightlifting. During my time here we have been fortunate to have several outstanding athletes: 5 state or American record holders with USPF powerlifting and one world record holder in deadlift. During a certification course I was introduced to kettlebells as they were being used by an athlete adjacent to our certification class. Since then I have learned what I could about kettlebell training through videos. As kids saw me practicing the techniques they became interested in learning so we occasionally took a day out of their training program to play with the kettlebells.

Like most S&C coaches I am constantly poring over results of training and looking for new ways to help kids achieve better results on their performance tests.

After attending a workshop with Pavel I began incorporating kettlebell basics into our daily workouts. In the course of 6 weeks we have seen some amazing results. Deadlifts went up between 15–25 lbs. and some of our larger athletes (220 lbs+) can now jump onto our 30″ and 36″ boxes. Our program is ending a hypertrophy phase so power is not an emphasis. These results would be understandable during our power phase. To see them now is new to me. We are currently meeting with other coaches on our campus to get kettlebells involved in all of our sports teams. Can't wait to see the results.

Note that Coach MacDonell mentions deadlift increases, as well. We sure have seen plenty of those in the RKC community, and now we have a study to document this. At the University of Copenhagen in Denmark, two groups of "recreationally weight trained males" (read "typical muscleheads") had their Romanian deadlifts, a lift in which they had experience, tested. One group started training RDLs, and the other took up overspeed snatching of light kettlebells. At the end of the study, which lasted several weeks, the deadlift group had improved their RDL by 5 kilograms (11 pounds) and the kettlebell group by 15 kilograms (33 pounds). WTH?!

Overspeed eccentrics are definitely responsible at least for some of the WTH effect.

If I set a 16-kg kettlebell on your foot, you will not even cringe.

If I drop it from 7 feet, it will break your foot.

If I slam it down, as if chopping wood with an axe, there will be nothing left to reconstruct.

The last scenario involves what Louie Simmons calls *virtual force*. The ability to generate this force is one of the most unique aspects of kettlebell training, as you can throw the kettlebell between your legs to load up for another snatch or swing rep. Such training remarkably improves one's jumping power.

Former Master RKC instructor Kenneth Jay, who is the strength coach for several Danish Olympic teams and a researcher at the University of Copenhagen, conducted an experiment in jumping power. He found that untrained subjects added 3 to 8 centimeters (or approximately 1 to 3 inches) to their standing vertical jump after just two weeks of explosive snatching of ridiculously light kettlebells (8 kg for women, 12 kg for men). In the same experiment, another group of untrained subjects added only an average of 2 centimeters (less than 1 inch) to their SVJ from doing plyometrics for the same amount of time.

I will cite Dr. Mel Siff:

One may produce the same force by moving a heavy load with a small acceleration or a light load with a large acceleration, but the training effect is very different. Explosive, low-inertia training targets involuntary, neuromuscular and central nervous processes more strongly than high-inertia training, which has a greater effect on static strength development and muscle hypertrophy.

With depth jumps, you can reduce your inertia only as far as you can reduce your bodyweight. And one has to be content with the acceleration of 1 G. Not so with kettlebell swings and snatches. You can go as light as you want, and you can throw the kettlebell down as fast as you can for an incredible preload for the next rep.

Siff coined a term for this type of training: *actively accelerated ballistics:*

> *Here you . . . rely solely on your muscles. Instead of lowering the [weight] slowly or allowing it to drop under gravitational acceleration, deliberately pull the [weight] downwards as fast as you can, stop the downward motion at a suitable point before the end of the movement and as rapidly as you can, try to accelerate the [weight] upwards into a powerful concentric movement.*

But to get back to the Danish study: The kettlebell group not only made greater gains, but their training was much safer, too. No matter how perfect your landing mechanics are—and I will venture a guess that they are not—with every landing, you are stacking the odds against yourself. Ask any paratrooper. You have no landings to worry about when you snatch your kettlebell. Of course, you will still have to master the jumping technique, but kettlebell snatches will go a long way here, as well.

While you will need to practice the foot and ankle action separately (Verkhoshansky recommends jumping rope), the hip, knee, and back extensors work the same way in kettlebell snatches and vertical jumps. And you also will learn what *Supertraining* refers to as *pneumatic shock absorption,* or how to pressurize your intraabdominal cavity before the amortization. So, you get to practice essential elements of jumping many times over and more safely than was ever possible.

It is interesting that one must use a light kettlebell to get the most benefits. Dr. Siff reminds us, "The important thing to remember is that this form of training, according to Newton's Second Law, focuses on force being increased by means of acceleration and not added mass."

When I met Brett Jones, he could parallel squat with a belt only two times his bodyweight, which many sources agree is a prerequisite to jumping well. Yet the 5' 9" Jones could not dunk a basketball until he started explosively snatching a 24 kg kettlebell. Later, he progressed to much heavier kettlebells and significantly increased his relative squat strength from 2.0 to 2.64, but he could not fly as high anymore. Now, to reclaim his impressive vertical, he is back to snatching his 24—the standard issue in the Russian military—and even a 16.

Presuming that you already have perfect kettlebell swing and snatch techniques, I am about to show you how to take them into overdrive. Start swinging a light kettlebell. To give you an idea of what how light is "light," we had Heath Evans of the New England Patriots—a 250-plus-pound man with a 550- to 600-pound squat—use a 24 kg. The kettlebell's mass is of secondary importance in this type of training. The kinetic energy imparted to the bell on the way down by your training partner, a rubber band, or even your own muscles is the key.

In the words of Louie Simmons:

> *Increasing velocity has a much greater effect on kinetic energy than increasing mass. [KE = mv2/2] Heavier weight will not add to the rebound phase as effectively as using an overspeed eccentric phase.... When slowing down the eccentric motion, we are limiting the energy that can be stored in the muscles and tendons.*

Hold the kettlebell with both hands. (Single-handed overspeed swings are harder to steer around the knees.) Swing to the chest level only. As Master RKC Brett Jones puts it, "The swing is about projection of energy; the snatch is about elevation of energy." If you want to go higher—snatch.

Now comes the interesting part: *Forcefully toss the kettlebell back between your legs, close to your groin, to load up for the next rep. Use your lats, long heads of the triceps, and hip flexors to explosively "hike pass" the bell.*

This is the simplest way to get an overspeed eccentric: by using your own antagonists. Jim Smith, RKC, and Jedd Johnson, RKC, of the Diesel Crew, have developed two more techniques, which are more involved but also more intense: with a jump-stretch band and with a training partner.

"Smitty" is getting spiked. Photo courtesy DieselCrew.com

A green band with a 24 kg is enough for a strong and fast man. Stand on the band with both feet, and loop it around the handle so it looks like an 8. "The goal is speed and explosiveness," comment the Diesels. "If the speed is compromised or slows in any way, stop the set. If speed cannot be achieved, lower the kettlebell weight." And/or pick a thinner band.

To do the partner version, after a couple of reps, have your partner gently push the kettlebell back once it has reached the top of the swing. With each succeeding rep, he should spike it progressively harder—within reason, of course. Doing a face plant is not going to make you faster or stronger.

With any of the above techniques, the reps should be limited. It makes sense to apply Professor Verkhoshansky's depth-jump guidelines: Experienced athletes should not exceed 4 x 10. Once or twice a week. This is exactly what is done by Donnie Thompson, RKC, the man who posted the highest powerlifting total of all time, 2,905 pounds: 4 sets of 10 spiked swings with a 48 kg "Beast," once a week. Given his deadlift in the 800s, a 106-pound kettlebell may qualify as "light." For less prepared athletes, 2 or 3 x 5 to 8 is sufficient.

Donnie Thompson, RKC, under the bar and with a kettlebell.

Since overspeed eccentric swings are related to depth jumps, the Russian breathing recommendations for plyometrics apply. From *Supertraining*:

> *Correct breathing is important during plyometric training. It is vital that the athlete holds the breath during the amortization and early propulsion phase to stabilize the body, offer pneumatic shock absorption and to increase the rebound force. Forced exhalation should accompany the remainder of the propulsion phase.*

The benefits of overspeed eccentric kettlebell swings are not limited to the jumping ability. The Diesel Comrades report "improved performance with general strength exercises: back squats, front squats, glute ham raises, back extensions, deadlifts, lunges, step-ups, clean & jerks, odd-object lifting... with sport specific movements: running, jumping, agility, speed, kicks, punching, striking, landing mechanics, throws." Jim Smith added 50 pounds to his deadlift, taking it from 485 to 535, in two months of "power bombs." Master RKC Geoff Neupert and I added 3 inches to the NFL player Heath Evans's vertical jump in one morning of overspeed swings and hip-flexor stretches. I believe that performing overspeed eccentric kettlebell swings and snatches is the new frontier in explosive training.

To perform an overspeed eccentric kettlebell snatch, start at the lockout. *Then throw the kettlebell through the stomach and quickly get out of the way.*

At the RKC, we have always advocated snatching as explosively as possible. However, we did not switch to lighter bells and thus maximized the overspeed eccentric overload effect until Kenneth Jay's unexpected, penicillin-like discovery.

Rif doing overspeed kettlebell snatches. Photo courtesy Mark Reifkind

The Danish researcher had set out to develop the most effective protocol for cardiovascular training. Having done his research, the Dane of Pain developed his VO2 max protocol using 16-kg kettlebells. Imagine his surprise when the subjects saw a dramatic increase in their vertical jump! As stated by Master RKC Mark Reifkind, who has been the most vocal proponent of going lighter and faster in kettlebell snatches, Kenneth has given us the "permission to go light." A much-needed permission, given the heavy lifting backgrounds of many of our Comrades.

Because the kettlebell travels a greater distance in the snatch than in the swing and has a chance to accumulate incredible kinetic energy, it has to be very light for the *girevik* to feel safe to accelerate it on the way down. If the bell is too heavy, he will not be giving it an overspeed eccentric and will miss out on the training effects of this amazing modality. A 16 kg hits the spot for most trained men. A 24 kg is enough for very strong men.

I believe one more reason that performing overspeed eccentric snatches with a light kettlebell is so effective in promoting explosiveness is nervous system disinhibition. Normally, you are subconsciously holding back and not expressing all your power out of a preprogrammed fear of injury. After having performed a number of fast snatches safely, you ease off on the brakes and really let it rip. But this will only happen if the bell is very light.

Overspeed swings and snatches are hard on the palms. Tracy Reifkind, RKC, has found an excellent solution. Her husband and coach, Mark, explains:

> *All one has to do is find a pair of medium-thickness socks and cut the top, elastic portion of the socks off. A 2-inch section is best, although one can cut 3 inches if they have very large hands. We have found crew socks, as opposed to tube socks, to work best, although feel free to experiment. New socks work best, as the fresh elastic helps to keep the sleeve in the right part of the hand.*
>
> *Simply slide the sleeve over the top of the hand, covering the lower portion of the fingers and the top section of the palm of the hand—just where the bell should sit, if properly held! That's it! Pick up the kettlebell and start snatching or swinging, and you will find there is considerably less friction in the hand right from the start but with almost no extra bulk to tax the strength of the grip. The sleeve doesn't roll up as you swing and encourages you to hold the bell in the correct part of the hand.*
>
> *You can use this all the time or just when you feel tender or hot spots on the calluses. A very simple but effective solution for keeping the hands in tip-top shape and keeping your training on track. Nothing worse than wanting to train but having to make adaptations because the hands are trashed. Enjoy!*

Use Jay's interval protocol of 15 seconds on and 15 seconds off: 15 seconds of maximally fast, up-and-down, snatches with your left; 15 seconds of rest; 15 seconds of snatches with your right; and so on. Make sure to get full hip and knee extension and a legit lockout with every rep. Keep going until you feel that your snatches are about to slow down. Snatch once a week, swing once a week, and do some heavy deads or squats once a week.

Other Hardstyle Drills

What about the WTH effect of other key Hardstyle kettlebell drills: the goblet squat, the get-up, the double front squat, the clean and press, and windmills?

Goblet Squat

Dan's goblet squat is awesome because it takes the brakes off your lower body. You cannot get very far if you are driving with one foot on the gas and the other on the brake. What is the point in making your hips strong if they are very tight? You cannot express this strength anyway. The goblet squat unlocks the hips and releases the power built with swings.

For Mark Toomey, Senior RKC and many others light goblet squats have built real strength. Photo courtesy Mark Toomey

Unexpectedly, the goblet squat also builds strength. Senior RKC, Mark Toomey has easily squatted 315 for 5 rock-bottom reps doing no squats other than kettlebell goblet squats in training. A short peaking cycle easily converts 315 x 5 to a 365 single, so Mark is a double-bodyweight squatter. This will not impress any powerlifter, but it is just enough for most sports. Consider that the double-bodyweight barbell back squat is usually considered the point of diminishing returns. Getting your leg strength up to that point dramatically improves your athletic power and performance. Going beyond does not help it, however, and sometimes retards it.

By the way, Toomey has legs that grow from his neck. If there is a man who was built *not* to squat, it is him. In case you are wondering about his exact protocol, he goblet squatted approximately every four days, alternating a "heavy" day of 48 kg x 5/5 (I put "heavy" in quotation marks because it is hard to use that word with 100 pounds in the squat) and a light day of 32 kg x 10/8 to 10 (reps/sets). Mark does not compete in a sport at this time. If you do, you would be better off spreading his volume over more days. Even with 70 pounds, 10 x 10 will leave the legs less than fresh.

What is a *goblet squat?*

Well, the funny thing about the goblet squat, much like the swing, is that it answers the question What do the hips do? And if, as we sometimes say, the kettlebell "reverse engineers" the action of the hips, especially in the swing, then in the goblet squat, the movement greases that key human motion: the squat. I read somewhere that we could evolve into a species that doesn't squat, and we seem to be doing everything we can to achieve that end. However, for those of us in sport, having mobile hips and strong legs is still something worth considering!

As I write this, I have just come in from a short goblet squat–focused workout in a hotel gym with 45-pound dumbbells. I "undid" a long flight, got a great leg workout, opened my hip joints, and got my heart pounding in mere minutes. The other gentleman in the spa/club/facility watched TV and spun his wheels on an exercycle. I would be interested in seeing how well he turns a caber!

The goblet squat simply spills over with odd benefits. My athletes have zero hamstring pulls. We don't have a lot of soreness in the preseason. Is it the GSQ? Why not?

My testimonial: I spent two years of my coaching career getting the groove right on the squat. I worked with the Bigger Faster Stronger program for a couple of years and found that kids who squatted correctly from the beginning squatted correctly after I coached them. If their early squatting had issues, it took a lot of time to fix it. Doing box squats, front squats, and all the rest got us closer but not there.

When I got to Juan Diego, I realized that I had up to 90 kids in a class. So, I decided I needed a process. At first, I used the PVC pipes that I brought in to do overhead squats, but that was a lesson in shoulder mobility, not real squatting. With the arrival of kettlebells, I continued to experiment with an effective teaching process.

So, we did sumo DLs (hands on the handles) and taught that miserably for a while. Greasing the hips seemed to help, but we still took months to teach the front squat. Next, we did Potato Sack squats—still a great move—where the athlete holds the bell and brings the weight all the way to the floor. The fingers will get smushed if they go too fast, so it taught control. But we still had the hips too high.

Then, I moved to holding the horns. I have this notion that the body thrives on a balance point, so for years, I've either used a finger or had the athlete touch their skin while doing a movement. It seemed natural to have the kids rub their elbows on their knees and . . .

And . . .

And . . .

That's it. That's it! From there, I just had the slackers (maybe five kids) push their knees OUT with their elbows, and the whole room was perfect. Chests were up ("heart to the heavens!"), knees were tracking, depth—it looked like squats!!!

I KNOW that I invented the lift, because nobody else on the Net's middle name is Arthur, has a passion for Holy Grail legends, and would instantly see the connection between the Grail stories (a goblet) and the lift. That's why when someone else "invented" it after I had it in my DVD and wrote a bunch of articles about it, it reminded me of the "gym" affiliate that invented the Slosh Pipe a few weeks after my article in *T Nation* came out.

A couple of years later, at the San Jose RKC, I asked Pavel if I could fix a young lady's squat issue. I whispered in her ear, "Let your elbow slide inside your knee, and feel the skin-on-skin contact." The crowd was stunned by her instant improvement. One of the Team Leaders turned to me and said, "These are the droids we are looking for!"

Pavel, of course, wanted to know the "secret," and it wasn't long after that when the "secret" became part of our standard of teaching.

Get-Up

Although the get-up is at least 200 years old, according to Dr. Ed Thomas, modern science views it as an exceptional exercise. Stresses Dr. Stuart McGill:

For many athletes, learning to lock the ribcage on the pelvis is essential for injury prevention and performance.... [A] terrific exercise for transitioning into performance is the Turkish Get-up, where the spine posture is controlled and the overhead weight is steered as the body learns more movement strategies that maintain torso stiffness while driving with other extremities.

The get-up promotes the shoulders' stability, mobility, and resilience. It improves one's strength in many events by teaching the important concept of linkage, while eliminating strength *leakage*.

The get-up is a very impressive developer for the whole midsection. Physiologist Bret Contreras took EMG measurements of over 50 exercises, midsection and full body. "The TGU was the only exercise in this experiment that had over 100% peak activation in all four core muscles that were tested. Good job, kettlebellers!"

The get-up deserves a whole book or two—and they have been written! In throwing, we are always discussing how to get that rotational work in. Well, the simple "punch and crunch" with a loaded arm seems to be the ideal way to work an athlete's middle area—and no, I won't say "core." It is the way you move in athletics: loaded, focused, one piece. Carryover? How can there *not* be?

The get-up has become the "go-to" exercise for fitness assessment. It is a full-body movement without peer, and it provides a complete workout in one long move. It can prepare you for a wrestling match or reteach an injured or elderly person how to move again. Here, let me make it clear: Do it!

Double Front Squat

The double-kettlebell front squat develops tremendous full-body tension, which translates into strength in "grinds" and into efficient, leak-free transfer of power in quick athletic movements. Dan stresses that it also gives you that solid feeling essential in taking punishment in contact sports.

Given the relatively light weights that kettlebells come in, the double-kettlebell front squat works the legs strengthwise surprisingly well. If Donnie Thompson finds that a pair of 48s or even 40s for 3 x 8 works him plenty, then I am sure there is enough weight for you.

Given the kettlebells' relatively light weights, the double kettlebell front squat builds leg strength.

The double-kettlebell front squat (DFS) is an exercise that takes time to appreciate. Now, like many others, I have done my time in the squat rack. I have squatted probably every variation and program you could list, and I have come away appreciating the serious growth- and strength-producing aspects of the movement. The cues and checklists needed to teach proper tension are almost endless.

So, learning the DFS taught me an instant lesson in having a natural lifting belt. This alone is worthy of the movement. You instantly lock yourself around the midsection to counter the bells. Also, without a doubt, the "cobra" muscles of the upper back—traps, rhomboids, and lats—leap into action when doing this exercise. So, if you are in need of a tighter body and powerful upper back and have any interest in stronger, more flexible legs, dip into the rich waters of the double-kettlebell front squat.

For a killer workout, try this:

- Perform 1 double-kettlebell clean and 1 double-kettlebell front squat.
- Without lowering the bells, go to 2 + 2, then 3 + 3, 4 + 4, and 5 + 5.
- Put the bells down and rest.

That thing you are brushing off your face is the floor!

Clean and Press

The kettlebell clean and press is not just another pressing variation. In the Hardstyle methodology, we emphasize the alternation of speed (clean), bracing (rack), and tension (press). This sequence is very important in contact sports.

The kettlebell C&P.

I shouldn't tell people this, but my new number-one "Armor Building," or hypertrophy, program is this:

- 1 double clean
- 3 double presses
- 2 front squats

Repeat in groups of 3 to 5. Why? Well, my athletes (and I) do this easy little variation and just keep banging away. The time under load for each rep can easily be more than 15 seconds. The clean and press—both the barbell and kettlebell variations (and I should probably add the sandbag lifts, too)—is the single best lift that I know. It is a total body workout, a total body conditioner, and a cool way to prove your strength all wrapped up in a relatively simple movement. The clean and press was the standard of strength until the bench press emerged as the answer to all questions in the early 1970s. Actually, it is just the answer to the question "Wadddya bench?"

The clean and press is a total body test of tightness **AND** looseness (if I can say that). You need to have strong legs, a strong back, and obviously a strong upper body, plus flexibility in all the major joints. Each repetition demands focus. For achieving most goals, doing a correct clean and press is a simple part of the journey.

I hate being any kind of anatomy geek, but I need to add one thing: The kettlebell clean might be the best "gun," or bicep, exercise ever made. Now, every school kid knows how to "make a muscle," showing off the bicep, and he soon learns that twisting into the "guns" position is also key. The third function tips us off as to why the kettlebell clean is superior for rapid gun advancement. As explained by Wikipedia.

> *The biceps brachii assists in forward flexion of the shoulder joint (bringing the arm forward and upwards). The short head of the biceps brachii also assists with horizontal adduction (bringing the arm across the body) when the arm is internally (or medially) rotated. Finally, the long head of the biceps brachii, due to its attachment to the scapula (or shoulder blade), assists with stabilization of the shoulder joint when a heavy weight is carried in the arm.*

Some people—especially Art DeVany, recently—argue that the deep stretch and rebound in the kettlebell clean make this lift a superior way to develop mass. In addition, at the start of the movement, all three functions of the biceps are easily noted in the basic kettlebell clean.

Windmills

The more I work with adults, the more I love the simple windmill. Yes, there is a learning curve. Yes, it helps to start on one knee. And yes, it looks difficult, to say the least. But for opening the hips, opening the thoracic spine, and clearing the shoulders, I can't think of a better move. You want to talk about developing your "core"? Slide down with a windmill, and get back to me!

For throwers, I suggest adding windmills to each session, either as a part of your mobility warm-up or as a way to break up the kinks after your performance work. I have had my javelin throwers do this for six years, and their shoulder injuries have vanished!

A Final Word on WTH Exercises

Quite simply, the WTH exercises need to part of every workout. If an exercise challenges an athlete's weak links, it needs to be done. Half-kneeling haloes can open up the thoracic spine for many locked-up athletes. Once "cured," that quick fix is going to be challenged in life and sport all the time. I think we might as well make it a simple part of the workout.

I think about WTH all the time. Is it that we finally accept the wonderful synergy of the human body and then BANG, our world changes? If you can get just a little taste of WTH, you will chase it with all your energy.

Professor Tom Fahey, Masters World Champion in discus, wrote about the only training he has been doing lately in addition to practicing throws with a variety of implements:

I have been experimenting with kettlebell training for discus. I do only three lifts, seven days a week: 40 one-arm kettlebell swings with 20 kg; 20 two-arm swings with 32 kg; and 20 one-arm snatches with 24 kg. My throws have improved by 10 feet, and my back feels a lot better. I am amazed at the effectiveness of such a small-volume workout. The ballistic nature of the workout is a lot easier on my old joints.

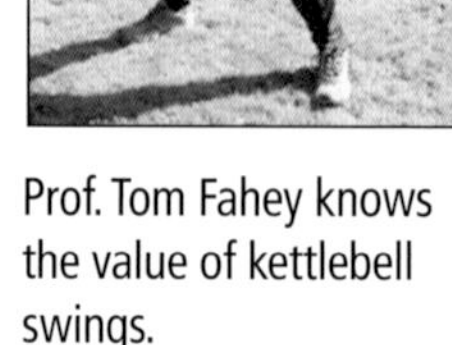

Prof. Tom Fahey knows the value of kettlebell swings.

Short-Term Muscle Memory and the Complex Method

Neuroscientists have a saying: "What fires together, wires together." Dan John knows. He alternates between throws and kettlebell exercises to ensure the transfer of strength built with the latter to the former via forming associative links between the two pathways.

I don't think I am dumb, but I have often been "there" and missed a great opportunity. For example, I could have taken computer programming courses in high school, long before people made billions using this technology, but I decided to take more biology classes instead. One day, I stood in line behind Nico Vlad when he was demonstrating the Romanian deadlift to a group of guys, but the only thing I was thinking about was that we were being served chicken again.

So clearly, I miss stuff. But at least I'm in good company. I have a buddy who told the current Miss America the he was "busy" when she asked him out on a date.

In junior college, I had the opportunity to work with several people who just basically knew stuff. At Skyline College (San Bruno, California) during the 1970s, I bumped into a lot of famous people. I talked with Tom Fahey on several occasions and never knew that I should have asked more than I talked. We also welcomed a decathlete from Germany named Wolfgang Linkman. Every day, he told me something, in his improving English—something I would spend the rest of my career relearning.

Technically, he was well beyond me, but he made sense. I had begun getting little insights into track and field from the Germans, and I would ask Wolfgang about them. My all-time favorite was asking him to translate a word that I couldn't find in any translation dictionary and that was the key to off-season training. After looking at it, he said, "Ah." Then he paused, looked up, and told me, "General manysidedness." (It was at that very moment I decided my career should be in history, theology, or something else besides language.)

Of course, I now recognize "general manysidedness" as either GPP or the basics of life in QI or QII. Linkman also tried to convince me of something else that took me decades to relearn—something he called "mixed training."

At the time, I was throwing at school and lifting at the Pacifica Barbell Club. Wolfgang wanted me to do some lifting DURING my throwing sessions. It was something the West Germans (East and West—it was a different era!) were doing and having a lot of success with. Of course, I ignored it.

A few years later, in my first coaching stint, we had a great set-up in the Nelson Fieldhouse, with an odd set of Olympic plates, a bar, and a throwing net. We had no "small" plates—just 45s, 35s, and 25s—so you had to think through a workout. With my young charges (and I really should apologize to all those athletes who ever had to watch me learn how to coach them), we mixed snatches off boxes with throws and then did some front squats and threw some more. Without a good place to do the Olympic lifts, I thought this program would work well. Of course, when the new facility opened, I tossed out this idea and went back to lifting here and throwing there.

In 1991, my eyes were opened again when Melody Torcolacci wrote about her experiences working with Boris Zaitchuk, the first man to throw the hammer over 80 meters. Beyond the great principles outlined by Melody, there was this short review of the training of Cathy Griffin, a discus thrower:

Practice (Discus)

Warm-up: *Yoga exercises (stretches and holds) + specific movements*
—Light throwing (20–25). Light = 5 meters less than max distance from previous practice
—Max throws (6 to 9)

Lift: *Lunge walk (3 x 10)*

—Medium throws (20 to 25) Medium = 2 meters to 3 meters less than maximum distance from previous practice. With medium throws the athlete alternated the implement weight, using a heavy (1.25 kg) and normal (1 kg) in her preparation phase, and normal (1 kg) and light (0.75 kg) in her competitive phase.

Lift: *Trunk twists (3 x 10)*

Here I was: a coach at a school without a field to throw in and without a true weightlifting facility who was also carrying an academic load (department head of theology) and working on an additional degree. So, I took this approach to training my throwers: Instead of throwing the discus, my athletes threw Powerballs (light medicine balls with handles) against a school wall. We soon found that mixing something as simple as Farmer's Walks with standing throws and hill sprints with full turns began to produce technical improvements in the discus.

The "why" was unimportant to me, because it was working, but others watching our training often asked that question. My only response—besides "Shush, it's working"—was to consider something that Mike Robertson recently commented on:

> *The basic principle here is this: If you don't have to coach or cue someone into the right position, if you can "trick" them into doing what you want, that's a powerful exercise. I like to call it* reflexive training.
>
> *We know goblet squats teach how to keep the chest up and out, open up the groin, and squat between the legs. Waiter's Walks and offset Farmer's Walks cue to stay tall and activate the core, all without having to think about it.*
>
> *The action is reflexive in nature: Hold a weight on one side of the body, and the body has this weird tendency to turn on the opposite side of the core to stay upright.*

My thought is this: Lifting weights between throwing sets seems to clue the body into what weightlifting is supposed to be doing for the thrower! If a lifting exercise is supposed to train the "core," then the core wakes up during the following throws. If you are supposed to use your legs first when throwing (or whatever sport you choose), then doing squats or hill sprints will wake up your legs to kick in while you do your sport.

It's that simple. It works, honestly, like a miracle, and you will be amazed you didn't thought of it before now. And here's the thing: You will probably stop doing it, because you will move on to some other fun tool. Well, at least I did.

As I discuss in the section on the WTH effect, a few years later, I tried kettlebells for the first time. Then, I began playing around with them a little and discovered how truly easy it was to keep one in my truck and carry it out on the throwing field and train with it while I threw. I rediscovered—again—the joy of lifting and throwing together. Remember, I am brilliant but not very smart.

Before I get too far along, let me note that as I progress as a coach, I begin to see less and less delineation between sport practice and conditioning. The concept of the quadrants is an attempt to explain this odd phenomenon. But honestly, one of the great leaps in my personal throwing career was grabbing my Dragon Door 28 kg and taking it out to the throwing field. At first, I did it as just a fun change-up, but I soon realized that it was a vein of gold—pure gold.

The workout ended up like what I've outlined below. But use your imagination in whatever you do, including swimming and winter sports, and see if this workout is a good fit for your sports. By the way, for your safety, do not do kettlebell work in the deep end of the pool. You have been warned!

Here is a simple workout template:

1. **Drag bell and discus to field.** Instead of general loosening stuff, try a few minutes of Waiter's and Suitcase Walks, with some goblet squats thrown in plus a few hip-flexor stretches.

2. **Easy standing throws.** After a few, do a few sets of swings to fire up the hips AND loosen up a bit more.

3. **Step-and-turn throws.** Add a few sets of one-arm presses, focusing on tightening down the whole body. Zip it up.

4. **South African throws.** Couple this dynamic exercise with some windmills. Carry that stretch into the ring, too.

5. **Full throws.** Play around with intensity on every single throw, and mix up some lifts, like snatches, goblet squats, and some clean and one-arm front squats.

Use the kettlebell to condition during the workout and enable the faster-looser feeling of big throws. And have some fun—really!

In team sports, use your imagination. I still think that tumbling drills should be a basic part of rugby, soccer, and football practice, so I don't see why adding kettlebells would be an issue. For defensive line players, kettlebells are a natural way to teach "punch," and foot drills are done famously well with moving swings. The problem would come from overkill. In the same way that football coaches overdo sprint work and conditioning, kettlebell work might be taken to excess.

Taking advantage of the short-term muscle memory allows the coach to instantly improve both the yin and the yang—the skill and the strength specific to it. In my *Martial Power* DVD sets, there are many drills of this kind. Using the straight punch as an example, let us see how it works.

The coach has the athlete throw a few hard punches against a heavy bag or a shield to establish the baseline in technique and power. Then, he has the fighter press his fist against some stationary object and imitate the final position of the punch. The coach then goes about adjusting the position, manually and with cues: "Move your foot here, . . . Push in against my hand with your knee, . . . Feel your lat, . . . Tense the right glute and get more upright . . ." The coach then takes hold of the right-front side of the athlete's pelvis and has him perform short pumping motions with his pelvis while driving with his right foot into the ground. The coach then instructs the athlete to perform *Fast & Loose* exercises for 10 seconds or so and without thinking—this is critical!—perform a series of punches.

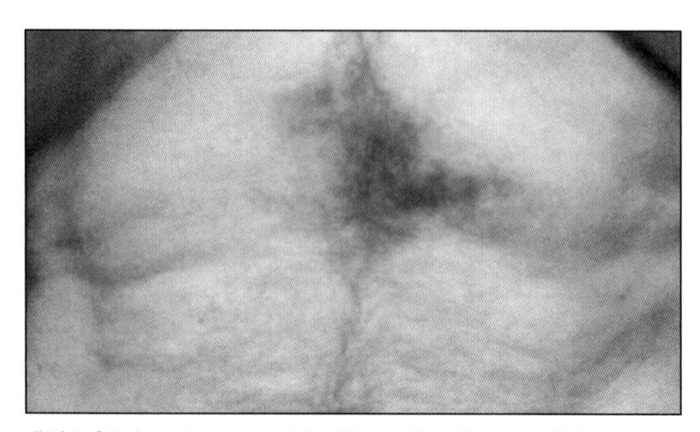

"Chief, I thought you might like a pic of how well the muscle memory punch drill works." Gary Music, RKC, a 6th degree black belt in Shurite Kempo, was punched by a petite lady with limited martial arts experience. Photo courtesy Gary Music

The drill never fails to deliver very noticeable improvements in technique and power—as long as the athlete allows his muscle memory to do the work, instead of thinking about technique. I love Brian Oldfield's quote, which I have heard from Dan: "You can't overthink a ballistic move!"

Since the effects of this type of muscle memory are short term, it is important to stop punching soon and keep practicing in a circuit of isometrics-relaxation-target technique. This will allow the skill to eventually go into long-term memory.

One of the applications of short-term muscle memory is explosive strength development that uses heavy and light resistance back to back. Explains Professor Yuri Verkhoshansky, the premier authority on the subject:

> *90% 1 RM or 5 RM and heavier weights . . . leave a certain trace, . . . a greater excitation of the central nervous system and a sustained mobilization, readiness to making a limit effort. A 30% 1 RM or approximately 25 RM resistance facilitates a quick rate of development of the working effort. As the exercise with this weight is performed on the background of the positive after-effect of the exercise with a large resistance, its training effect is significantly increased.*
>
> *As a result of the combination of such different-in-their-character training stimuli, the organism*

Three Methods of Explosive Strength Development

(Verkhoshansky)

1. 1–3 RM lifts
2. 5–10 RM lifts done for low reps, 3 or 4, and with the focus on the maximum rate of force development
3. The most effective is the *variable* or *complex method* of explosive strength development, which uses heavy and light resistance back to back.

The first is the *large effort method* if the lifts are heavy but not maximal and the *maximum effort method* if they are. Yes, heavy weights can make you explosive.

The second is the *dynamic method effort.* It helps to tap into a higher percentage of your absolute strength in a brief effort—a useful technique, once you have some strength to start with.

The third, *complex* or *variable method*, rules.

The Complex Method of Explosive Strength Training

(Verkhoshansky)

1. Repeat an exercise twice with a heavy weight and twice with a light weight.
2. Do 8 to 10 repetitions with the light weight, with the accent on explosiveness.
3. Repeat the whole series 2 or 3 times, with 6 to 10 minutes of rest in between.
4. Practice relaxation and flexibility exercises, easy and loose limb swings, and jogging in between. Refer to my DVD *Fast & Loose*.

States Verkhoshansky:

> *The possibilities of using the complex method of "explosive" strength development are significantly expanded by using jump exercises, jumps from a squat on two parallel gymnastic benches with a kettlebell (16, 24, 32 kg) held in hands, jumps off both feet following a 60- to 75-centimeter [approximately 2- to 2.5-foot] depth jump.*

Explosive Leg Strength Complexes by Verkhoshansky

Perform the drills in the order specified 2 or 3 times with 8 to 10 minutes of rest in between. Obviously, only do one complex at a time.

Complex 1

1. Barbell back squat (5 RM, 1–2 sets).
2. Jump exercises, such as triple or quintuple standing broad jumps (x 6–8).

Complex 2

1. Barbell back squat (5 RM, 1–2 sets).
2. Jumps from a squat with a barbell loaded with a 20 RM weight or a kettlebell (2 x 10).

Complex 3

1. Barbell back squat (5 RM, 1–2 sets).
2. Depth jumps (2 x 10).

Complex 4

1. Jumps from a squat with a kettlebell (2 x 8–10).
3. Intense jump exercises, such as triple or quintuple standing broad jumps (x 6–8).

Verkhoshansky proceeds to offer more complexes that emphasize strength, speed-strength, and jumping ability.

Strength and Speed-Strength Complexes by Verkhoshansky

Repeat each complex 2 or 3 times. Practice one complex at a time. The standard frequency for all complexes in this section is 3 times a week.

For Leg Extensors: Strength

1. Pistols (x 8–10 per leg) or squats with a partner on the shoulders (x 8–12) or heavy barbell back squats (x 6–8).
2. Vertical jumps up from a deep squat (x 6–8) or forward kettlebell throws from a swing (24–32 kg x 6–8).

3. Do the following:
   a. Easy accelerations up to 80 or 100 meters or jogging 200 to 300 meters.
   b. Easy basketball play into one hoop (5–8 minutes).
   c. Running drills (6–8 minutes).
4. Shaking the muscles and other relaxation exercises, stretching.

For Leg Extensors: Speed-Strength

1. Vertical jumps up from a deep squat (x 8–12) or alternate pistol jumps (x 8–10) or jumps with a 24- to 32-kg kettlebell for max height (x 8–10).
2. Take two or three steps and jump off both feet, reaching up for a hanging object (x 8–10), or repeatedly jump up, bringing the knees to the chest (x 8–10).
3. Easy accelerations or jogging (6–8 minutes).
4. Shaking the muscles and other relaxation exercises, stretching.

For Calf and Foot Muscles: Strength

1. Walk 30 to 40 meters with a partner on the shoulders, rolling from heel to toe and coming up on the ball of the foot with a "spring." Spring 2 or 3 times per step. Or do barbell calf raises on a 4- to 6-centimeter block (x 8–10).
2. Straight-legged hops on a mat (x 20–30).
3. Muscle shaking, jogging.

For Calf and Foot Muscles: Speed-Strength

1. Springy straight-legged jumps with a barbell on the shoulders (x 15–20) or springy rocking on the balls of the feet on the edge of a bench (x 10–20).
2. High, intense, straight-legged jumps off both feet (x 8–10) or jumps from foot to foot going for height and distance (15–20 meters).
3. Muscle shaking, jogging.

For Hip Flexors: Strength

1. Lie on your back on a bench or a pommel horse and lift one straight leg with an 8- to 10-kg weight (x 6–10), or stand and lift the knee with a 24-kg kettlebell hanging on the foot (x 6–10).
2. Run, lifting your knees high.
3. Easy accelerations or jogging.

For Hip Flexors: Speed-Strength

1. Lie on your back and repeatedly bring your knees toward your chest at a high pace against your partner's resistance (x 10–15).
2. Sprint, lifting your knees high.
3. Easy accelerations or jogging.

For Trunk Extensors: Strength

1. Prop your elbows on a bench behind you, your straight legs in front of you. The position is similar to the bottom position of the bench dip, except your hands are hanging off the bench. Extend your body—or bridge—against your partner's resistance (x 8–10). Or sit with your back to the stall bars, reach up with both arms, and grab a bar. Arch and lift your body, pushing down with one foot. Stretch the free leg forward in the air (8 x 10, switching legs).
2. Run, emphasizing the hip extension and trying to kick yourself in the butt.
3. Speed good mornings with an empty bar on your shoulders (x 6–8).
4. Shaking and stretching drills for the hamstrings.

Prof. Verkhoshansky's trunk extensor strength exercise.

Do snap-ups from a mat (x 6–8). (Lie on your back and place your palms on the ground by your ears, as if ready to bridge. Flex and lift your hips until your knees are over your face, as if ready to tumble back. Simultaneously explosively push your hands into the ground, extend your hips, arch your spine, and stand on your feet. Push straight down.) Or sit with your back to the stall bars, reach up with both arms, and grab a bar. Arch and lift your body, pushing down with both feet (8 x 10).

For Trunk Extensors: Speed-Strength

1. Back hypers (x 6–8).
2. Run, emphasizing the hip extension and trying to kick yourself in the butt.
3. Do snap-ups* from a mat (x 6–8). Or sit with your back to the stall bars, reach up with both arms, and grab a bar. Arch and lift your body, pushing down with both feet (8 x 10).
4. Shaking and stretching drills.

Bondarchuk "can confidently say that in the future, in the track and field speed-strength events, we will see the complex method of constructing separate training sessions." The above heavy-to-quick sequence is but one example of the complex method. The professor is referring to the broad concept of stringing along different training means in order to take advantage of the after-effect and the pre-effect phenomena. In his words, "Specialists are more and more leaning toward this which is substantiated by [our] data." This is a brave new field, which awaits coaching and neuroscience discoveries.

Variable Practice

Another tool that an astute strength or skill coach has in his quiver is *variable practice* (VP). It can be effectively used with athletic skills, SPP, and GPP drills.

Variable practice is a powerful alternative to conventional constant practice. *Constant practice* (CP) refers to doing the same thing in every consecutive trial. Multiple sets with the same weight (e.g., 440 x 5 x 5) and a series of maximal throws or punches are examples of CP. In VP, on the other hand, the effort waves up and down on every attempt. Many motor-learning studies show that subjects practicing under variable conditions perform at least as well as the constant practice group—and frequently, better!

Eastern Europeans' weightlifting sessions are variable. When Russians hit heavy doubles or triples, they often alternate them with singles or doubles with a weight reduced by 5% to 10%. Bulgarian Angel Spassov's programs are also variable. Everything is heavy and ugly, singles and doubles, yet the degree of heaviness and ugliness varies all over the board. To understand why this wavy approach is better than multiple sets with a static weight, we will have to take a geek detour into the science of motor learning.

Dr. Richard Schmidt, director of the Motor Control Laboratory at UCLA, proposed the *schema theory* to explain the effectiveness of variable practice. If a quarterback has practiced throwing the ball 10, 20, and 40 yards, he will have no difficulty passing it 30 yards. The athlete has formed a *schema:* a mental diagram that relates various outcomes to the corresponding parameter values. He may never have thrown a given distance, but by practicing at a variety of other distances, he has figured out what needs to be done. On the other hand, if the quarterback has only practiced 40-yard throws, or *overspecialized*, he will be unable to perform effectively at any other distance.

By the same token, a weightlifter who does multiple sets with the same weight will have a hard time demonstrating his strength with a different weight. You might go from snatching 115 kg x 1 x 5 to 115 kg x 1 x 15 without adding a single kilo to your total. The solution is variable practice: *Constantly vary your training weights. Train to "snatch heavy," not to "snatch 115"* (e.g., 115 x 1, 90 x 1, 100 x 1, 95 x 1, 120 x 1, 100 x 2, etc.).

"Most important," writes the UCLA professor, is that the process of forming a schema "allows the learner to make a movement he or she has never made previously." Say your best snatch is 125 kg, and you want to try for 130 kg. If you have been varying the weights like a Bulgarian, your nervous system will estimate the required force from the stored schema and run the snatch motor program with the 130-kg parameter value. Bingo, another PR!

On the other hand, if you have been doing endless singles with a static weight (e.g., 115 x 1 x 10), your *skill plasticity*—or the ability to alter and improve a given skill—will be compromised. An athlete who overspecializes, or does not mix up his training weights sufficiently, will "flat line" and have a tough time performing outside those numbers.

In a study of long jumpers by Rewzon, the subjects did not jump their maxes in training, yet they were required to jump various submaximal distances and be precise about landing at specified spots. The subjects *generalized* their skills and improved their maximal jump! The researcher who conducted the study found that practicing over a wide range of parameters was much more effective than simple repetition of the task with fixed parameters. As Schmidt himself put it, variable practice teaches "much . . . more than just the specific movements actually practiced." In this light, an athlete seeking explosive legs should consider researching *Parcours* jumps—not the crazy kind that could put you in the hospital but the kind that calls for precise landings.

When Jeff Armstrong came over one weekend, I noted that he needed to ease off on his 56-pound weight tosses, as he seemed to have a speed barrier. He was aware of the "Soviet drill", from my book *The Contrarian Approach to the Discus Throw.* For those of you who missed it (yes, I know—no more Soviets), the drill is called the Soviet drill.

I learned about this drill years ago as a way to break through the speed barrier. After marking the best throw, step off about 15 feet for most high school athletes (for some, 20 to 25 feet) back toward the ring, and put a large marker there. Cones work great; towels and bags are fine. If you have many throwers, you might have a little colony out there.

The Soviet drill is simply a series of 20 full throws in which the athlete tries to hit the marker as easily as he can. Many athletes simply can't do this! Yet once they get the hang of throwing with less, they soon find that that they can easily surpass their previous one-throw mark by using good technique and rhythm. Also, this drill comes in handy when the pressure is on to qualify for the finals at a meet.

Like most strength athletes, Jeff couldn't grasp how easing off could help him throw farther. Then, I asked him, "Do you max squat every day?" As the words came out of my mouth, I thought to myself, "You know, you should practice what you preach!" I have a journal entry where this concept whacked me on the head again:

> *November 7, 2000*
>
> *Great trip to Las Vegas and Phoenix. Really enjoyed watched ASU come back from 35–6, only to lose in double overtime. My Cardinals defeated the over-inflated Redskins, as well. While at the Orleans, I got in a nice workout with two 50-pound dumbbells. I did about an hour of clean and press, one-arm snatches, and one-arm presses. Last night, after getting off the plane, I did a nice workout of power snatches (six singles with 155), power clean, and push jerk (six singles with 195), then some real snappy clean pulls and Romanian deadlift clean pulls (a bunch with 235). This is the kind of workout that seems to give me a lot of long-term benefit. When I drop back to the "one lift a day" style of training, it really helps to have this volume with snappy, fast workouts in my quiver.*
>
> *I had a nice talk with John Powell on this trip. We ate three meals together and went bowling for a couple of hours. We both agreed that one of the real secrets to increasing your throwing distance and your lifting maxes is to push your 60–80% lifts/throws up. In throwing, you try to see how easy you can toss 80% of your best.*

In lifting, you try to dominate those lighter weights. If you have the patience to back off, you can shoot ahead later. This doesn't mean what most people think. We have a saying, "I said it was simple, not easy." It is simple to do, but not easy. For me to back off, I have to have something to back off from!!! Too many guys don't put the heavy training in early, so they can back off later.

I wouldn't consider this method of training until you at least snatch bodyweight. These fast, snappy workouts should still have some nice weights on the bar, too. Don't use vinyl dumbbells from Sears to do your "heavy" day squats, if you know what I mean. Use your journal to minimize the number of times you make the same mistakes. Sure, you won't nip every mistake in the bud the first few (five, ten, fifteen) times, but if you take some time each year to review your journals, it is like mining a vein of pure gold. Try comparing one season to another, try the countback when you peak, and keep looking for those insights that you may have forgotten. It is part of the road to success.

In addition to the heavy-hitting motor learning reasons, varying your weight up and down from set to set offers other power advantages. Lighter sets facilitate recovery for the next heavy wave and painlessly increase the tonnage. The latter is very important, as upping the volume with heavy metal makes you stronger through the process of *synaptic facilitation*.

This leads us back, of course, to the great question of the role of strength training in sports. Shouldn't I be doing some kettlebell throws? Should I have my quarterback take a 5-pound plate and practice his throw? Should I take a 32-kg kettlebell and shoot free throws with it? Well, no, but . . .

Sport-specific drills have their place—sometimes. I can think of no better way, far from competition, to relearn a basic skill or reinvigorate the "beginner's mind" than to overload an athlete. I have found that throwing heavy balls helps a javelin thrower rediscover the hips, that Powerball throwing makes a discus thrower stop thinking of the arm, and that doing loaded carries will work marvels for an off-season football player. It is also a great way to train inside in a snowstorm.

But caution must be observed: Whereas almost all heavy shot put throwing helps a shot putter almost any time of the year, overweight work will cripple an athlete who relies on the fastest movements—like sprinters, hurdlers, javelin throwers, pitchers, and perhaps even kickers. It's too close to the real thing, and I'm not sure if it upsets the delicate timing of a fast movement or if it simply causes a response from the body in the wrong direction. (Pulling a slow sled might indicate that the adaption necessary is wallowing like a pig, to paraphrase Coach Ralph Maughan.) In fact, the reason matters little.

A wise coach and athlete should probably err on the side of less when trying to get cute with sport-specific work. Now, there are cases when it works—like in the shot put and the lifting sports, obviously—but once you dial up the speed of the movement, it doesn't seem to work. Why doesn't anyone add weights to their swimmers?

Skill transfer is always the question, Hamlet. The genius of fine athletes, like fine typists and musicians and artists, seems to be to do less to make more. An elite performer displays a certain effortless elegance that seems to make the complex simple. Overloading a cellist's wrists with a weight would probably hurt the performance (and the cello).

So . . .

So is one of my favorite words. Growing up, my mother would say it when there was a lull in the conversation. It's also a nice word to use right now, as we look at all the various things spinning in the air that an athlete could do. Part of the key to balancing an intelligent strength and conditioning program is understanding that what the athlete *could* do is miles from what the athlete should do.

After all the discussion about elite athletes and QIV thinking and systematic education and systemic education, I feel that most readers now have the equivalent of elite "sticker shock." But I have some good news for you! Relax. Breathe.

Really, for the bulk of us, there is some good news—boring but good. Simply doing general conditioning—along the lines of kettlebell work, some powerlifting, and some easy, basic calisthenics—is all you will ever need to reach your goals.

Imagine, if you will, the yin-yang symbol. On one side—let's pick black—stands your general conditioning. On the other side—white—stands the technical needs for your sports or interests. For most of us, simply improving the black will help with most of our "bumping-through-life" goals. Essentially, most of us will be very happy and very productive living our life in quadrant III. It will help us move couches, play pick-up games, wrestle with our buddies, and look good enough to interest someone in continuing our genetic code into the next generation.

Actually (and this is rude), most people I deal with don't have any goals. So like the cliché says, "Any road will get you there, if you don't care where you are going."

And we can make that circle of the yin-yang bigger. That's what many of us do: We add kettlebell drills and pull-up contests and all kinds of other things to make our couch moving easier, even when our sister moves to the fourth floor. It's those two little dots that are the issue for most people—the specific little conditioning exercises that mimic our sports and often actually lead to more failure and folly. In religious studies, we always note that it is very difficult to relate to something that is totally "other." The dots remind us that there are feminine traits in men and masculine traits in women. The dots, my friend, are the key to specific preparation!

And, I need to add, the dots—those little drills and lifts that we all invent in the gym and dojo and field that are lifting/throwing/grappling/whatever moves—are usually the things that lead to injury. Moreover, throwing a 25-pound plate like a discus probably does more technical damage to the actual discus throw than simply just going home and eating another steak.

Here's the question: If you can improve your sport through general training alone and actual performance work in your sport, then why should you do the extra junk? And here's my answer: You shouldn't.

I like to think that the phenomenal "what the heck?" effect is actually related to this insight about simply enlarging the yin-yang symbol. But plugging the WTH effect into a program is difficult, as many of us will attest to. Even so, I think that most of us who have experienced that odd sensation of the WTH effect will be able to later glean the actual process of what was really going on in the total program.

In reading Tommy Kono's remarkable second book, *Championship Weightlifting: Beyond Muscle Power,* the interested athlete will find some great training gem leaping off nearly every page. Tommy's career is unparalleled. As an Olympic lifter, his gold medals at the Olympics and World Championships, along with his world records and extraordinary career as a coach and author, place him at the top of the game. Many forget, however, that he was also Mr. Universe.

In the very last chapter of his book, Tommy writes about the "right place at the right time." He reviews his life story, from his childhood sicknesses to his discovering weightlifting at a WWII internment camp. (For the record, after you have read both of his books, you will be ready to stop feeling sorry for yourself.) Struggling from ailments, Tommy struggled to learn how to lift those weights, even out of the box.

Near the end of the book, Tommy makes an interesting almost "throw-away" comment: "I would train for a weightlifting contest but as soon as the contest was over, I would immediately start 'pumping' up." He goes on to describe how after a few weeks of bodybuilding movements, he would feel himself becoming interested in heavy movements again.

This is a simple idea—one that many readers likely pass over. Yet Tommy recommends lifting in as many Olympic meets as you can during a year. That means the athlete would probably have several intensive six-week periods preparing for an Olympic lifting meet, followed by maybe three to four weeks of "pumping." Don't worry about the specifics—worry about the career.

There is a genius insight here. First, how long can an athlete do just the sport alone? With basketball, it seems that a small percentage of athletes can play year-round for decades and achieve the highest level. They are rewarded with multimillion-dollar contracts. Some nations have massive state-funded sports programs that take literally tens of thousands of young athletes and end up with a handful of champions (or survivors).

Other than these two extremes, I strongly suggest adopting Tommy Kono's approach. Train hard, focus on a competition, and then move into something that is complementary. Many throwers, for example, find that Highland Games competitions provide the perfect tonic to a long track season. "Same but different."

Professor Issurin tells the story of a coach who decided to get rid of general exercises and make his athletes' preparation exclusively "sport specific." Seven months later, the athletes not only failed to reach PRs but could not even repeat their previous bests. Such stories are common. Don't repeat others' mistakes.

It is true that hyperspecificity works with the right genetics, the right support system, and the right reward at the end of the day. For most, however, there is a need to have the "same-but-different" approach.

Unlike "peaking" programs, alternating naturally between specific and true general work seems to lead to a longer, healthier approach to elite sports.

CHAPTER 7

Strength Training Planning

"Training is putting money in the bank to spend it on the fight night."
—Steve Baccari, RKC

For the past few years, I've become infamous for two heretical beliefs:

1. I don't believe in *peaking*.
2. Connected to that, I really don't believe in *periodization*.

Now, it's true that there are people who've peaked. I'd argue, however, that there are far more people who've trained to peak and failed to peak. For proof, just look at the Olympics. It isn't uncommon for an athlete to have his worst performance in years at the Olympic Games. One can argue that it's the pressure, and I'm fine with that insight. But I believe that the pressure is caused by the imagined need to peak, the change in training to allow a peak, and, ultimately, the pressure to respond to the need to peak.

According to German sports scientist Alfons Lehnert, only 20% of Olympians post their year's best performance at the Olympics. Clearly, contemporary models of periodization and peaking have severe limitations.

As for periodization, my argument is simple: By the time you finish with all the charts, graphs, percentages, and number crunching, the athlete can barely load a weight on a bar. "I need to do 6 reps with 83.4% of my 4 RM in a 9-3-2 tempo and a 26-second rest between sets for maximum hypertrophy." The math alone will paralyze the lifter. True, I exaggerate, but not by much.

Verkhoshansky makes this amused observation:

Many Westerners seem oblivious to the fact that the general paradigm of periodization was based heavily upon the philosophies and methodologies of communism. The cyclical nature of periodization was strongly influenced by the "five-year plans" and other cycles of productivity in the Soviet system, while the precise calculation of training quantities reflected attempts to minimize the unscientific factors of subjectivity and emotiveness."

So, before you get enamored with all things Russian, consider these examples of Soviet-era folklore:

Q: Why is the Soviet system the best?
A: Because it is always overcoming the challenges absent in other systems.

Q: Can socialism be built in the US?
A: Yes, but then where would Russia buy wheat?

Q: What would happen if we built socialism in the desert?
A: There would be sand shortages.

I am as opposed to mind-numbing complexity and inflexibility as Dan is. I am for *periodization* defined as "planned according to certain principles of variation of the training variables such as specificity, intensity, and volume within a specified period of time culminating in peak performance." This does not imply computerized charts.

Whatever the terminology, we have to talk about training planning. And it has to follow certain rules that have come to be associated with periodization: building capacity while taking care to vary or *cycle* the loads, then switching to more intense and specific yet lighter-in-volume training to *peak.*

Consider the following set of recommendations for training and peaking the deadlift by Dr. Ken Leistner, who is decidedly not a fan of Eastern European training methodologies:

- Two weeks of easing in, five or six weeks of hard training, and two more weeks of easy training.
- Train a muscle group twice a week: once heavy and once light (technique, etc.).
- Alternate heavy and medium deadlifts every other week.
- Build strength; then "convert" it into the powerlifts.
- Do weekly low-rep skill practice, but do not max.
- To peak the deadlift, train with 2 to 4 singles, with 30 seconds of rest between them.

When you step far enough away, you will see a pattern of similarities between apparently very different successful training plans.

First, we will discuss "putting money in the bank" and then "taking it out on the fight night."

"The two major tasks of all [training cycles] are the creation of movement potential and its realization," stated Dr. Atko Viru, a Soviet superscientist. It is critical for a coach to understand that *building* performance potential and realizing it are not the same thing. Many Russian specialists believe that one trades long-term gains for instant gratification of high performance.

According to powerlifting coach Alexander Faleev, maxing out is a missed opportunity for 5 x 5s. Two decades before him, Dr. Fred Hatfield stated that 5 x 5s build strength and singles only test it. Both views may be a bit extreme, but most professionals would agree with them at least in principle. "When one is after long-term adaptation and aims at significant structural, and not just functional changes, the volume of loading is increased first and foremost," explains Dr. Leonid Matveyev. "When, on the other hand, one aims to realize the acquired ability as a sudden increase in athletic performance, the training intensity gets top importance." In other words, off-season training is simply about what Dan calls "punching the clock."

If we stay with the saving-and-spending-money analogy, neither blowing every dollar that comes your way nor denying oneself everything and going to one's grave with a fat bank account without having enjoyed the fruits of one's labor will bring one happiness. One needs to know when to save and when to spend. As Dr. Robert Roman reminds us:

> *Athletes are often afraid to lower the workload during the competition month, reasoning that they would get out of shape. And there are other examples when athletes . . . start sharply lowering the volume . . . two months before . . . a non-important meet and taper for every such meet. It is wrong. In the first instance the athlete fails to completely realize his potential. In the second . . . the athlete hits the same PR every time as he fails to build his base. . . . Either case is a brake for growth of athletic performance.*

Konstantin Rogozhnikov offers an example illustrating how much competition preparation may set an athlete back in the long term. According to the Head Coach Powerlifting Team WPC Russia, making weight to drop 5 or 6 kilograms (11 to 13 pounds) rewinds your strength by three months!

One must understand that "high" volume in the preparatory period is relative—relative to the volume in the competition period. Ben Johnson's 12 reps of squats (2 x 6) in the off-season may sound low compared to some arbitrary bodybuilding number, but they are high compared to the 4 to 6 (2 x 2 or 3) he did when a race was around the corner.

Increasing training volume to crazy levels has been tried in all sports. Sometimes it has worked, but more often it has not. Thomas Kurz is talking about the *principle of economy of effort:* "The coach should use the least training load necessary to deliver a desired result. . . . Research by Costill et al. (1991) showed that swimmers who worked out twice daily and swam more than 10,000 m per day made the same improvements as swimmers who worked once per day and swam approximately half that distance per day."

Today's trend is toward lowering the volume. According to Dr. Bondarchuk, the training volume of jumpers and throwers was chopped in half in the late 1980s to the early 1990s, compared to the late 1960s to the early 1970s. And the records have substantially gone up. World and Olympic champion weightlifter Tommy Kono was way ahead of this trend back in the 1960s. He recalls:

> *My approach to Olympic weightlifting has always been based on quality training in order to cut workout time to the minimum and yet get a maximum benefit. . . . After a certain amount of exertion time, any more may be detrimental. . . . Instead of improving, the excess training, the extra efforts, and the extra time spent may just undermine all the positive effects achieved to that point. . . .*
>
> *There is a "diminishing return" for an excessive amount of work. When your workload gets to the point of fatigue, all the previous good lifts performed beforehand will be erased by sloppily performed or imperfect lifts. . . .*
>
> *When a great volume of work is performed, the quality of movement is lost. Too many repetitions destroy coordination. Fatigue becomes a big factor in employing the wrong muscles to complete the movement. The athlete no longer lifts like an athlete but like a laborer performing work. . . .*
>
> *The American system is finding the quickest way of doing things, so that we have more time to pursue other goals.*

Arthur Jones and Mike Mentzer may have taken a wrong turn in their quest for maximally efficient training, but their goal was and still is worthy. Consider the logic of Konstantin Rogozhnikov, who is dedicated to the same purpose. This elite powerlifting coach finds the classic set-and-rep scheme of 3 x 5 or 6 from the famous US study by Berger the ultimate in efficiency:

> *The mistake of many athletes is they do not know how to stop in time. It always seems to them that they are not doing enough and they ought to do more. For example, if in the [bench] press you confidently pressed a heavy weight for 6 reps in two sets, you can be certain that you will press that weight 5 times in a third set, 3 or 4 in the fourth, 1 or 2 in the fifth. This means that you should stop on the third. In the later sets you are starting to draw on the organism's reserves, which will be needed for recovery. Three work sets are more than plenty for . . . a quality workload. More does not mean better.*

Of course, this is not the only efficient approach to building strength, but you get the point.

Restraint equally applies to your lifting and your sport practice. Here is how Charlie Francis used to coach his sprinters: "If I hear Ben's feet hit heavier on the track, that's enough. Top athletes need to be controlled from overmotivation."

Nikolay Ozolin is on the same wavelength: "Appearance of the feeling of some fatigue is usually the signal to terminate the exercise which demands primarily quickness, strength, [coordination]. . . . Such exercises, usually performed with high intensity, high nervous strain, should not be continued after the onset of fatigue."

Russian scientists differentiate between two types of training load: *external* and *internal.* A sharp coach has to pay attention to both. The former is easily quantified in kilos, reps, and the like. The latter is the body's reaction to a given external load.

Obviously, it is a lot trickier to measure the internal load than the external one. Daily monitoring of the athlete's resting heart rate is "one of the simplest and most practical of the accepted methods of monitoring athletes," according to Vladimir Issurin. Find your base-level heart rate by measuring it on a morning when you know you are well rested and not overtrained. From that point on, an increase of less than 6 BPM indicates good recovery. If you are between 6 and 10 BPM, you are adapting to the load but have not fully overcome fatigue. A range of 11 to 16 BPM flags a high level of fatigue, and if you have exceeded 16 BPM, overtraining alarms are going off. This does not mean you should always religiously keep your pulse within 6 BPM of the norm and worship perfect recovery. If your workout was heavy deadlifts for 5 x 5, you have to redline around 10—just don't go over.

Verkhoshansky and Siff stress that heart rate monitoring is valuable not only in endurance sports but also in explosive and other nonoxidative activities to estimate levels of both physical and mental stress. Other parameters tracked by Russian coaches include the rate of perceived exertion, willingness to train or compete, perception of fatigue, breathing, and even face color.

Traditionally, the *rate of perceived exertion* (RPE) is logged on a 1 to 10 scale, but I like my father's method better: a percentage of an all-out effort. Looking at his training log entries before his latest deadlift meet—in which he pulled a PR 380 at 181 raw (not even a belt) at the age of 73—helped me make adjustments in his cycle. The last three workouts were planned like this:

- 325 x 3/3
- 335 x 2/2
- 345 x 2/2
- Meet

Three weeks out, my dad pulled 325 x 3/3. According to my calculations, this was supposed to be a moderately heavy, 80% RPE or so, effort. Yet to him, it was 90%. For one reason or another—anything from an improperly laid-out cycle to not getting enough rest—things were not going as planned. (I learned the answer later: Without my knowledge, my father had maxed—after a 5 x 5 workout not long before!) So I made adjustments, hoping he would listen this time, to allow him to come to the meet fresh, not burned out. The new plan looked like this:

- 325 x 3/3—last workout
- 275 x 3/3
- 275 x 3, 295 x 2, 315 x 1
- Meet

I first dropped him way low—just over 70% of his 1 RM—for a few triples to unload him. Then I gently reintroduced him to heavier—kind of heavy, barely 85%—weights. I was not worried about detraining, as my dad had done five 5 x 5 workouts in the cycle and had a durable base.

According to Russian research, strength built with volume lasts. Besides, as Professor Issurin points out:

Older and more experienced athletes are more accustomed to any kind of training stimuli; consequently, their response is less pronounced and their improvement rate is lower. However, the higher long-term adaptation level determines the lower rate of ability loss. As a result, older and experienced athletes have longer training residuals, which allow them to perform a smaller training volume. This is consistent with the real sports world, where training volumes for elite older athletes are 20%–25% less than for their younger counterparts.

Paying attention to the perceived rate of exertion allowed my father to overcome the consequences of a bad training decision. This is how it all panned out:

- 325 x 3/3 (RPE 90%)
- 275 x 3/3 (RPE 85%)
- 275 x 3, 295 x 2, 315 x 1 (RPE 86%)
- Meet: **380 PR**

A part of my father's DL plan is a light Monday workout that never changes: 225 x 5/5. It serves several functions: First, technique work. Second, maintaining muscle mass in the later weeks of the cycle, when the volume on the heavy days drops dramatically. Third, keeping him out of trouble, as my old man loves training and will find something to do if I do not do it for him. (To give you an idea, a few times a week, he climbs the stairs to the top of a 17-story building.)

Throughout the above cycle, his PRE readings for the light day read:

60%, 50%, 49%, 48%, 47%, 46%, 44%, 43%, 42%

You might say: "You have got to be kidding! 42%?! No one can define his perceived effort with such accuracy." True. In my father's system, such increments simply mean that the weight felt a hair lighter than the last time. And I was very pleased to see the pattern, as the light workout stayed the same for the duration of the cycle, and apples could be compared to apples. He was obviously getting stronger.

Nikolay Ozolin recommends asking the athlete to rate his willingness to go through a training session or competition on a 1 to 5 scale before the warm-up. 5 = very large desire, 4 = large, 3 = average, 2 = low, 1 = unwilling. This is very important, especially before competition. In principle, the willingness to train should always be high. It indicates proper training load and recovery.

If the athlete is not game, have him warm up thoroughly till he sweats. If he is still unwilling, he has been overloaded too much or not recovered enough. You are witnessing early symptoms of overtraining.

Note that willingness to train is specific to the event. An athlete tired of intense sport-specific training may be very game for GPP. It is instructive that Vladimir Dyachkov would have his athletes take their last intense sport-specific training load 10 days before the competition. After that, they would maintain their edge with intense GPP. Very Tommy Kono.

So then, gentle reader, you may wonder how I train athletes. Years ago, I came across a simple formula that has elements of peaking and periodization yet also allows for the natural fluctuations of this thing I call "life."

Life? Yep, think it through: How many times have you finally put together an ideal training program and training environment, only to have some "life" just sneak up and clobber you? You know—sick kids, sick dog, broken car, best friend's bachelor party, that "job thing," and just plain life.

Planning Training: The "Do This" List

1. First, realize that you are powerless NOT to do something stupid. So accept that. Embrace it. Now, promise yourself the following: *The goal is to keep the* GOAL *the goal.* Anything you add to your plan that is **NOT** part of the goal is going to be the problem. Don't do it.
2. Steal other people's paths. There is tons of information available for anything you are attempting. Success leaves tracks: Follow them.
3. Assemble the tools, supplies, and information needed for correctives. If you are going to use a foam roller in this program, get a foam roller. Allot about 10% of your training time to restorative work, correctives, and any kind of voodoo that you think helps.
4. If you are involved in a sport, 80% of your training time should be spent doing that activity. For most of you, 10% of your time should go to developing strength and another 10% to correctives, but the bulk should be spent on the specific activity.
5. Evaluate any program or system every two weeks. Make small course corrections when you are still basically on target.

How often should you change training programs? That is a good question, because there seem to be only two kinds of trainers:

1. **Those who never change anything—ever:** Go to most gyms, and the guys come in and walk for a minute, bench press, do lat pulldowns and curls, and go home. They have done this for years.

2. **Those who never stick to anything—ever:** This condition is described with a lot of names, but I like "Internet Warrior." Or better yet, insert my name. This condition is usually caused by people (like me) who are convinced that somewhere, someone is doing something smarter, better, and faster.

I strongly suggest that most people learn to work in two-week blocks: building up certain qualities in some blocks and other qualities in other blocks. Here's a simple kettlebell-related answer:

- **Two weeks of the Program Minimum (PM):** Swings two or three times a week, get-ups two or three times a week
- **Two weeks of *Power to the People!* (PTTP):** Five days a week of deadlifting and pressing
- **Two more weeks of PM**

Now, here is the key: When you move back to PTTP, try to maintain the loads from two weeks before when you moved to the PM.

I get these bizarre phone calls and e-mails from aging elite athletes who take my advice on alternating the two weeks of PTTP "grinds" with the more dynamic program minimum. A typical conversation goes like this:

> *"Um, I feel like I'm not doing enough."*
> *"Oh?"*
> *"Yeah, I'm competing and doing better than I ever have, but I don't feel like I'm doing enough."*
> *"So, you are meeting all your goals and enjoying training and performing well?"*
> *"Right."*
> *"And, you want to change that?"*

I won't name names, but I work with several people—multi-Olympians and Olympians-to-be—who truly struggle with the concept of less. One elite athlete is setting marks at one-third the effort but still e-mailing me with concerns about doing more!

Will it work for everyone? Well, first run this through the quadrants. If your sport or goal is in QIII, the answer is "yes."

This is an example of Russian *block training*: the most cutting-edge yet simple-to-implement type of periodization. Be forewarned that this particular supersimple template—alternating two different modalities every two weeks—works only if you stick with these two for several months.

Explains Arbeit: "It is one of the most important training principles: Do not change the rhythm of the loads.... The biological system must get exact information about the direction of adaptation." That is why if you follow the two-week rotation, you must stick with the same two blocks for several months in order to gain what Marty Gallagher calls the "training momentum."

After three or four rounds of this (i.e., three or four months), do a detailed assessment of your mobility, your strength levels, your general fitness ("Do these pants make me look fat?"), and your performance. For athletes, refer to the quadrants to assess the impact of the training on your performance.

If there is a gap, fill it. If there is clearly a lagging issue, take a few weeks to address it with a clear focus. Don't just wave your arms and do a whole bunch of "stuff," because you read about something in an article.

Moving from a program as interesting as Armor Building to a program that asks for little in the way of excitement, like Easy Strength, MUST be done according to a calendar. Armor Building is something that we do:

1. Months ahead of a season
2. Every workout session after the age of 28 or so
3. As a tonic during a season to recharge

Easy Strength is something that we do:

1. To build a platform for superlative performance
2. As a way of holding on to qualities for a long period of time
3. To keep an experienced athlete incredibly strong with minimal effort

The human body is amazingly adaptable, and that adaptability explains why humans do so well in just about any environment. But the elite athlete doesn't want a bunch of adaptations. The generalist can impress you with a laundry list of "this" and "thats." But in line with the old saying "Jack of all trades, master of none," the generalist will fail when measured against the elite athlete. And no, it doesn't matter what it says on your T-shirt. One can't simply claim to be elite.

So, be calendar wise when moving from important training programs. I would suggest never just doing something like Armor Building here and Easy Strength there. Keep a little bit of Armor Building through a long season, and enjoy some quality workouts with Easy Strength far away from competition. But anyone in QIII or QIV must really focus in on the narrow band of qualities needed for elite performance. It is not an easy concept to explain, and it is even more difficult to practice, but the coach and the athlete have to live in "unbalanced balance." And that is also why so few people make it to the top.

Should you train with kettlebells year-round?

One of my principles of training is simply "It is about movements, not muscles." I still follow the basic movements:

- Push
- Pull
- Squat
- Whole-body explosive move
- Deadlift
- Anterior chain
- Rotational movements and single-limb stuff

From there, you can break it down in vertical, horizontal, and diagonal work, but it really just muddies up the subject. I believe that a solid training program "plays" with every movement, every day.

You have many tools at your disposal to do these movements, and I think it is important to explore each movement with various tools.

Bodyweight

- Push: Push-ups
- Pull: Pull-ups
- Squat: Free squats
- Whole-body explosive move: Multiple jumps
- Deadlift: Vertical jumps
- Anterior chain: V-ups

Kettlebells

- Push: Presses
- Pull: Swings
- Squat: Goblet squats
- Whole-body explosive move: Snatches/Swings
- Deadlift: Deadlifts
- Anterior chain: Get-ups

Barbells

- Push: Military presses
- Pull: Rows
- Squat: Front squats
- Whole-body explosive move: Cleans
- Deadlift: Deadlifts
- Anterior chain: Suitcase deadlifts/Barbell rollouts

Even from these short lists, you can see that some movements can be done with any tool and others probably lean toward one. The press is excellent any way you decide to do it, but the kettlebell get-up has convinced me that it is the King of Core.

So, while there may be times during a specialized period that this point may not be true, for the most part, I am open to any and all tools. I train my adult groups with nothing but kettlebells and let them work with barbells on their own. I have noted that adults are good at grinding but struggle with balance and ballistics. So, that's what we do together.

An adolescent boy might need more barbell work for his set of goals—often, simply to get bigger and faster. A wise coach focuses on what the student does NOT want to do, rather than the "candy" part of the workout.

Speaking of a workout, heed these rules distilled from Russian research to better plan workouts and training weeks:

- Keep your training sessions short, one hour or less. Multiple shorter sessions are preferable to a single long one. Even half an hour of rest makes a difference.

Beware that the idea behind twice-or-more-a-day training is to fragment the existing workload into smaller pieces—not to add more volume, at least not initially.

- Severely limit the number of training foci—at times, all the way down to one—and modalities per training session. Combining strength and endurance training in one workout is an especially bad idea.* The research is clear: you have nothing to gain and a lot to lose. A mere 2-mile run after a strength workout reduces the strength gains by 10%! If you are confused about the goal of your workout, so will be your body.

- The following qualities demand CNS freshness: skill (especially new skill), speed, power, strength. Train them first in the workout, and plan your training weeks in such a manner that you are coming to the gym fresh. If you train more than one of these qualities (skill, speed, power, strength) in one session, you may stack them in any order. There is research demonstrating that speed work improves the quality of the following strength work and vice versa—although one should not do intense plyometrics before strength exercises. After intense jump training, the CNS functional condition is reduced, according to research by Dyachkov.

- Following are examples of effective workout arrangements:
    - — Speed, power, sport skill
    - — Strength, speed, sport skill
    - — Skill, strength, skill
    - — Skill, power, skill
    - — Speed, strength, static passive flexibility
    - — Strength, static passive flexibility, static active flexibility
    - — Sport skill (nonexhaustive), power
    - — Strength, sport skill
    - — Dynamic flexibility, sport skill, power
    - — General (aerobic) endurance, passive flexibility
    - — Dynamic flexibility, technique, anaerobic endurance, passive flexibility
    - — Dynamic flexibility, anaerobic endurance, sport-skill endurance (stressproofing a mastered skill), passive flexibility

- Do not learn new skills or train speed, power, strength, or hypertrophy on the same day or the day after a hard endurance workout—any type of endurance.

- Only very easy endurance training—any type of endurance—is acceptable on the same day or the day after a hypertrophy workout.

- For motor-learning reasons, periodically take days off from practicing your sport skill. States Ozolin, "Effectiveness of skill mastery increases if after a series of frequent practices (4–6 a week), . . . one takes a 2–4 day break."

- The next session after a hard workout of any type should be a light or medium one, focusing on a different quality.

* There are some exceptions. For instance, a low volume of kettlebell snatches facilitates following low-rep "grinds," presses, pistols, and the like.

- Do not schedule the hardest workout of the week after the weekend or a day off. It is a common misconception that after the weekend, because you are rested, you will do your best. Not so. All the processes in your body have inertia, and it takes a couple of days to get into the swing of things. I am sure your boss has noticed that Monday is not the day you do your finest work. As one Russian employee wrote in his explanatory note, "I did not show up for work on Monday, because my appearance did not match the photo on my security pass." Could this be why Russian strength plans often place the hardest workout on Wednesday?

- Unless prescribed otherwise (e.g., the complex method), do your special strength exercises following a low-volume, general strength workout: right after, later in the day, or on the next day. Barbell exercises have a positive strength influence even the next day, according to Dyachkov.

- QII athletes, do not schedule back to back more than two workouts from either the left column or the right column:

Speed Power Strength	**Any type of Endurance**

Let us talk about recovery. Following are the recommendations of Ozolin, typical of a Russian coach:

- Get a minimum of eight hours of sleep at night, surrounded by fresh air and silence—and total darkness, I might add. No blinking alarm clocks or cracked shades. Read *Lights Out: Sleep, Sugar, and Survival*, by T. S. Wiley and Bent Formby, Ph.D., for details. If you cannot fall asleep, count till 3:00 a.m. If that does not work, count till 3:30 . . .

- Take naps, as well. Russian folk wisdom has it that sound sleep not only extends life but also shortens the workday! If possible, snooze for 60 to 90 minutes after lunch. It is best not to lie down right after eating but to take a 20- to 30-minute walk first. If you have a very intense training schedule and you are a "trust fund baby," you should try sleeping three times in 24 hours: 1 hour after breakfast, with the morning workout taking place before breakfast; 60 to 90 minutes after lunch, with the main workout before lunch; plus 9 hours at night. The total sleep time may reach 11 hours. Powerlifting great Mike Bridges reportedly could do better than that at night alone, and so can my father. Power loves rest.

- Allowing even short, 10- to 30-minute relaxation periods between exercises or attempts in competition is helpful. It is best to lie down, elevate your feet, and mentally remove yourself from the training environment. Perhaps listen to music.

- Relaxing in a hot tub for 10 to 15 minutes is recommended for recovery after a workout or competition—but not before!

Russian specialists have determined that passive rest is not always the best way to restore the athlete. In 1903, Ivan Sechenov discovered the phenomenon that he named *active rest.* The Russian physiologist observed that the work capacity of one arm recovered quicker if the other arm worked, as compared

Mike Bridges knew that power loves rest. Photo courtesy *Powerlifting USA*

to passive rest of the same duration. This principle was successfully implemented in Soviet prison camps: If you got tired swinging an axe, it was time to pick up the shovel and "rest."

Seriously, Russian coaches have made extensive use of this phenomenon for decades, always carefully paying attention that the active rest exercises are indeed easy. Light windmills would make for great active rest after kettlebell swings; heavy snatches would not. I like doing various correctives, like the "Brettzel," and easy local strength drills, such as neck work, between sets of global exercises. I often sandwich splits and other lower-body stretches between sets of upper-body exercises. This not only improves recovery, but it allows me to reduce training time.

Here is something that I have been doing for just the past few weeks, but it seems to work: during the strong movements of a workout, do all the correctives and foam rolling and mobility issues work. During the rest periods of a strong point, do the extra "stuff." During the rest periods of the movements being addressed the weak points—simply rest.

The reason behind this is simple: The focus on the weak points MUST be the weak points. However, with mastered movements, you have some extra mental free space to turn the focus to other things.

A warning, though: For whatever reason—perhaps it is a neurological quirk—some correctives can steam up the metabolism. So, you might experience some odd huffing and puffing from doing a mobility fix on the shoulder, for example. Enjoy it! You are getting better.

The day after a hard practice, Russians like activities such as easy jogging in the woods, rowing, biking, swimming, and skiing for 30 to 40 minutes. According to Ozolin, this

> *lowers psychological excitation [and] normalizes the activity of the cardiovascular and respiratory systems, the metabolic processes.... Such active rest the day after a large training load promotes a quicker elimination of fatigue. But the intensity in such exercises must be low, approximately on the level of 100 to 120 BPM heart rate, sometimes a little more. Exceeding this intensity could add to the athlete's fatigue.*

If you are not accustomed to the particular activity, take it even easier. Hartmann and Tünneman add, "Recovery training involves the training of less loaded muscle groups and thus helps to prevent injury."

It must be stressed that a competitor who wants to have a long, successful career must have multiple gears. You must know when to take your body and mind into overdrive when competing in your sport—and to take it easy and simply have a good time playing beach volleyball (unless beach volleyball is your sport). Don't race a runner passing you on your active recovery mountain jog. Be content knowing that you can deadlift two to three times more than him, and let him pass. The right gear for the right job.

An effective form of active rest combines high physical demands with high positive emotions in events far from the athlete's main sport. A mountain-climbing trip for the wrestling team is a good example. Games, water skiing, windsurfing, and downhill skiing all make great active rest events. S. Yananis discovered that proper active rest reduces the stress on the athlete's nervous system.

A few words from Ozolin about active rest after competition:

> *It has been noted a long time ago that athletes, psychologically fatigued from many months of training and competition in their sport, do other exercises with pleasure. However their selection must be related to their athletic specialization in order to effectively maintain general and special preparedness on a high level.*

For examples, throwers and weightlifters do long jumps, high jumps, and skip rope; jumpers and sprinters play volleyball; and so on. Kono knew this decades ago:

> *I believe that my switching from Olympic weightlifting to bodybuilding exercises almost immediately after a big weightlifting competition prolonged my sporting career. Switching back and forth . . . kept my enthusiasm high in both endeavors, hence I kept improving.*

Onward to annual strength programming.

Most of your year should be dedicated to "punch the clock" training in a series of Easy Strength and Even Easier Strength cycles. Stay on an ES or EES plan put together according to the guidelines we gave you earlier—"sort of max" with singles or low reps—and then move on to another. Change most, if not all, loading parameters—the exercises, the sets, the reps, the frequency, and so on—for every cycle. Just keep everything within the parameters set in Chapter 3, the "Easy Strength" chapter. As a rule of thumb, make the change every three to six weeks, unless advised otherwise, as in Bob Gaynor's DL plan.

In fact, this could possibly be the ONLY kind of training that an athlete needs!!! The more I work with athletes on the Easy Strength, 40-Day Workout, and Even Easier Strength programs (which honestly are all about the same thing when you are dealing with advanced athletes), the more convinced I am that we need to simply continue to pick two "weaker or lesser" movements and address them over a brief window of time—then find two more. With the other movements, the "stronger" ones, you still keep doing them, of course. The athlete keeps the strong movements and builds up either the ignored movements or the weaknesses.

If you are not yet ready for the radical step of going ES/EES 100%, occasionally run an intense strength specialization or hypertrophy specialization program—for example, twice a year for both. Strength specialization cycles can be as short as three weeks or a lot longer, if you are using a powerlifting cycle. Remember that muscles take longer to adapt than the nervous system, and make your hypertrophy cycles 6 to 12 weeks long, as recommended by Hartmann and Tünneman.

A strength specialization program is something unfriendly, like 5 x 5 with the same weight in all sets, the Russian Squat Routine, or a plan out of *Power to the People Professional.* Neither such a strength plan nor an Armor Building one is compatible with serious speed, power, technique, or endurance training, so you must plan your year accordingly. Pay attention to the recommendations from *Supertraining:*

> *One must work on improving technique daily, especially in speed-strength and complex-technical types of sports, with "freshness" of the body being an important prerequisite for development of technique. Separate tasks of technical training which do not require maximum intensity of effort can be performed with the body in a lowered functional state, but the execution of other tasks under such conditions is unacceptable. . . . Thus, one may recognize two successive stages of technical training in the preparatory period. During the first stage, one performs those components of*

> *technique which need improvement and during the second, the emphasis is on executing the* sport exercise *as a whole with high intensity of effort....*
>
> *Speed work is excluded totally from the concentrated loading stage. However, it is possible during this stage to perfect this athlete's motor skill, which directly determines high speed of movement.*
>
> *This motor proficiency requires efficient intermuscular coordination, when there should be no tension in the muscle groups which do not directly take part in executing the motor tasks. This involves a specific sequence of tension and relaxation of the working muscle groups to perfect the general coordination structure of the given exercise. This type of work is quite compatible with the athlete's decreased functional state, provided it is executed in the optimal range of intensity of effort and frequency of movement.*

And heed this advice of Dietmar Schmidtbleicher: "When one increases the number of training units devoted to strength and power training, he/she should elevate the proportion of 'lengthening gymnastics' (stretching, physiotherapeutic procedures, etc.)." That means *Super Joints, Fast & Loose, Relax into Stretch,* and professional soft-tissue work.

Thanks to a lot of sunlight and fresh fruits and vegetables, summer and fall are the best times for strength or hypertrophy specialization training—if your competition calendar allows it. Americans take for granted having fresh produce year-round.

To give you an idea of how the Russians made due, in the service, we were given raw onions in the winter to stave off scurvy. When I was a kid, a friend of mine snacked on raw onions at school. Civilians grew their own green onions. You stick an onion bulb into a glass with a little water on the bottom, set it wherever it can find some light, and wait until it first sprouts roots and later leaves. The chives are tenderly clipped, washed, and chopped and lovingly placed on top of some starch—that is your meal. This qualified as a "vegetable." Valerie Hedlund, RKC, who visited the Soviet Union in the 1980s, told me how she was surprised when she was scolded by her host for not eating the parsley on her plate. What goes by the name of "garnish" in the West was a legit "vegetable" in Russia.

There was the competition calendar, as well, and some other peculiar circumstances that demanded "periodization" of training. In the 1980s, Soviet powerlifters and bodybuilders often took summers off and played with kettlebells, pull-ups, and dips, because government-run gyms were often closed for repairs in the summer. Very scientific.

When competition nears, you must be back to ES or EES.

Never stack strength specialization and hypertrophy specialization cycles back to back. Separate them with at least one six-week block of ES or EES.

In your tough strength specialization blocks, you need to remember some rules of thumb about pushing and backing off "cycling". From *Supertraining:*

The optimal duration of continuous training is 5–6 weeks, and with concentrated loading, the duration is 3–4 weeks, after which a recuperation period is necessary for activating the compensatory processes. . . . The trained athlete is able to tolerate three such sequential blocks of loading, separated by short recuperation pauses (7–10 days). After this, a longer recuperation period is necessary to facilitate stabilization at the new level of adaptation.

Charlie Francis was very smart about simple strength periodization. Ben Johnson's strength training had the following phases: accumulation, intensification, and maintenance. Following six weeks of accumulation, Johnson would really crank it up in a seven-week intensification phase: three weeks hard, an unloading week, another hard three. The maintenance phase could go on for a long while; its duration depended on the proximity of the next competition. According to Dr. Joseph Horrigan—whose writings have been very helpful in tracking down gold nuggets about Charlie Francis's methodology—Johnson took his last hard workout seven weeks before running a 9.83 world record in Rome in 1987, but he still kept lifting the same heavy weight, albeit for doubles and triples.

Francis had his sprinter work all the qualities all the time, albeit not equally hard. One modality was emphasized, another deemphasized. If the athlete did more strength work, his explosive training took the back seat, and vice versa. So, when you are not on a strength or hypertrophy specialization cycle and doing your ES or EES, you should stress other qualities—power, and so on.

Cycling the loads is probably done best on a very simple scale. Honestly, for the bulk of the athletes and people I work with, having a volume workout one day a week and a heavier workout one day a week seems just about right.

I need to stop, because that statement just opened up 1,000 questions. But I had a fine New Zealand coach, Kevin Brady, teach me a simple formula in college that simply worked miracles for me and many others:

- **Sunday:** Off or easy recovery.
- **Monday:** 70% in the weight room. Lots of volume (and that means a million things).
- **Tuesday:** No lifting. (There is an assumption here that this is an athlete doing lots of sport work every day.)
- **Wednesday:** 80% to 95% in the weight room. Heavy work, low reps, lots of rest after heavy attempts.
- **Thursday:** No lifting.
- **Friday:** 80% for a SINGLE in some key lifts to excite the nervous system.
- **Saturday:** Compete.

I have used this formula for myself and countless others, and it is a simple path to success. Insert appropriate lifts for your sport or goals, but keep the loading simple.

Over a career, one will soon find that a "heavy year" should proceed an important year. For example, the year before the Olympics should be extremely heavy in terms of lifting and, well, any kind of heavy work the athlete can do. During the Olympic year, the training needs to be both eased up and sharpened.

Ponder an insightful comment by Ozolin about biological rhythms:

It must be stressed that waviness [of loads] also has to do with a gradual transition to rest after each training practice and day, after a training macrocycle and competition, during transition to active rest in the end of annual training, and when quitting the sport due to age or some other reason. A sudden transition from large training loads and high levels of organs and systems functioning to physical inactivity leads to disruption in the finely balanced work of the whole organism, decline of health.

Now, the problem is that the athlete will feel so good that he will join a basketball league, sprain an ankle, and lose a chance to make the team.

The US Marines have more men down from basketball games than from combat. I am not joking. I believe that the responsible thing for an elite athlete or for a front-line military man is to pass on hazardous activities that do not contribute to his athletic or operational performance. I gave a piece of my mind to a friend—a special operator with many combat deployments under his belt—for going snowboarding, taking a hard landing, and seriously injuring his lower back.

There is a time and a place to man up. The war is it; the basketball court is not—unless basketball is your war.

Cycling loads should be done in a deliberate manner weekly, monthly, and yearly. Any plan to play with loading will work, which underscores the popularity of Jim Wendler's simple 5/3/1 program. So few people have ever systematically played with any loading parameters that they are frankly amazed at the immediate benefits of trying different weights and rep schemes. It certainly isn't complex, and one does not need a supercomputer to attempt this stuff.

You **WILL** cycle loads. Sure, a raw beginner will be able to train in a linear line that slowly moves up, but that will end soon. Moreover, it only works ONCE in a career (so enjoy it!). If you try to prove me wrong, you will blow something off and have to taper because of surgeries or athletic tape. That was my "system" for most of my athletic life.

Indeed, why does one have to crash after a peak? Many coaches and scientists have pondered that question. From *Supertraining*:

Matveyev ... posed the intriguing question: "Why not retain sporting form permanently as a state which is optimal for the athlete?" This would obviate the need for detraining after a competitive phase or including transition phases, which are commonly part of the "off-season" in the West. In asking this question, he is clearly re-examining the entire rationale behind his model, thereby suggesting that one must be very circumspect before taking any training model at face value.

For one reason or another, an athlete cannot keep improving continuously. Eventually, he will exhaust his adaptive reserves. Explains Viru:

> *Prokop pointed to the dependence of the performance dynamics on the exhaustion of adaptivity in sportsmen. According to him, a sportsman has to exhaust a great part of his adaptivity to reach the top performance. Thereafter, a decrease in the performance level will follow. In this situation, continuing training with high loads unduly magnifies the drop in performance, while reduced training helps overcome the decrease in performance and ensures a new improvement. This consideration fits in with the experiments with sportsmen. Against this background, reduced training is recommended when the top performance has been achieved.... The temporary loss of adaptivity has made it necessary to employ a cyclic structure in training.*

Here is a thought: Perhaps if we did not "exhaust the adaptivity," we would not have as many problems associated with periodization and peaking, including unreliability, possibility of burnout, and lost training time from periods of lower volume before and after competition.

Francis must have been on to something:

> *It is always better to undertrain than to overtrain. You will still supercompensate, but not to the same degree. Once you overtrain, your body will plummet and fight to retain a balance. Smaller CNS demands over a longer period of time result in more acceptance and greater improvement, while the rush to get more done leads to uncertainty down the road.*

The second part is so important, let us hear it a second time:

> *Smaller CNS demands over a longer period of time result in more acceptance and greater improvement, while the rush to get more done leads to uncertainty down the road.*

As we wrote in the "Easy Strength" chapter, we should coax the gains, not force them. PRs without maxing, even in your strength specialization cycles. After competition or a limit workout, the nervous system needs at least three weeks to recover, according to Ozolin. After an important competition, this is understandable. But after a workout—why waste three weeks of your training?

It is true even in powerlifting. Andy Bolton, 1,000-plus-pound puller, warns, "A big mistake is training deadlifts with a max effort. These should only be done in competition. Try holding back a little, and watch your deadlift fly."

Anatoly Bondarchuk has had remarkable success keeping his Olympians in top form for up to nine months! He reveals that "it is most important 'not to excite the dragon' but as much as possible entertain' him and if at all possible 'fool him.'" Bondarchuk is poetically referring to not abusing the body with maximal loads and to rotating exercises every three or four weeks.

Try applying the Easy Strength philosophy to all aspects of your training, not just strength.

A careful reading of this passage from *Supertraining* offers more food for thought:

> *The need to increase loads and progress towards maximal loading is based on the thesis that physical loads which are most capable of significantly disrupting homeostasis elicit the greatest training effect.*

Have you noticed that the need for max loads is not a fact but a thesis: "an unproved statement, especially one serving as a premise in an argument"?

Another quote from the same source:

> *Although today's athletes attain a high level of sport proficiency, there is still no basis to state that this is the result of a precise methodology of special strength training. To a great extent they achieve proficiency through a large volume of strength work and colossal expenditure of energy. Generally, the selection and use of means for organizing special strength training has a number of weaknesses.*

Without ever meeting Steve Baccari, Ivan Ivanov—who formerly coached the Bulgarian national gymnastics team—talks about training as "putting money in the bank" and "increasing, rather than exhausting, the energy." This theme runs throughout the training philosophies of Ivanov, Francis, Baccari, Ross, John, and many other highly accomplished coaches. Perhaps it is high time you listened and started focusing on building up your athlete's "bank account," instead of finding new ways of draining it by smoking him.

To stay with the banking analogy, sophisticated periodization and peaking procedures may be compared to buying a fancy house with no money down and an adjustable rate mortgage. It has worked for a few, but it has bankrupted a lot more. On the other hand, those who live within their means do not have to juggle their bills and resort to Enron-type accounting. They just write a monthly check for a house they can afford.

Kurz writes:

> *These are the general rules for changing the dynamics of training loads:*
>
> - *The lower the frequency and intensity of workouts, the longer may be the ascending phase of the wave, but the amount of improvement from workout to workout is very small;*
> - *The higher the intensity of the workouts and the means of recovery used in the interval between them, the more frequent are the waves.*

Research and experience show that the higher the loads, the more one has to "wave" them, which is a headache even for a high-end professional. Just consider the circa-max squat cycles practiced at Westside. Pure rocket science. Or look at the training plans of Powerlifting Team IPF Russia. Its members' monthly volume fluctuates enormously—for instance, from 80 to 400 tons.

When loads are modest, one does not have to walk the edge of injury, overtraining, or burnout. Training planning becomes simple if you are training "within your means."

It is fascinating that Tommy Kono's once poor health may have helped him to become an Olympian by teaching him not to push too far:

Starting with poor health, I learned to exert myself only to a certain level and back off; otherwise my condition would reverse itself. All this helped me define quality training. For me, it wasn't the volume of work but the quality of training *that was important.*

Pieces of paper are cheaper than surgeries. Write out your goals, specific dates for achieving them, and a general plan based on what has worked in the past and what has worked for others. This is 99% of success in planning.

Next, grab a calendar and make a few big red-letter Xs on the dates when you know things are coming up. And then, don't be surprised when things come up. Also take a yellow highlighter and highlight the days with "issues." They might include things as simple as school finals or appointments for the dog.

In most situations, the day before competition should be an 80% day (hard to define, but most people have a feel for that). But TWO days before should be 60%—perhaps just a warm-up. The "two-day lag rule" has survived the test of time. If the event is really important, you should completely rest three days before it and perhaps four days, if possible. Don't try to stuff weeks, months, or years of work into the last week.

You may have the best laid out training plan yet still fail to get the results you are after, for the very simple reason that you are alive, complex, and affected by a great many variables that you cannot possibly account for—from moon phases to the health of your cat. Fine-tuning your training by closely monitoring the condition of your nervous system will help you make the necessary adjustments and prevail.

When the chips are down, the nervous system decides everything—and one has to watch it. But there is more to "watching it" than not letting oneself reach a state of eye-twitching nervous exhaustion.

Nerve cells can function in three modes: *normal, forced,* and *pathological.* Using a jet analogy, the first corresponds to cruising, the second to flying on afterburner, and the third to crashing.

The *normal* mode is characterized by a stable, moderate function that can be maintained almost indefinitely. It is like paying cash and living within your means. The meat-and-potatoes moderately heavy training you do throughout the year should be done in this mode.

The *forced* mode of the powerlifting competition, and one or two heavy sessions before it, is "tapping into your savings." Your performance spikes for a short period of time and necessitates a prolonged recovery and replenishment.

Stay in this mode too long, and you will have gone "bankrupt," entering the *pathological* mode of overtraining. No matter how hard you try, your performance will nose dive as your nervous system shuts down the operation to protect itself against your stubborn stupidity. Keep at it longer, and you will get nervous exhaustion. Remember Inspector Clouseau's boss, who sings "Somewhere Over the Rainbow" with his eye twitching?

One must plan and tweak training in such a way that most of it is done in the normal mode. Peaking and competition belong in the forced mode, and the pathological mode should be left to your competitors. Venturing into the forced mode without falling off the edge into pathology is very tricky. The following Russian techniques for monitoring and influencing the work capacity and tonus of the CNS will be of great help.

It was 1961, and Russians were flying high. Yuri Gagarin was the first man in space. Valery Brumel was breaking world records in the high jump. Every day, Brumel's coach, Vladimir Dyachkov, tested his grip strength. This coach extraordinaire knew that this was the simplest way to gauge the work capacity and excitability of the athlete's CNS—the single most important variable in posting great results.

One day, the chart showed that the sportsman's grip had suddenly spiked. The coach shook his head, fully aware that this indicated premature peaking. He did not want his star jumper to leave his best performance in the gym—to get "discharged," as Russian athletes would say. So, Brumel took a harder-than-planned workout, and the excitation came down. Then, several days later, it started climbing again. Another workout, a light one this time, brought it down once more.

Coach Dyachkov's adjustments worked like a charm. On the day of the championship, Valery Brumel's grip strength was off the charts, his nervous system in peak form, and another record fell.

Soviet coaches had known for decades that the condition of the athlete's nervous system is the most important variable in posting an elite performance. Moreover, breakthrough neuroscience research by their fellow countrymen had given them an undeniable advantage over the rest of the world. Simple and effective tests of the CNS tonus were developed: the grip, the standing vertical jump, the critical blinking frequency, the latent reaction time, tapping with a pencil and hitting a maximal number of dots in 5 seconds, and so forth.

Take a page from the Russian book, and use one of these tests to tweak your training when necessary, the way leading US coaches already do—Dan John with tapping, Louie Simmons with the grip, Chad Waterbury with the SVJ. But before getting down to the procedure, you need to know that there is more to these tests than flagging overtraining.

Indeed, an overtrained athlete will lose his grip strength and jump height, and as you would expect, these are signs to take it easy. But surprisingly, rapidly climbing numbers can also be a cause for concern, especially in the days before a competition. A "peak", by definition, is narrow, and once you have hit it, the only way to go is down. "Early peaking is dangerous," observed great Yuri Vlasov six weeks before the Tokyo Olympics. "You must avoid maximum concentration. Such concentration of energy destroys strength."

Decades ago, Ivan Pavlov discovered that nerve cells cannot fire on an "afterburner" for a long time. The scientist established that when neurons are pushed to their limit or even way above the normal level for too long, they experience *defensive inhibition*—a fancy way of saying that they hit the brakes to avoid hitting the wall. This sharply decreases the neurons' work capacity and tonus—and your competitor takes home the trophy. Russians learned to manipulate CNS excitability, keeping it on an even keel for most of the training and then carefully—but never too early!—bringing it up before competition.

The desired pattern is to keep your grip strength more or less even (of course, you should expect a drop the day after heavy deadlifting), then to increase it for several consecutive days before the competition, and finally to hit your highest value exactly on the big day. The day after the event, your grip strength, along with your CNS, will predictably come down.

"Several" days sounds vague, and indeed it is. Everyone is different, and you will have to find your sweet spot through trial and error. Months of measurements and several competitions will teach you whether your grip strength should start climbing two, four, or some other number of days out in order to hit its max on the big day. Then, you will know when and how to tweak your training load, if the peaking process does not follow the best-case scenario.

Listen to the following recommendations by Professor Ozolin:

- Buy a hand-grip dynamometer, of the kind used in physical therapy clinics, and test yourself daily. Never change the testing protocol: Do it at the same time of day, with the same hand, in the same posture, with the same warm-up or lack of thereof, and so on. Do only one test.

- The number itself does not reflect the level of your CNS excitability; it is the dynamics charted over time that matter. When your training load is appropriate, there will be little daily variance—1 or 2 kilograms (2.2 to 4.4 pounds). A greater decrease indicates an excessive training load, an insufficient recovery, a nervous fatigue, an early phase of overtraining, or some disturbance in your regimen or your life. A slight drop for one to three days following a competition is normal.

Continues Ozolin:

> *Analysis of daily values of grip strength gives the opportunity not only to objectively control changes in the nervous system excitability, but also to guide it into the right direction with the help of the daily regimen: massage, training, and pharmacology. A reminder: a calm and long cross-country run through the woods lowers excitability and brief but intense work, including strength work, increases it. Training in the pre-competition days and a warm-up the day before the competition restrains an increase in excitability, while passive rest filled with thoughts about the upcoming competition sharply increases it.*

Obviously, if your sport demands serious grip training, the above procedure will be inaccurate. Use the SVJ test or the tapping test.

The Soviet champion, scientist, and coach offers more advice on fine-tuning your CNS condition in the days before the competition, ensuring that you will be at your best when it counts:

1. When training loads sharply increase before competition, the CNS reaches its peak performance in just one or two days. Without training, the peak will be lost in two or three days. The peak can be kept up for five to seven days with 85% to 90% loads and lower volume.
2. One can maintain fairly high CNS function—but not a true peak—for several weeks with intense training, but this leads to burnout.

3. Don't rest longer than 24 hours before the event.
4. Perform a warm-up specific to your event 24 hours before the competition.
5. Do a light workout if nervous on the days leading up to the competition.
6. Skip the workout if you don't feel like training after the warm-up.
7. An easy tonic workout—with lifts not heavier than 70% to 80% in speed-strength sports—four to six hours before the competition is helpful.
8. It is normal for the grip strength/CNS excitability to go up for the first two or three days after arriving for a competition in another city or country. Traveling excites.
9. Events other than training (feeling happy, sad, etc.) can have an effect on grip strength/CNS excitability, which may last for several days. Advises Ozolin, "In the end, one must remember that it is the athlete himself who changes the level of excitation through his interpretation of various external stimuli, his thoughts and decisions."
10. Don't push it on the days after an unsuccessful competition. No point in "Monday morning quarterbacking," Train light, and do exercises that are not specific to your sport. Back-cycling after the competition is essential in order to prevent CNS burnout.

It is interesting that losing sleep over worrying about an upcoming event might spur you on to greatness! Have you ever dragged your tail into the gym and set a PR? You probably shook your head and decided that you would never bother trying to understand your body.

Drs. William Kraemer and Steven Fleck offer a surprisingly simple explanation:

> *Chronic sleep loss can compromise physiological performance, but limited sleep deprivation from typical sleep patterns has been shown to create a higher physiological state. This higher physiological state is created by increased nervous system sensitivity and higher levels of catecholamines . . . released by the adrenal glands in situations of stress.*

So, if you have not slept well before a competition or a heavy workout, keep a great attitude! It was all for the best.

CNS testing will help you get a lot more out of your Easy Strength training plan—not a highly structured plan, like Justa's singles or the PTTP linear cycle, but a flexible one like the flexible wave cycle from *Power to the People! "Grease the Groove"* from *The Naked Warrior,* or the *40-Day Workout,* which, as Dan has pointed out, is just "an organized 'Grease the Groove.'"

Aim to keep your grip strength steady. If you see a drop, reduce your intensity and volume. Keep both down until your nervous system rebounds. On the other hand, take advantage of the days when you see a sudden jump in your grip strength, and test your "sort of max" or go for a low-rep PR. As Dan summed up Easy Strength training, "Punch the clock. Then, on the days things are grooving, you go after it." And don't forget to immediately back off.

Keep in mind that the above template does not aim to squeeze the last drop of performance out of you, as a true competition peak would. (That would take some days of planning, building up, and backing off.) It is just an opportunistic approach to setting PRs—a "tactical peak," so to speak.

Back to real peaking—peaking for competition. In many sports, shock-intensity, low-volume loads are used in precompetition days to sharply increase the CNS function. Experience shows that one can "spike" the CNS twice starting 14 days before the competition: once or twice in week 1, again once or twice but more intensely in week 2.

Concludes Ozolin:

> *There have been attempts to follow this scheme for three weeks, but the result of the competition in the fourth week was unsuccessful. Based on the fact that the athletes' work capacity in the workout of the third week was successful, as well as on the positive experience of competitive preparation with shock workouts in a two-week cycle, one may make a conclusion about high effectiveness of such a scheme.*

As Dan says, "I am always three weeks out from a meet." Thanks to Louie Simmons, that is now common knowledge among US strength athletes and coaches.

Russian specialists have concluded that the more important the competition, the longer the grip strength and CNS tonus should climb in order to reach a higher peak. Yet start to peak too soon, and you will leave your best in the gym.

Peaking is a lot like playing blackjack. A perfect hand of 21 corresponds to hitting the highest CNS excitation exactly on the day of the competition. A good hand—maybe winning, maybe not—is in the high teens. It corresponds to conservatively coming into competition with a high, although not maximal, nervous system tonus shortly before the real peak. A "bust" with 22 or more is what happens when you peak before the big day.

A new idiom is begging to be coined: "a Saturday morning quarterback." Knowing when to say "hit" and when to stay "stand" is a science, an art, and a gamble.

Boris Sheyko is careful not to leave his powerlifting champions' best lifts in the gym:

> *Some young coaches test their athletes' maxes 7–10 days before the meet. It is probably the sign that the teacher, rather than the student, is having doubts. Such flops happened to me too in the beginning of my career.... This resulted in the athlete being empty, squeezed out like a lemon on the day of the competition. Records were out of the question. It also happened that due to unloading too late, the athlete had enough strength but not enough freshness in the muscles and speed.... Based on my experience working with high-level athletes, I came to the conclusion that for an athlete on the level of Team Russia, it is sufficient to lift 90% weights for their opener 2.5–3 weeks before the meet.... [I tell them]: "No need to test your max. You already did it at the Russia Cup. Now you just need to lift your opener with ease and grace."*

And up-and-coming athletes should not gamble at all. Dan and I insist that they say "stand" early on and pass on the "hit" of high-intensity CNS priming—especially with their event.

Russian lifters do not leave their best lifts in the gym.
Photo courtesy *Powerlifting USA*

"Stand" or "hit." Playing blackjack is an excellent metaphor for training an athlete getting ready for competition. Years ago, I watched a youth football coach note that the team he was about to play lined up in an unusual formation. So, he gathered his team—a group of preadolescent nose pickers and video game players—and went through a detailed explanation of the formation, the dangers of the formations, and the scheme to stop the formation.

When the game began, the coach's team forgot their normal defense and, of course, the other team never used that formation. Knowing young football players as I do, it could simply have been the case that 5 of the 11 just went to the wrong place.

Trust me, that is not unusual. I once had an insane parent yell at me and my coaching staff for having only ten players on the field for a punt. I turned to my assistant and said, "Ten? Actually, that's pretty good for us. Usually, we have nine."

What's my point? It is crucial to learn to "stand." In team sports, there is a saturation point where enough is enough. The late, great football coach Bill Walsh used to love to show high school coaches his highly complex "if they do this, we do that" stuff, simply to confuse the group enough that they would be receptive to the real message of his talk. There is a point where, to quote that great disco song, "Enough is enough is enough . . ."

For individual athletes, the error comes usually from "more." Tommy Kono—and I know I mention him too often for some (but honestly, he deserves even more kudos)—emphasizes this point over and over in his vast works on the Olympic lifts. His point is simple: *Less is more*. Yet the fear of competition makes many of us want to try "just one more" and then leave it in the training hall.

There are some wonderful books about playing blackjack and beating the house. Simple rules state what to hit and what to stand when the dealer shows this or that. I'm no expert, but here is my idea for winning at blackjack: Don't go bust. Make the dealer beat you by the numbers, not by the fact that you hit on 18.

Yes, that is a poorly disguised metaphor: Make the opposition beat you. Don't go bust **BEFORE** the game begins!

Recall that CNS excitability is affected not only by training. A less-than-elite athlete is likely to be so nervous before the competition that he will not need any help in getting himself worked up. Just the opposite needs to happen—he needs to come down.

This is where Dan's warm-up style practices of the event (such as 50% deadlifts for a powerlifter), as well as take-it-easy, GPP-like games and cross-country jogs, come in. In case you think you are too advanced to pursue such a lowly strategy, consider that weightlifting legend Tommy Kono used to do bodybuilding exercises for two weeks before a meet, claiming that such training kept him strong, fresh, and eager to lift in the meet.

There are two additional reasons for an inexperienced athlete to avoid intense skill practice before competition. First, a less-than-stellar showing is likely to psych him out. Second, he might pick up bad habits. When the CNS is highly excitable, new skills are easily learned—intentionally or not. Ozolin emphasizes, "Incorrect movements performed on the background of pre-competition nervous strain are very easily solidified."

In power sports, the nonspecific stimulus of heavy lifting done by muscles less involved in one's sport can produce a powerful "spike" before competition while simultaneously acting as active rest. Explains Bondarchuk:

> *In sports practice, the process of restoration and activation of competitive activity can be favorably influenced by several types of exercise. For example, many jumpers use different forms of press exercises when preparing for competition on the following training session. Sprinters and hurdlers also use these exercises. Throwers frequently use the half squat with the barbell at 95%–100% of*

maximum weight. An overwhelming majority of athletes in speed-strength events in track and field came to the conclusion, through trial and error, that in the last training session before competition, it is necessary to use strength exercises with the barbell.

Russian specialists recommend finding the optimum excitability for the given athlete in the given sport, to be reached in the precompetition warm-up. While power sports call for high excitability, it is interesting that endurance sports with events lasting longer than 2 minutes need just the opposite. Some top long-distance runners will tell you that they do not like the "on" feeling before the start, as it reduces their endurance. They prefer feeling a little low on energy. This is not surprising, as the name of the game in endurance sports is to pace your efforts over the long haul, not to focus them on one moment in time.

Citing many studies, Ozolin explains that excessive (from the endurance athlete's point of view) CNS excitability makes the CNS perform at a level consistent with a more powerful effort and makes it use up its capacity sooner. Increased excitation makes runners use up too much energy early in the race. That is why elite middle- and long-distance runners are known to take a moderate run of up to an hour long as close as six hours before the competition! Amazingly, in an experiment by R. Kazmin, medium- and long-distance runners who were given mild sedatives (valerian and bromium) showed superior run results! And Russian pistol shooters have been known to take a shot of vodka before competition "to settle the nerves."

The airline industry was made safer by the use of checklists. So, use this simple formula for success: Make checklists and follow them. If you need a checklist for your warm-up or mobility work or whatever, make one. (I am reminded of the football team that showed up to a game without footballs. I am reminded of this because I was the team's head coach.) Use checklists to free up space in your brain for focusing on the work at hand.

Be sure (!!!) to plan something for the successful completion of the program, season, or system. Look beyond the finish line, so to speak. Answer the question Now what? long before you get to that point.

The first and most important consideration in "peaking" is understanding that to peak, the athlete needs "a lot of water under the bridge." And I mean **A LOT OF WATER!** Nothing drives me more crazy than someone telling me that he is peaking for some low-level crap lift or event.

Before we can even begin to discuss this "peaking" thing, the athlete has to be up the pyramid a little bit. In other words, you don't peak for a 200-pound bench press. You simply bench press for a while, ask someone to spot you, and then make it. Now, a 1,000-pound bench press—which is something I can barely imagine, much less comment on—will definitely demand some peaking.

If there is an issue that really clouds American Olympic lifting, it would simply be the number of times someone should compete in a year. Tommy Kono recommends that a lifter compete "often." The greatest American lifter notes that sadly, all too often today, lifters focus on just one

That's not enough. Years ago, Dick Notmeyer explained my "monkey brain" issue to me. During training, I tended to think in a certain way. I was calm, intelligent, and focused. I also had as many attempts to complete a lift as I wanted to have.

But on the competition platform, things were different. Even though I went 17 for 18 in my first three meets, I was overpowering everything, because it was so light. When the lifts became heavier and heavier, I started missing. I could always get it "the next time." But with only three attempts, I really started to struggle.

The answer wasn't time on the couch with someone asking me about my childhood. The answer was more meets. Dick had me go to every little meet he could find. I made progress, learned the ropes of dealing with the odd stress of sitting around while more and more plates go on the bar, and soon graduated from a "monkey mind" to a "tranquil mind."

When in doubt, remember this: *Tommy said so.*

Moving ahead, years later, I was challenged to compete in the Masters Nationals. My game plan was right out of vintage Dick Notmeyer and Tommy Kono—to compete in as many meets as I could with one caveat: Strive for six for six. (In lifting, there are two lifts: the snatch and the clean and jerk. You get three attempts, so "six for six" means you went on the platform and made every lift. Easy to write, hard to do.)

My game plan worked. Even though I had all kinds of struggles, I was able to pull off a win on my last clean and jerk. There are many reasons for my success, but I am convinced that I had developed the tranquil mind needed to deal with any issues.

Here's what I have discovered while working with athletes for several decades: You need to back off and let success happen. (Caveat: First, of course, you need to have done a little accumulating and tapping up of the intensity.) Now, everybody knows this.

One of the things we began to notice years ago is that our "peaking" athletes were getting a little pudgy, a tad bit soft. We also began to see that, without a lot of direction, the athlete who'd trained so long and so well began to play pick-up basketball games (and lose the season to an ankle injury), volunteer for the couple's dance in the school production, or find some other way to destroy a few years of work.

This observation led to the *transformation program.* We drifted back in time to the simplest, most basic program we could find: 3 sets of 8 with 1-minute rests. We also decided to move to the weekly format of push-pull-squat, too. The best decision was to take all the best "stuff" we'd learned through the year and keep those new toys, skills, or drills as part of our package.

Issurin adds:

It is widely held that high-resistance exercises prior to competition suppress precise neuromuscular coordination and negatively affect fine sports-specific feelings. Many athletes reduce or even exclude such exercises from their precompetitive program. However, and this has also been noted by prominent coaches, the exercises for maximum and/or explosive strength allow athletes to maintain the level of force application in sports-specific technical skills. Moreover, the exercises producing an anabolic effect prevent reduction of muscle mass induced by stress hormones associated with emotional tension.

The professor offers a high-profile example:

The world-famous swimmer Alexander Popov, who earned five Olympic gold medals, systematically used dry-land maximum strength exercises for upper-body muscles within his tapering program. These exercises were followed by low-intensity technical drills that didn't reduce his sensitivity and fine technical skill. According to Gennadi Touretski, the athlete's personal coach, these exercises served to maintain the contractile abilities of the muscles and prevent suppression of the immune system. The latter is very important, because long-lasting emotional stress combined with highly intense workloads can provoke various health disorders.

It is good news that, according to Russian specialists, a reached level of performance in many qualities, including strength, can be maintained with twice-weekly, 70%- to 80%-intensity loads.

We also decided to keep a weekly "game" day, realizing that our athletes needed a low-key competition as well as some fun. Soccer and flag football were the best choices, as they included a lot of running yet little contact. Playing indoor games with big, powerful athletes is not a good idea—trust me.

For legs, I still like squat variations, such as front squats and overhead squats, and some hill sprints are also useful. Maybe some sled pulls would be fine, too. That ain't much, folks, but it will keep you going.

Have some fun playing ultimate Frisbee or flag football. Keep some pressing and ab work in the program, and don't be afraid to work in something like Turkish get-ups. We found that the best of all pulls for the peaking athlete was the clean-grip snatch.

You can shift the days and the movements around to fit any situation, but these principles are key:

1. Stay tight on the diet, and keep the workouts fast to keep some of the pudge off.
2. Don't try to go crazy and make some massive leap overnight. Enjoy the benefits of all the work you've done up to this point.
3. Have some fun. Enjoy yourself. Reap what you have sown.

What you actually do here doesn't matter. The key is to keep yourself "in shape" and not give away all your hard work by blowing an ankle in a pick-up game at the schoolyard. You might find, like I have, that the rewards of achieving your goals outweigh the thrill of beating your buddies in some game one afternoon.

Here is the Russian coaches' favorite bit of black humor relevant to this period: "It is too late to drink mineral water when the kidneys have failed." This is not the time to be training to get stronger, more technical, and so forth. Just don't blow it.

The greatest resource for peaking is simply answering this question: How did you do it before?" I "mine" my journals like a prospector seeking clues to unusual performances. I also follow the directions from other successful ventures and apply them to my next goal.

I know there is nothing shocking here, but so few people do it. So, if there is a rule number one for peaking, it would be this: Compete. Then sit down with your journal or a piece of paper, and write down what did and didn't work.

Distinguished Coach of the USSR Dr. Anatoly Bondarchuk measured his throwers' results with a regulation-size hammer, a lighter one, and a heavier one three times a week for a year. This allowed him to chart the patterns in his athletes' condition: increases and decreases in work capacity and CNS tonus. He then worked back from the date of a competition and designed individual training plans that took the lengths of these phases into account. The results spoke for themselves.

Everyone ignores this advice, so mentally, I watching people skip this section to find the "real truth." Go ahead. I am sure you will all be back.

OK, let's pick up again: Every great lesson I have from peaking comes from my athletes or my experience and the discipline to spend some time noting what worked. Here is a million-dollar hint: Make a list of things to bring to a competition.

Listen, I don't follow my own advice here! Years ago, I went to a national weightlifting meet with my wife's lifting card. I didn't double-check before I left, and I was naked on a scale in Louisiana when my error was discovered. One of my athletes, Paul Northway, laminated his checklist to his training bag. And days before a meet, he always pulled everything out of his bag and then rechecked and restocked everything.

I discovered years ago that packing three to seven days before a meet actually ensures success better than a bunch of percentages on a computer program. I think it puts one in the championship mode early. Following this little practice also allows the athlete to begin to move into "meet mind," versus what most people have on game day, "monkey mind."

So, Peaking 101 involves two basic principles

1. **Learn from your own experience.** Mine will be different from yours. I react to this or that and need to do this and that to be ready. You need to figure these things out for yourself. I found, for example, that reading chess books before lifting really helps me on the platform. The depth of analysis seems to allow me to relax physically and put my mind miles away. Then when it is time to hit it, I seem clearer. This might not work for you, though.
2. **Prepare long before the morning of the competition.** Organize your gear, your travel issues, your nutritional needs, and any other details well in advance. Not having to worry about such matters helps me keep a clear mind for competing, in my experience.

Notice that I haven't once mentioned reps and sets. I probably won't.

The key to peaking is and always will be *mental.* There is a phrase in throwing: "Long warm-ups are poison!" In other words, tossing a good throw while warming up before competition is a good way to make sure that you will falter during competition. So, I plan my warm-up to ensure that I won't throw well, and I have taught my athletes the same thing. Do drills and throws that get you warm, prepare you mentally, and feed your ego some other way besides trying to win the warm-up. For the record, I believe that most people give away more championships than they win. Stop doing that!

The mental side of peaking involves lots of little steps. For example, I know that at the state high school track meet, the athletes will be huddled into chairs, not allowed any music or coaching, and then marched out on the track to perform. So, why wait until the morning of the meet to let the athletes know that? I talk about it every day and every week and even come up with strategies to poke fun at the all-too-important officials. At one meet, when the athletes came out, one of my throwers decided to strut like a member of the marching band. A few minutes later, she broke her old personal record, while the other competitors seemed to forget where they were that day.

Actually, my issue with peaking might be better explained with an analogy involving parenting. If I am really tired one evening and my daughter pukes on me, I can't simply say "Sorry, I'm dead tired tonight, but you can bet I'll be a helluva dad next Friday!" Honestly, the meet or competition is **TODAY**. Show up and compete.

The longer you play the game, the more you will know about your peaking strategies. As I got into my forties, I discovered that my last two weeks of going into something important was crucial. Now, it wasn't crucial in terms of load or volume but in terms of not **RUINING** everything! I found that all I needed during this time was really light weights and really gentle technical work, including an honest assessment of last-minute weaknesses that I could address. I learned this, of course, by studying my journals.

The lesson is clear: Don't blow it in the last few days before something important by making bad decisions and tossing away all your hard work. Like having the bachelor party the night before the wedding, bad timing can destroy months of planning and determination.

CHAPTER 8

Learning Your Lessons

"Truth comes out of error more readily than out of confusion."
—Francis Bacon

Everything Old Is New Again

Whenever somebody tells me about something new in the world of physical conditioning, the first thing I do is make sure my wallet is secure. Next, I reference John Jesse's book *Wrestling Physical Conditioning Encyclopedia*, published in 1974. I picked up a copy as a young lad and promptly ignored all the excellent advice because, well, in technical terms, I am an idiot.

No matter what new and exciting thing has emerged in the last three decades, Jesse already wrote about it. The list of topics includes isometrics, sandbag training, ligament strengthening, Olympic lifts, grip work, swingbells (which look a lot like kettlebells), combining sprinting with calisthenics (I thought I invented that), get-ups, and flexibility training that still outpaces what most of us do today.

Also consider Jesse's recommendations for starting a new year, which have stood the test of time. They are simple and have all the hallmarks of a great program. He recommends this basic weekly approach:

- Three sessions of strength development and injury prevention, with near-maximum loads
- Three sessions of flexibility exercises
- Three sessions of endurance training

- The strength development, injury prevention work, and flexibility exercises should be done one day and the endurance training another
- The strength development, injury prevention work, and flexibility exercises should slowly increase to 1.5 hours a day and the endurance work to 1 hour. This will total 7.5 hours' training time each week.

It's hard to argue with such fine advice! Again, not much has been said since Jesse published his book that can trump his excellent weekly overview.

Sadly, I even had trouble finding anything new or exciting in the field of strength and conditioning. Not long ago, noted nutritional expert Lyle McDonald, a good friend, loaned me a book called *Physiology of Strength*, by Theodor Hettinger, MD. This book was published in 1961, yet everything we know today about strength is in there. As I often say in referencing John McCallum, author of *Keys to Progress*, the rest of us are "footnotes."

Here are some of my favorite insights from Hettinger's book:

- The calves can increase in strength 6% a week, the glutes 4%, the triceps 3%, and the biceps 2%. When I fall back into my "hunter" paradigm for understanding why humans react to training, I shouldn't be surprised to see the sprinting muscles respond to training quite quickly.
- The research notes that it is easier to train in the summer, and vitamin D might help that, too. No surprise here, but it's amazing to see the graph that shows me why January training is so lousy. I thought it was just the snow.
- Men are stronger than women. In tests, some parts of women are 55% as strong as men (forearm extensors), but in the hip area, it rises to 80%. Anyone who's ever coached women will find this research to be absolutely true. Like one of my female friends, women tend to have the odd ability to bench 135 for 10 reps yet their max will be 140 for a single.
- Strength peaks in the late twenties, maintains that level for a long time, and then gradually declines with age, especially in untrained individuals. Oh, that is sadly true, based on my personal experience.
- Injecting testosterone seemed to make everybody train better for a long time. Welcome to the modern world of sport! For many athletes and coaches, this illegal method is "the answer to all questions."

If you missed the point, here you go: Almost everything we know about the science of strength training was discovered **BEFORE** I was born. Moreover, if you read Sandow, Cerutty, Hackenschmidt, LaLane, or any of the countless other pioneers in the art of strength training, you might wonder why anyone today can claim originality in anything in weight training.

Still not convinced?

You want to know about exact reps and sets? Well, Dr. Thomas DeLorme worked with some guys rehabbing from World War II and found that weightlifting worked wonders for their injury rehabilitation. Originally, he thought that doing 7 to 10 sets was the key but later revised his thinking: "Further experience has shown this figure (the number of sets in a workout) to be too high." The number of sets was reduced from 7 to 10 to a much more realistic 3 sets. During the first set, the weight was at 50% of the person's 10 RM. In the second set, it was increased to 75%, and it finished at 100% of the subject's 10 RM. This became known as the *DeLorme technique*, although a guy named Watkins co-authored the study.

I'll be honest: The system still works. And even though we can add all kinds of tempos, rest periods, and other insightful elements, nothing I have found works so much better than this that I can't continue to marvel at DeLorme's simple program design.

Maybe you are not yet a "giant" yet, but you have some wonderful tools right in front of you. I would argue that the greatest tool you have is your training journal. Now you just need to learn to "mine" it.

Mining Your Journal

That's right—*mining*, like a miner in a tunnel. You need to dig out those treasures from your own experiences!

About a decade ago, I worked with a young man—let's call him *Ed*—who had all the physical tools, listened to everything I said, worked hard in my presence, and then went home. But he couldn't get himself to follow my most important commandment: *Keep a journal.* The second year I worked with him, I found out that he did absolutely no training on weekends, virtually nothing all summer, and slumped over any extended break.

Any strength and power athlete who can't train alone is going to fail. Sometime, sooner or later, you must stand alone.

I took an idea from the Soviet track coaches and quit going to meets with my athletes, when appropriate. Why? So they had to deal with their own problems. Forgot your throwers shoes? Deal with it. Mean judges? Deal with it. Bad conditions? Deal with it.

My wife, Tiffini, still thinks it is funny when I get telephone calls on mornings throughout May that start with "Dan, I won the state championship!" and usually include the question "Have you had coffee yet?" I'm often in bed when the newest member of the State Championship Club calls.

Well, Ed never won a state championship. With a couple of years of hindsight, I am now convinced that he gave it away by refusing to use the most important tool in the athlete's toolbox: the training journal. Writing in his journal would have helped him learn one of the keys to athletic success: *Try to only make the same mistakes over and over again a couple of times.*

What? Simply put, we tend to repeat our errors. We want to be successful, so we increase our volume and intensity to make the big leap. But then we find ourselves hurt, injured, or sick. Of course, a week or so after the flu, we hit our season's best mark. Next year, we do it again—train too hard, get hurt, then improve. By the third year . . . Well, now it is "Fool me twice, shame on me."

Without a journal, Ed relied solely on others to discover his path to success. He didn't understand one of the great tools of athletic success: mining your journal. Your training journal contains a gold mine of information—if you take the time, every day, to record your workouts, your attitudes, and your life in general. Years later, you can sift through this material to discover what makes **YOU** tick!

Sometimes, the answers aren't apparent. For example, in 1991, I was coaching at the Upper Limit Gym in Utah. I had access to wonderful facilities, lots of training partners, and great enthusiasm about the strength sports. I began to really push my back squat poundage. Some weeks, my squat went up by 20 or 30 pounds, as I was shamed into lifting more by excellent powerlifters. I topped out at 605 for 3 reps. I remember realizing that the weight was bending my rib—and I also noticed something else: *This increase in squatting weight did not add 1 foot to my discus throw.*

I threw 190 at Utah State and never went over 405 in the squat, yet 605 got me to 181. Two years later, John Powell—twice the bronze medalist in the discus at the Olympics—told me that he had quit squatting heavy years before he began to really "bomb" the discus. He said that heavy squatting "didn't feel good," so why do it? This made no sense to me at all. I was stronger, so I should throw farther.

Then, in 1994—after not squatting heavy for three years and doing mostly rapid squats up to sets of 8 and lots of hill sprints—I dropped a 184 throw. I weighed less, my waist was smaller, I felt better—and I threw farther.

So, how did I mine my journal? I went back to 1991 and looked at the videos of my throws. I compared them to the videos from 1994. I looked healthier, but it was hard to see any other difference. Then, I thought about the hill sprints. In 1994, my finish was smoother somehow—I held together better. Could doing all the hill sprints have been the key, or did dropping the heavy squats make the difference?

You know, I don't really know the answer. I can say, however, that my journal entries revealed no injuries in 1994. They also revealed lots of energy and lots of inside jokes and fun with the group. My entries from 1991 talked about buying ankle wraps, knee wraps, and wrist wraps and making biweekly visits to the chiropractor.

Clearly, increasing the load with my squatting got me hurt but provided little payoff. Maybe, it was simply what I thought about a month ago: Heavy squatting makes your hips and legs strong. But the body is one piece. When you throw, you snap off your whole leg and you are only as strong as—your ankle. If you cave at your ankle, you lose your finish. Hill sprints seem to be an ankle/calf builder with no peer.

John Price reminds me often of another key to athletic success: *You are only as strong as your weakest link.* For me, and probably everyone else, the goal should be to bring your weak points up to the point that they become your strong points.

So, we have seen the first technique in mining your journal: reviewing one season in the light of another. Big deal, everybody does it—or do they? How often have you cracked open your old journals and read them carefully? I would argue for doing this at least twice a year. Obviously, the off-season is a good time to harvest the knowledge you learned but forgot in the past. The next best time is just before peaking. What gems have you forgotten? What mistakes are you about to repeat?

My favorite in-season use of the journal is the "countback." I take the four weeks prior to a "hot" performance—a day when nothing goes wrong or you are just in the groove—and look at the month.

Several years ago, I began doing heavy back squats and power snatches every workout and tossed in heavy, heavy jerks twice a week. One weekend, I had an Olympic lifting meet in the morning and a track meet in the afternoon. I had the opportunity to do this two weekends in a row. A week later, in a three-day period, I tossed 181' 7" in a left-handers' wind, put the shot 50' 9", and snatched 314 (clean and jerked 358, cleaned 402 and missed the jerk). Then, I went into a six-month tailspin of injury upon injury.

What did I learn? Well, I thrived on power snatches, but the heavy jerks and heavy squats all led to injuries. It would take me a couple years to really mine the events of this season!

The AIT Formula

Some time ago, I got a wonderful insight about the training of the German track and field team. I was told that they had a simple three-part formula: Accumulation, Intensification, and Transformation. In Chapter 1, I referred to this as the AIT formula.

Certainly, *accumulation* relies on having a marvelous PE program in which you are taught the skills, rules, and basic mastery of dozens of sports and games. As I mentioned in Chapter 2, this is called *systematic education*, and sadly, it is missing in most people's training. It takes up to two years to even begin to master the Olympic lifts, but I have had people tell me they became "experts" after a two-hour workshop! Think about how long it takes to master math or language skills, and then consider what true mastery takes in sports.

The second part of the formula is *intensification*. Throughout your career, you should keep adding new ideas and challenges to measure you as well as to keep you interested. However, there does come a time when you need to ramp up to the next level. Now, everybody knows this—it's as old as Milo and the calf. But I bet most of the people you meet in a typical gym never ramp it up.

Over time, I have learned to hold these four points in mind when I decide to "jack it up:"

1. Be open to new ideas and new experiences, and don't be afraid to plug in some fresh approaches to your training.

2. When you learn something new, check to see where you struggle. It might hint at an area to consider when setting your biggest goals.
3. Take time to think about the "political prisoner" question, raised in Chapter 1. What's important?
4. When you do decide to test yourself, ease off, but continue to keep an eye on your waistline and your general fitness level. Also provide a suitable outlet for your new level of energy. Don't blow all your hard work doing a lay-up at the schoolyard basketball court.

Let's review the "political prisoner" question: Suppose, for whatever reason, that you were only allowed to train 1 hour a week in three 20-minute periods. Thinking about your goals in sport or life, what would you do? If you have any sense, your answer for how to spend those 20 minutes is the very core, the key, to achieving your goals!

When you really decide to go after it as an athlete—or really, in pursuing any worthy goal—the intensification stage is when, to paraphrase Andrew Carnegie again, you put all your eggs in one basket. And, my friends, you better keep an eye on that damn basket!

On Winning and Losing

You see, it's all about staying focused on the goal. Most people are going to miss the point here. So let me start off by reminding myself that most people miss the point of anything related to success anyway, so I shouldn't worry too much about all of this.

The point? Well, please bear with me a little bit, but the basic idea is this: Sometimes, **NOT** achieving a goal or fulfilling a dream is what spurs people on to make their greatest impact on the world. And, the reverse is true, too: Reaching a goal or realizing a dream can flatten a person out for years to come.

I have known a lot of college English majors who spent four years writing their own work in creative writing and literature classes and then stopped—never writing another poem or story or essay. As teachers themselves, they may spend hours red-penning semicolons and comments like "transitive verb" all over students' papers, but they will never again write their own compositions. They earned the degree and stopped writing.

Many athletes sweat and fight through four years of high school sports to get a scholarship to college but then quit during the first weeks of college practice, often because "it doesn't mean anything" to them. I am reminded of this nearly every year now. I'm not sure how it was when I was playing in high school, but I have a clear view of things now. Some parents spend up to $2,000 a month ensuring that Bobby or Cindy is on the most "elite" team money can find. Sadly, if you do the math, you might find that these kids get minimal scholarships, at best, and the club coaches and their promises are long gone.

If Junior does make it to the next level, one of the hardest things to watch is the quick exodus of so many of these athletes. The reality of playing Division I sports is one of constant and overwhelming pressure and competition. For many, it's too much, and the number of two-year lettermen drops dramatically at most schools. So sometimes, success leads to failure.

Mark Twight, the author of *Kiss or Kill* and one of the world's foremost mountain climbers, noted the same thing at my dinner table not long ago. Faced with the decision to keep climbing and probably die on Mount Everest or to come back down to base camp, he came back. But, he noted, he learned far more from this failure than would have from succeeding.

In a sense, being successful can dilute the lessons of life. No, I am not telling you to fail; it is just that success seems to prod most people into rethinking their purpose, their journey, their path.

Joseph Campbell commented on this several times regarding the fact that he—the most renowned person in the field of comparative religion—never got his doctorate. Campbell chose not to pursue this degree and often encouraged his students not to go on, either. He also warned them of getting buttonholed in a job that would stop them from exploring all the directions that life presented. He noted that people who earned their terminal degree and were then appointed to their dream job often flattened out. Earl Nightingale offered much the same warning: "A rut is a grave with the ends kicked out."

Every two years, the world turns it attention for a few weeks to the Olympic Games. I am not exaggerating when I tell you that one of the worst-kept secrets of Olympic sports is how many athletes quit (in fact, they can barely stomach thinking about it) their sport after the games. Even gold medalists abandon the pool, the track, the rink, and the slope. After all their dreams of victory, plus all their sacrifice and pain, it's just not fulfilling to be told "Here is your medal—thankyou very much. Next!"

Many of the Olympians who fail to make their goals turn to coaching, writing, and other forums for expressing their athletic goals. Or they take the lessons they've learned and parlay them into a successful life doing something else. In any case, they don't just drop their dreams and walk away.

Now, I'm not encouraging failure or the initiation of a so-called culture of failure. I coached football at a school for a long time and realized something very unsettling: When we began losing games, my athletes were getting more out of losing than the winners were from winning.

After you win a game, your team goes into the locker room, and before you can untie your shoes, your coach is already talking about next week. The total amount of celebration time in a winning locker room—for true winners—is usually pretty short! But the losers—they hear long speeches and get hugs, tears, and kisses, usually from the prettiest girls. While the victors are thinking of yet another week of "nose to the grindstone," the losers are being cuddled and caressed back to a smile. OK, I'm exaggerating—but not a lot!

Don't let success flatten you or let failure enroll you in the Loser's Club. Learn from failure—enjoy it, if you can—but then find another expedition to the top.

When you win, be gracious. And when you achieve your goals, set new goals. Usually, when you reach one goal, you already have a whole new set of goals lined up.

To repeat perhaps the greatest lesson of life: it is the journey, not the goal. Very often, the day or moment you finally achieve a long-sought goal, you have the somber realization that it brings little satisfaction.

A few random ideas:

- Always—and I mean **ALWAYS**—celebrate the goals you achieve. It can be very simple and private, like a bowl of ice cream, or something more elaborate, like a dinner party. I don't care—but always acknowledge attaining your goals.
- Be sure to set a few goals that are hard to get. Don't set a bunch of goals like "I will go to school tomorrow and sit in a chair." Come up with a couple like "I will change the world by creating a pollution-free method of creating energy." Whatever draws your interest, the point is to set goals and then celebrate them.
- Enjoy the process of taking the journey on the way to the goal. Enjoy every step and look around often. You'll see where real living occurs.

So, back to *intensification*: How do you know if the wonderful things you add during this period are truly worthy? As much as I love systematic education, in which you build one concept—or one year, even—upon another, there is another system you need to know about: *systemic education.*

In systemic education, we use the image of a tree. If you don't know what a tree is, move out of the city.

You are the tree. The seed that you came from is your genetic inheritance. Some of you are oaks, others are cedars, and a few of you are bonsais (and for that, I am sorry). The soil can be considered the environment you grew up in. So, if you grew up in a town with phenomenal success in wrestling, you might become a wrestler.

At the risk of beating the model to death, the rings of the tree represent your years of experience. Like many of us, I have some thin years and some thick years—years that went bad and years that went well. The key to this model is this: Your continued growth relies on the previous rings!

Let me cut to the point: You go to a workshop and hear about a wonderful new supplement. What do you do? This is the core of systemic education. When you add something to the "soil," you need to test it by sampling the "fruit" that it bears. The problem? Well, when you go to a workshop, you tend to add 50 new things to your training, and you can't measure what worked and what didn't!

Do you remember our friend Billy, from Chapter 2? Each time young Billy reads an article or goes to a workshop, he's enthused beyond anything he's felt in all of his 14 years. So, he begins to take 20 fish oil capsules an hour, does depth jumps off boxes with the bar in the overhead squat position, sprints like a Canadian Olympian, performs ring work, eats extra chocolate protein Wizzbangs, and snorts six hits of sugar-free psyllium every hour. Within days, he's a mess. What happened?

Well, if you have a tree and add ten ingredients to your soil—nine of them healthy but the tenth poisonous—how will you figure out what effect each one has? That, my friends, is the issue. When I'm learning all these wonderful new things and ideas, how do I discern what works and what's killing me? You need to do it systematically!

This is how I approach new training ideas: I immediately fall back on one of two workouts. I have two basic workout models that I've used over and over and for which I have a feel for what's going on with the balance of training load and recovery over a few weeks.

The first standard workout that I use is the Transformation program. (Don't worry about the name.) Basically, it involves three days a week of lifting, with one day devoted to pulling movements, one day to pushing movements, and one day to leg work. I do only two exercises and keep the rest periods at strict 1-minute intervals. Generally, I like 3 sets of 8, but any reasonable rep/set combination will work. One other day a week, I do a few hill sprints (very few!), and on another day, I do a fun activity like hike, bike, or play a team sport. This is an easy program to manage, and I know that my joints will feel good, that I'll have a lot of energy, and that I will generally look "okay" doing it.

The other standard workout I do is the One Lift a Day program. I might even simplify the workout a bit by doing just a push day, a pull day, a squat day, and a whole-body day (snatch, clean and jerk).

By choosing to train in a program that basically covers everything at an easy to moderate level, I'm pretty sure that I'll be ready for the experiment. The experiment?

Yes, now I add the new groovy thing I learned at the workshop. If after two weeks, my knees hurt so bad that I can't press the gas pedal, I will deem this new thing a failure. But if after two weeks, young supermodels are throwing themselves at me (again), then something good is going on and I'll keep doing this new thing! You know, this approach sounds so logical, so simple, but very few people follow it! If you learn five new things, it might take a few months to run them all through your training program to figure out which ones do and don't work for you. Keep testing the fruits of your labors, not the hype in the advertisements.

The Rules

Let's review:

Rule 1: Set yourself up with a basic training routine that you can count on to keep you fresh but in shape.

Whatever "in shape" means to you might be different than what it means to your training partner, but I like basic lifting measurements and throwing distances. You might use a ratio of your upper-arm measurement to your waist measurement. (My long-term plan is to have a 1:2 ratio in the arm to waist. I just need to get my arms to 27 inches.)

Rule 2: Add new lifts, variations, and ideas to your training program one at a time.

I bought a set of chains a year ago, and for the first month, I used them only with front squats. The next month, after discovering how excellent the chains were for acceleration, I tried them with deadlifts. Now, I use them for all squats, deadlifts, and presses. But in fact, I might not have realized their benefit if I'd added a bunch of things at the same time.

The next simple idea is that some things work only for a short amount of time. Throughout this book, I have used the term *quiver* to describe all the lifts, exercises, and routines that I can draw on through a training year. For example, doing thick-bar deadlifts provides real value sometimes. But you don't want to constantly train with oversized bars, because even though your grip will get better and better, you will never truly push your posterior chain.

Rule 3: Some great ideas work sometimes but not always.

In fact, I keep a chart of all the training tools at my disposal, and I review it whenever I feel like having a little instant variation. In nutrition, the formula is a little harder. I live by this two-part mantra: "If it works immediately, it's illegal. If it works quickly, it's banned."

I recommend that you set yourself up with a standard eating plan. Here are a couple of things I insist on for your standard diet:

1. I like my athletes to eat three meals before they train with me: breakfast, lunch, and a snack somewhere. This almost instantly helps most modern teens.
2. Eat protein at every meal. I like the simple rule of "about a fistful at least."
3. Water should be your base beverage.

If you're doing these things consistently, now try to add the "magic food." I did this a few years ago with fish oil capsules and became an instant missionary for this inexpensive but wonderful supplement. Again, though, think *systematic!* With dietary changes, you may not notice any difference.

I look for improvements in blood profiles (I have an expansive yet inexpensive blood profile once or twice a year), skin health (less acne, more glow, better elasticity), and your moods. The latter one is hard for you to notice, so ask your friends and family about your moods. If they all smile and move back toward the exit, it's not a good sign.

So, what's the point of all of this? You have to learn what works for you through personal experience. It's not a perfect system, but find a basic training regime that you can count on for a few weeks and a basic approach to diet that you can live with for a month or so. Then, add the magic—only one new thing at a time—and see what happens. After that, of course, you can pester me with questions about whether doing the clean and jerk with 400 pounds will build your biceps.

If you are not an elite-level athlete, you can thrive for a long time playing around with my insights about systemic and systematic education:

1. Try something new. Join a team, a club, a sport, or take up a new hobby. Meet some new people. Learn some new skills and have fun.
2. Continue your chosen sport, or continue working on your body-composition goals. Monitor your progress in all the usual ways: "before and after" photos, body fat measurements, and athletic achievements.
3. Through the lens of your new endeavor, rethink and reimagine your primary goals. This, of course, is the key to the whole process.

I applied the rule 3 to my discus throwing a few years ago. I played in the Fast Action 5 on 5 football league and found I was "losing a step." Now, I was also 40 years old, but my numbers in the weight room were excellent. Then it hit me: I'd been doing hill sprints regularly for nearly a decade but had recently changed training facilities and there was no hill. Sure, my lifts were good, but I was lacking my two days a week of charging up the hill. I bought a sled and starting madly sprinting in the area behind my home. Within two weeks, I had found my "lost step."

Without the football league, I might have missed an obvious deficit in my training. I'm always amazed at how easily we can lose sight of the big picture when we keep a single focus. Open your eyes by opening yourself up to new opportunities.

For the elite athlete, you simply don't have the wiggle room to move too far from nearly total specificity. But keep this in mind: For every sport, there is a visionary like Dick Fosbury, who decided to pop over the high-jump bar in a radically different way and changed the sport forever.

AFTERWORD

Experts have defined the art of strength coaching as finding the optimal balance of two sets of opposites. Work and rest. General and specific. For every athlete, the balance is different. And it is a moving target. Dan and I hope that this book will help you hit it.

We have made the case that a simple way is the best way. "The most amazing thing about cheap and simple fixes," wrote the authors of *Superfreakonomics*, "is they often address problems that seem impervious to any solution."

We insist that you stop seeing "smoking" the athlete as the answer to all training problems. "Heroes are in demand where there is a shortage of professionals." This cruel Russian saying was born out of a history of ordering men into bayonet attacks against tanks.

Last but not least, we are behind Professor Matveyev's categorical statement: "Strength is the foundation for development of the rest of physical qualities."

Don't you forget it.

Recently, I had a discussion with an elite, high-level athlete who simply **COULD NOT** understand the basic principles of this text. I was dumbfounded. Really?

We then began discussing the athlete's pedigree. Like dogs, most of us in the strength and conditioning field have this odd ability to tell the "story of the story" and list the "whos and whats" of our careers. Trust me, I hold my mentors dearly, and most quality athletes can tell you who taught what to whom.

The "unbeliever" listed a series of fine coaches who had issues ranging from severe alcoholism to near insanity. All of them had trained with massive amounts of anabolics and had detailed programs that assumed a certain amount of anabolic loading. In contrast, my references were Hack, Certutty, and Kono—clearly, mentors who had never had the opportunity to even discuss anabolics, as the drugs weren't around during any part of their formative education.

When the athlete noted "I have never heard any of this before," I simply replied, "Well, this is **BEFORE** before."

How does one apply this information? First, the easiest task of the strength coach is to ensure that the athlete gets stronger. Honestly, this is by far the easiest task in sport. Not to dismiss the fine work done in the gym and on the field, but the legions of strength coaches have to agree that increasing strength is far easier than mastering the free throw with no time left on the clock and a national championship on the line.

Of course, we have also addressed the second point to death: Even if I make my team or group the strongest, will it really carry onto the field of play? Add to this my final point: If your client wants to lose a few pounds of body fat, do you really need to act like this is the final checklist for the Mars exploration team?

If all you do is not hurt your athletes by doing something stupid, then you are miles ahead. I hate to say this, but I actually enjoy the stories of elite athletes and how they ruined their careers with some dumb idea, whether in training or from just being stupid. "Do no harm" should be on the wall of every gym, right next to all the motivational posters and pithy sayings. "The Road to Success Is Always under Construction." Fine, but am I the only guy who's tired of driving five miles an hour around the traffic cones?

Both the strength coach and the athlete need to apply the tools of systematic education in developing the athlete's career. Certainly, it is possible to be successful using a limited toolbox of training techniques. Although an athlete may never actually need to do a deadlift or a snatch to achieve greatness, it isn't a bad idea to know the correct way to do both classic movements. Just don't teach them the week of the Olympic trials! Over the course of an athlete's career, there is a need to teach and correct a whole laundry list of movements on the track, in the gym, and in the weightroom, but it should be done with a plan that encompasses years of the athlete's training life. And that's obvious, I know!

Basically, Pavel and I are arguing that we need to develop an athlete (or anyone doing anything, really) over a period of time and insist on laying a broad foundation that can be reinforced and built on over the years. This isn't earth-shattering news, but sit down and take a moment to ensure that this essential foundation underlies your whole program. Then, after creating this solid base, refine and specialize and peak and periodize and intensify.

If you have a solid base, then you're equipped to try the newest gimmicks and tricks and idiocies you read about on the Internet. One of those new, fun training toys might revolutionize sport and training, like the article in *Milo* Magazine, "Vodka, Pickle Juice and Kettlebells," spawned the kettlebell revolution. Or it might just end up in the dustbin of training ideas and nutritional tweaks and magic potions, which most of us will laugh at later for having spent our money and time in search for the next real phenomenon.

In addition, take some time to revisit what quadrant you are playing in. If you are QIII and training with someone preparing for football season, lift for lift and stride for stride, then you are wasting your time, your energy, and perhaps even your goal!

Beyond addressing your quadrant, also have some system that you trust to assess how you are doing overall. I can't praise the Certified Kettlebell–Functional Movement Specialist (CK–FMS) enough for targeting mobility issues, and every sport has some kind of chart of where you should be at your level. Again, strength training is by far the easiest method of improving performance in practically everything, but how do you know when enough is enough?

You see, that is the "secret: striving to get as strong as possible as easy as possible and having the courage to stop there and focus on the other qualities needed to reach your goals. The concept of Easy Strength actually angers some people, as they begin to wonder "How come it is so easy?"

It's OK. Breathe out. We're just the messengers.

INDEX

A

B

C

F

G

H

R

S

T

ABOUT PAVEL

Pavel Tsatsouline, is a former Soviet Special Forces physical training instructor, currently a subject matter expert to the US Navy SEALs and the US Secret Service.

Although Pavel's expertise lies in training gun carrying professionals, his "low tech/high concept" training methods have been increasingly and successfully used by elite athletes and their coaches. Among them are UFC star Joe Lauzon, 200m sprint women's world record holder Allyson Felix, and Donnie Thompson who posted the highest powerlifting total of all time.

Pavel is the author of several bestselling strength training books, including ***Power to the People!***, ***The Naked Warrior***, and ***Enter the Kettlebell!***

In 2001 Pavel's company and Dragon Door introduced the Russian kettlebell to the West and launched RKC, the kettlebell instructor course, which became the industry's golden standard.

ABOUT DAN JOHN

Dan John has been teaching and coaching for well over thirty years. He has taught theology, history, economics and weight training in the classroom and has coached track and field and football. He continues as a full-time on-line religious studies instructor for Columbia College of Missouri and contributing writer to ***Men's Health***, ***t-nation*** and ***Hardstyle*** Magazines. Originally from South San Francisco, Dan came to Utah to throw the discus for Utah State University and recently returned "home" after 35 years away. He currently lives in Burlingame, California.

Dan has Masters degrees in history and in religious education, as well as intensive work at the American University in Cairo, University of Haifa, and Cornell. Dan has written articles for ***Catechetical Update*** and ***Utah Historical Quarterly***, as well as being a columnist for the ***Intermountain Catholic***. Dan was also a Fulbright Scholar in 1985.

At home, he is humbled by his lovely wife, Tiffini, whose middle name is not "long suffering" no matter how often it is repeated, and his two daughters, Kelly and Lindsay.

In his athletic career, among many other championships and records, Dan has won the Master Pleasanton Highland Games twice, American Masters Discus Championships several times, the National Masters Weightlifitng Championship once and holds the American Record in the Weight Pentathlon. Of all his titles, he holds "Senior RKC" most dear.

The Graduate Course In Instant Strength Gains

"I went from 5 to 10 pullups in one week."

"Last night I did 15 one-arm pushups with each arm. Two months ago I couldn't do one complete rep."

"I could do one wobbly one-legged squat... [Two weeks later] I did 5 clean, butt-to-ground pistols."

Have you noticed—the greater a man's skill, the more he achieves with less? And the skill of strength is no exception. From the ancient days of Greek wrestling, to the jealously guarded secrets of Chinese Kung Fu masters, to the hard men of modern spec ops, warriors and allied strongmen have developed an amazing array of skills for generating inhuman strength.

But these skills have been scattered far and wide, held closely secret, or communicated in a piecemeal fashion that has left most of us frustrated and far from reaching our true strength potential.

Now, for the first time, Russian strength expert and former *Spetsnaz* instructor Pavel has gathered many of these devastating techniques into one highly teachable skill set. In *The Naked Warrior* Pavel reveals exactly what it takes to be super-strong in minimum time—when your body is your only tool.

- **Gain more brute strength in days than you did in years of bodybuilding or calisthenics**
- **Discover how to get a world-class powerlifter's quality workout–using your body only**
- **Get a harder, firmer, functionally-fitter body–and be as resilient as hell whatever you face**
- **Master the one-arm/one-leg pushup for crushing upper body force**
- **Forge super-piston, never-quit legs with the Spetsnaz favorite "Pistol"**
- **Discover the magic of "GTG"–guaranteed the world's most effective strength routine**
- **Be tow-truck strong–yet possess the rugged looks of a stripped-down racer**
- **No gym, no weights, no problem–get a dynamite strength workout at a moment's notice–wherever you are**
- **Discover the martial secrets of instant power generation–for rapid surges in applied strength**

The Naked Warrior

Master the Secrets of the Super-Strong–Using Bodyweight Exercises Only

By Pavel

#B28 $39.95

Paperback 218 pages 8.5" x 11"

Over 190 black & white photos plus several illustrations

"Pavel's *Naked Warrior* DVD is worth its weight in gold!"

You just thought you knew about bodyweight exercises!

"Pavel's DVD is a treasure trove of information for any beginner or expert strength trainer. I was trained by Bill Starr in Power Lifting and Weight Lifting(Olympic Lifting to the ignorant.) and was a personal trainer/instructor 26 years, Military Police/Correctional Officer for 11 years and coaching/instructing Judo and Ju-jitsu for the last 8 years, and I was in the Marine Corps, Navy, and the Guard for giggles and grins, so I have some knowledge on the subject matter. I can honestly say that Pavel is 100% correct! Give his DVD or book a shot (hell, I bought both!) and you'll see that you don't need hundreds of reps or dozens of different exercises to become rock hard and strong as coiled steel." —James Copelin, Texoma Judo-Jujitsu - Wichita Falls, TX

The Naked Warrior

Master the Secrets of the Super-Strong–Using Bodyweight Exercises Only

with Pavel

DVD #DV015 $34.95

Running time 37 minutes

Invest in the set of Pavel's *The Naked Warrior* DVD and book–and SAVE...

Item #DVS009 $69.95

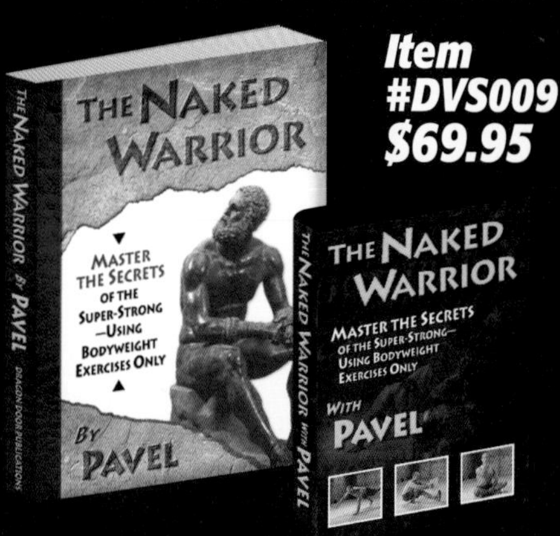

www.dragondoor.com

1·800·899·5111

Order *Naked Warrior* online:
www.dragondoor.com/DV015

HOW TO MASTER ADVANCED KETTLEBELL DRILLS—AND EXPLODE YOUR STRENGTH!

Thoroughly master Pavel's *Enter the Kettlebell!* program and you can consider yourself a "Kettlebell Black Belt". But once you're a Kettlebell Black Belt, then what?

Well, say hello to *Return of the Kettlebell*, which takes it for granted you already own those Black Belt fundamentals—and offers you a dramatically tougher, yet highly systematic program for explosive and massive muscle gain.

Return of the Kettlebell's protocols were born from Pavel's insights while training elite power athletes. Several champions made astonishing, almost mysterious, strength and muscle gains—at least two broke new powerlifting world records—thanks to kettlebell training. Pavel decided to reverse engineer this "What the Hell" effect experienced by the champions—so all others could benefit from their success.

Return of the Kettlebell presents the final fruit of Pavel's research—combining the very best of ancient lifting wisdom with modern day scientific breakthroughs.

Like the Breakfast of Champions, consume what's on the *Return of the Kettlebell* menu and watch yourself grow—and grow!

"I have used kettlebells in my program for years with fantastic results. The combination of movements provides the professional athlete with a unique challenge available from no other piece of equipment. I have followed Pavel's principles in designing my training systems. Now with *Return of the Kettlebell* you can take your training to the next level. The guidelines outlined in the DVD and companion book are ideal for athletes who must be strong and explosive. The book has excellent program design hints that allow you to adapt the training to the specific goals you seek. The book and DVD are a STRONG combination that everyone should have in their own personal strength and conditioning library."—**Stan Kellers, Assistant Coach of Strength, Cleveland Cavaliers**

"Pavel is the reason I started using kettlebell exercises with all my clients so I was anxious to get my hands on *Return of the Kettlebell*. Pavel, as always, gets straight to the point with his concise, logical, and entertaining writing style. The pictures perfectly depict what you should and shouldn't do to master these awesomely explosive lifts. The book is loaded with tips, tricks, and proven training principles that will supercharge your body and performance.

The Return of the Kettlebell DVD is the best kettlebell resource I've seen to take your physique and performance to the next level. Pinpoint technique is essential to your success, and Pavel knows it. He shows each exercise from every angle and explains what you should and shouldn't do to get the greatest reward. This DVD, plus hard work, equals your best body."—Chad Waterbury, neurophysiologist, author of Huge in a Hurry

"Pavel's *Return of the Kettlebell* is a no-nonsense guide to advanced kettlebell training. This DVD is for people who have mastered the fundamental of kettlebell training and understand the importance of linked motions and good spinal biomechanics in developing strength and power. He has incorporated new research on high velocity power training and the stretch-shortening cycle to maximize strength fitness using minimal equipment. His emphasis is always on good technique. *Return of the Kettlebell* will improve fitness and performance in any experienced power athlete. This is a 'must have' DVD for any serious student of sport."—**Thomas Fahey, Ed,D., Professor of Kinesiology, California State University, Chico**

"As a strength athlete and a coach, I applaud the effort and quality of this DVD. Although I am known for my hyperbole so I need to be careful here, but let me say this: if you only have one DVD on the shelf for the game of strength and conditioning, this is the DVD. I enthusiastically recommend this work without hesitation to anyone interested in any facet of fitness and health."—**Dan John, author of *Never Let Go***

Return of the Kettlebell

Explosive Kettlebell Training for Explosive Muscle Gains

by Pavel #*B40* *$39.95*

Foreword by Donnie Thompson, RKC, World Super Heavyweight Powerlifting Champion

Paperback 146 pages 8.5" x 11"

DVD

by Pavel

With Kenneth Jay, and Missy Beaver, RKC

#DV062 $34.95

DVD Running time: 48 minutes

Purchase Pavel's *Return of the Kettlebell!* book and DVD as a set and save... Item #DVS019 $67.95

www.dragondoor.com

1-800-899-5111

Order *Return of the Kettlebell* online: www.dragondoor.com/B40

continued on next page...

Smash Your Training Plateaus, Overcome Injuries, Make Unprecedented Strength Gains and Grow More Muscle... with a Classical Education in the Wisdom of the Past — and the Scientific Breakthroughs of the Modern Day Masters

The fight for greater strength and muscle is the story of a constant struggle against conflicting forces...

Since ancient times — when strength meant survival — to the more modern goals of competitive excellence and physical culture, we've fought a never-ending battle with our own bodies to achieve and maintain maximum performance.

Because our bodies don't want to change! And if we make them, they'll do their best to sabotage us!

Let's face it... our bodies are reluctant partners in the strength game...Anyone who's been around the block, knows this only too well:

The story of strength training is the story of constantly adjusting, constantly engaging in a guerrilla campaign of trickery and skullduggery against our obstinate bods. A small victory here, a setback there, a sudden breakthrough, another setback, another breakthrough, a long stalemate, another breakthrough ... it never ends!

And many of us simply give up from sheer frustration. We quit, when perhaps we could have stayed ahead... We become content to slough back into slackness and physical mediocrity...

And that's mostly because we never got the education we needed — to know how to win — and keep winning — the guerrilla war against our own bodies.

Of course, it doesn't help, in this day and age, that we also have to fight the myth-mongering marketers of strength training half-truths, preying on our ignorance to make a quick buck out of the gullible...

We have to fight against the machines, the gizmos, the quick fixes, the absurd claims — and the downright foolishness of most of what passes for 'training advice' in the magazines and gyms of our country.

Fortunately, there is a solution to all the confusion, ignorance and uncertainty...

When all else has failed you...

Pavel has spent his life immersed in the study and practice of practical strength and muscle training... as it applies in the very hard testing ground of both American and Soviet Spec ops, of the US Marines, SWAT, professional athletes, martial artists, gymnasts, powerlifters, weightlifters, Olympic champions and numerous other tough, tough competitors — where results are everything and failure is simply not on the menu.

Pavel has, frankly, done the research for you... plundering both the classic and the little-known strength texts from past and present... networking and comparing notes with many of today's great masters... submitting his own body to the pain of infinite experiment. And Pavel has trained thousands of troops and police whose life might depend on his tips... hundreds of athletes and martial artists with the chance to achieve their dreams thanks to his advice.

And of course, tens of thousands have gone to the dragondoor.com strength forum to share the astonishing gains and results they have achieved by employing Pavel's strength advice...

In *Beyond Bodybuilding*, you get the essence of most-all of the strategies, tips, routines and fine points Pavel has developed over many, many years for these elite men and women of the strength game. (Beyond Bodybuilding represents a compilation of many of Pavel's best magazine articles over the course of the last few years.)

Now, with *Beyond Bodybuilding*, there are simply no more excuses for not excelling in strength, continuing to gain, continuing to reach new heights in your performance.

Defeat the enemies of progress

Now, as you'll quickly discover in *Beyond Bodybuilding*, a close ad-herence to classical strength training principles is the true recipe for strength and muscle building success. What are these key principles? You'll find them all in *Beyond Bodybuilding*.

But as mentioned, it's not-by-far enough to just know and employ these key principles. Because without an additional bag of tricks, your body will inevitably find a way to escape...

continued on next page...

Pavel has trained thousands of troops and police whose life might depend on his tips... hundreds of athletes and martial artists with the chance to achieve their dreams thanks to his advice.

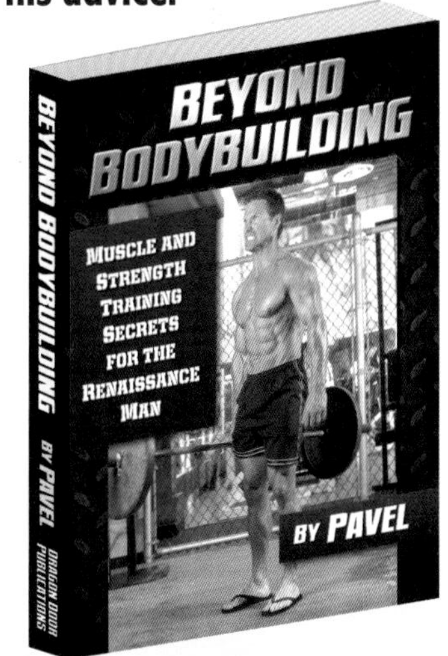

Beyond Bodybuilding
Muscle and Strength Training Secrets for The Renaissance Man
By Pavel
8.5 x 11 Paperback
365 pages • 255 Photographs
38 workout charts
#B31 $49.95

Beyond Bodybuilding—a treasure chest of strength training secrets

Discover the finer points of technique... that separate the champs from the chumps

What finally distinguishes Pavel from almost any strength author on the planet... is his ability to zero in on the finer points of adjustment to the body's continuing effort to sabotage your progress. That—and the sheer breadth and wealth of the fine points Pavel has to offer...

Because to truly succeed with your strength training you need to become a master at making these adjustments...

It's a Good Cop, Bad Cop kind of thing:

You need to know how to cajole, torture, sweet-talk, seduce, beat up and lie to your body... to bend it to your wants! But you also need to know how to feed it, maintain it, make it happy, care for it, sensitize it, protect it... yes, all that good guy nice stuff too.

Trouble is, the rules keep changing on you...When's it time to give the body a good smacking and when's it the time to lighten up?

Pavel steers a path for you through the minefield...

Now, you can stop butting your head against the wall and stride through the door Pavel has opened for you...The already highly skilled amongst you will find a treasure trove of new strategies for elevating your game. After all, give a consummate professional the correct adjustments at the correct time and they can surge forward in their gains... give a championship caliber team the right coaching tips and they can win it all...

For the regular bodybuilder or strength athlete, Pavel gives you the ultimate road map for progress and success. You'll be fired up all over again, as you experience one great breakthrough after another... with your new understanding of the skill of strength.

Fight these crimes against the body:

If there's one thing that makes Pavel as mad as hell... it's the insidious sissification of the body that has been perpetrated in this country, in the name of bodybuilding and fitness. *Beyond Bodybuilding* is a masterplan to eliminate those cheap, cosmetic, skin-deep looks... and move to strength-from-the-inside-out.

Experience a new level of confidence as your power does the talking for you.... Armed with the new knowledge Pavel gives you, you'll find yourself with the power-body of a wild animal — but the mindset of a skilled strength-scientist.

After all you've put yourself through already, you owe it to yourself to get Pavel's short cuts to strength-skill mastery — and make history of your past failures.

Section One: Power Training

- The real secret to spectacular strength gains.
- The basic laws of successful practice—follow these and you can't help but gain and gain and gain. Page 2
- The perfect number of reps for greater strength.
- How to finish a workout feeling stronger than when you started! Page 2
- The method that did more for a SWAT instructor's strength in a week -- than conventional training in ten previous years! Page 4
- 'Neurological carry-over training' -- the secret technique that resulted in a 1,200 pound squat.

- Stuck on your bench press? How the surprising addition of a piece of wood can help you blow through your current plateau. Page 12
- This high-tonnage program will easily pack ten to fifteen pounds of beef on your frame in less than two months. Page 13
- A Soviet Special Forces method to pack on the pounds with kettlebells -- despite sleep deprivation, excessive exercise, stress and a limited protein intake. Page 13.
- How to cheat the 'law of accommodation' -- and gain beyond your wildest dreams. Page 19
- The only training structure for consistent physical gains that is reliable in the long haul. Page 19
- How to jolt your system into fresh gains -- without changing any of your favorite exercises.
- Discover why the Smolov routine has achieved a cult status. Page 21

- The little-known secret of extensor reflex training can give you a championship edge.
- Be as strong as an ox! How to use 'after-effect' overloads to make you stronger.
- How to fool your internal 'governors of strength' into agreeing to let you be stronger.
- Russian champions consider this the critical component of any strength training. Page 31
- Build greater strength by employing these three fundamental principles of motor learning.
- The critical secrets for super-strength
- Quick! This crash course in the neuroscience of strength may alone be worth the price of this book. Page 41

- The most reliable muscle and strength building method... period.
- Worried you are wasting your time with obsolete routines? Find out which ones work the best, now.
- How to take advantage of 'delayed transmutation' to gain, after going nowhere. Page 44
- Feeling burnt out from heavy, heavy lifting? Here's the perfect remedy.

- Build might and muscle with this classic 'countdown to power.'
- 7 classic set and rep schemes to build a dense, lifter's physique. Page 46
- Bench press stalled? Jump start your bench with this cool and effective routine. Page 49
- How even the busiest person can still make surprising gains thanks to the Setchinov principle.
- Sarkis Karapetyan set a teenage world record by deadlifting 3.14 times his bodyweight -- using this simple-as-can-be cycle. Page 52

- Shoulders going nowhere with your military press? Shock them into life and great new strength/size gains with the 'RKC ladder.' Page 54
- Why explosive lifting can be disastrous for your strength program -- but when it might increase your max by up to 15%. Page 55
- How to correctly use eccentric contractions to stimulate muscle growth.
- This may be the most effective glute exercise in existence. Page 58
- Weak ankles bothering you? This one technique will do a fine job of fixing ankle strength.
- Why the little-known secrets of tendon training are a must for experienced iron athletes of all persuasions. Page 59
- How to train your connective tissues to be maximally tough.

- How and why integration, not isolation, is the key to elite performance.
- How to use 'active negatives' for power, muscle and safety. Page 64.
- The three major benefits of active negatives.
- Are your joints in agony from so much heavy lifting? Protect them better, reduce pain, with 'virtual tissue leverage.'

- Try the 'dead squat' program -- two fortysomething guys added at least five pounds a week for a year with this.
- The seven fundamentals you must know to succeed in the iror game. Page 76
- How to sculpt a classical physique with 'retro' lifts.
- Could these be the most important 'lost' bodybuilding secrets of all time? Page 81
- Exercises you should avoid like the plague -- and exercises you should rush to embrace.

Section Two: Training Planning

- Are you confused about when and how often to hit each bodypart? Discover how to customize your iron schedule for greater gains in strength and muscle.
- Understand the pros and cons of full body workouts versus split routines. Page 99
- The most foolproof training schedule for high-yield results.
- How and why you must cycle your loads to keep succeeding in the iron game.
- What is the optimal volume/intensity ratio for strength gains? Page 104

- How to take advantage of the

continued on next page...

'adaptation lag' -- and its tremendous impact on your strength and muscle training. Page 107

- Want this too? Many bodybuilders have reported sensational gains after using this particular workout. Page 108
- Confused about whether it's okay to train twice a day? Page 112
- How 'controlled overtraining' can be gain-superior to 'total recovery training.' Page 115
- Are you a dissatisfied bodybuilder? This approach could breathe new life, vitality and progress in to your strength and mass program. Page 117
- How a used phone book could help you add 15 lbs to your bench in just one month.

Section Three: Back

- Nothing on the planet beats this exercise for all-around back development! Page 125
- This unique drill -- an incredible back developer -- helped Matt Dimel squat 1,010. Page 131
- Shouldn't this vital back-saving skill be made mandatory in our schools? Page 134

- Discover 3 Russian 'low tech/high concept' programs for pullup power and exceptional lat development. Page 138
- Essential pullup techniques you must know to excel and gain.
- The single best exercise for developing huge lats.
- According to Mike Mentzer, this is the King of back exercises. Are you about to disagree?
- How to take carefully measured doses of 'poisonous' exercises to prevent injury and raise your tolerance levels.

Section Four: Legs

- How to forge truly powerful, traffic-stopping legs.
- Try this little-known, killer squat-deadlift combo for greater flexibility, better form and surprising gains. Page 165
- Do you really know how to squat correctly? Precious few do! Here are the fine points you must know to safely make huge gains. Page 175
- Do you have aching, creaky knees? These two tips alone might save you from a fatal date with the surgeon's knife. Page 195

Section Five: Neck and Shoulders

- Worried about your weak neck? You should be! This unique old-timer's version of the back bridge will give you a resilient, powerful neck—and perhaps keep you out of the hospital. Page 199
- The ONE secret to real success in pressing.
- How to be hard on your muscles, but easy on your joints.
- It's the hallmark of an elite athlete! -- How to own a magnificent neck and traps.

Section Six: Arms

- Cheaters will lose! How to stay honest and build truly huge biceps. Page 225
- The elite Soviet climber secret to bulging forearms and uncanny finger strength. Page 226
- Are you making these serious mistakes with your curls?—3 insider tips help you escape elbow pain.
- Learn from the masters—the top ten Russian arm training secrets revealed.
- Add up to two inches to your arms in just two months with this potent mix of old-timer discoveries and cutting-edge research.
- Experience unbelievable strength gains when you employ this little-known neurological law. Page 233

- Blast your muscles—not your tendons—with this unusual 'control' technique. Page 234
- Enlarge and strengthen your biceps with this powerfully simple growth formula -- guaranteed to grow your guns by at least an extra inch. Page 235
- Blast your way to thick, ripped tris with this excellent, powerlifters' favorite. Page 236

Section Seven: Chest

- How to go from average to superior in your bench press—discover the finer points that separate the champs from the chumps.
- The effect of this martial arts technique on your bench is nothing short of amazing—immediately add 5 reps to your 7-rep max! Page 254
- This favorite of many power athletes will quickly pack on slabs of beef on your chest—thanks to the extreme and unusual overload it generates.
- This tip from strength icon Dr. Fred Hatfield could advance the development of your pecs by light years. Page 261
- This dirty little secret of bodybuilding not only blasts your pecs but builds bigger pipes better than curls. Page 276

Section Eight: Naked Warrior

- Discover the Russian Special Forces ladder to power—it's common for veteran soldiers to add many reps, in short order, to their pullup max...
- Get them here! The secrets of proper pushup form to amplify your strength gains. Page 284.
- Failing to do this during an endurance feat can mean the kiss of death.
- Discover how to take advantage of the 'central pattern generators' in your nervous system -- for longer-lasting energy.

- How to add one inch to your chest in ten days with pushups.
- How to develop cut and muscular legs with the Dragon Walk. Page 295
- The Lizard, an explicitly evil Soviet Spec Ops drill... delivers driving leg power and a ripped, mean, upper body. Page 298

- How to assault your body with a brutal workout—yet save your knees to fight another day. Page 301
- Learn the key mechanics for max body strength.
- Some little-known methods to make bodyweight neck bridges even harder. Page 307
- How to ace the Marine pullup test with the 'Russian rest pause.'

"I wholeheartedly recommend *Beyond Bodybuilding*. I view it as a summation of the accumulated knowledge Pavel Tsatsouline has gathered to this point in his career. Every body part is covered and a blueprint provided for how to build and strengthen every conceivable muscular target. The detail and description is tremendous. The mix between text and photos is spot on; the clarity of the exercise description leaves nothing to the imagination.

Every aspect of training is covered in Pavel's *Beyond Bodybuilding* from flexibility to all types of strength development, U.S.M.C. training, R.K.T. training tips from many of the greatest strength experts around the world, plus a glossary of exercises to fit everyone's needs. I salute Pavel and *Beyond Bodybuilding*."

—Louie Simmons, Westside Barbell

Beyond Bodybuilding

Muscle and Strength Training Secrets for The Renaissance Man

By Pavel

8.5 x 11 Paperback • 365 pages

255 Photographs • 38 workout charts

#B31 $49.95

Are Rigid Muscles Robbing You of Your Strength?

Traditional stretching programs weaken you — but stop stretching altogether and you'll doom yourself to injuries and mediocrity. Discover the world's only stretching protocol specifically and uniquely designed to increase—not reduce—a powerlifter's strength. Skyrocket your strength now—and reduce the wear and tear on your joints—by mastering the secrets of *Strength Stretching!*

- **How to gain** up to 15% on your pulling strength
- **How to arch higher**—and bench more—without killing your back
- **Master the Kettlebell Depth Squat** — the Russian powerlifting secret for teaching perfect squat and pull form and developing championship flexibility
- **Discover how** to release the hidden brakes that are silently sabotaging your deadlift
- **How to relax** your turtle traps—and up your dead
- **How to squat with the big boys**—without killing your shoulders and elbows

"*Strength Stretching* is a virtual must for the powerlifter, novice or advanced. Strength Stretching has helped **Westside Barbell** enormously and I know it will help everyone who is in powerlifting at any stage of the game."—*Louie Simmons,* Westside Barbell

"**Pavel** is a fitness visionary. He has been teaching people about whole body functional training when sports scientists and exercise leaders were emphasizing aerobics and muscle isolation bodybuilding techniques. He formulated his methods by combining training principles developed by Soviet and eastern European coaches and scientists, worldwide sports medicine research, and personal experience. His books and DVDs will help athletes increase power, functional flexibility, and neuromuscular control, while minimizing the risk of injury. Coaches, athletes, and sports scientists will benefit from his unique training courses."—*DR. THOMAS FAHEY,* **Exercise Physiology Lab, Dept of Kinesiology Track and Field Team , California State University, Chico**

Strength Stretching is well worth the money.

"I recently received the ***Strength Stretching*** DVD. This is another quality product from DD. I was surprised at how much information was on the video, considering the price it is a great bargain. This is a must for people who squat, bench, or deadlift. And I believe it's worth owning for anyone who lifts weights, or kettlebells. I don't do any of the powerlifts, I only train with kettlebells but I believe that using the information will definitely improve my kettlebell lifting. I really like that DD is putting out products now for specific athletes, i.e. powerlifters. A great product."—***Jonathan Frost*** **- Naples, FL**

If you are a PLer this is a must have

"After suffering several nagging injuries from PL I finally came across this valuable resource. There are several exercises within this DVD that I implemented into my training program immediately. I am confident that the stretches and techniques mentioned in Strength Stretching will not only up my total, but keep me injury free in the years to come. I recommend this DVD highly."
—***Thomas Phillips,*** **Senior RKC - Marlboro, NJ**

"Pavel's stretching ability is unbelievable. As World Class as it comes!"
—*Brad Gillingham,* 2 times World Superheavyweight Powerlifting Champion

"I loved the DVD. A viewer might discover that they may already be doing several of the Strength Stretches but might quickly discover, as I did, that one additional idea or factor can turn that stretch into a game changer. Good Stuff!" —*Dan John,* National Masters Champion in Discus and Olympic Lifting, Salt Lake City, UT

"When I consume a teaching resource, I look for two things; first does it have something I can use immediately, and second does it mention something that I have been playing with in the gym. *Strength Stretching* hits both points several times. Great for both new and more experienced PLers. Very few things have my full endorsement, but this does."
—*Jack Reape,* Armed Forces Powerlifting Champion

Strength Stretching

For a Bigger Squat, Bench & Deadlift

with Pavel

#DV024 $39.95

DVD Running time: 38 minutes

www.dragondoor.com

1-800-899-5111

Order *Strength Stretching* online:
www.dragondoor.com/DV024

Who trains with kettlebells?

Hard comrades of all persuasions.

Soviet weightlifting legends such as Vlasov, Zhabotinskiy, and Alexeyev started their Olympic careers with old-fashioned kettlebells. Yuri Vlasov once interrupted an interview he was giving to a Western journalist and proceeded to press a pair of kettlebells. "A wonderful exercise," commented the world champion. "...It is hard to find an exercise better suited for developing strength and flexibility simultaneously."

The Russian Special Forces personnel owe much of their wiry strength, explosive agility, and never-quitting stamina to kettlebells. *Soldier, Be Strong!*, the official Soviet armed forces strength training manual pronounced kettlebell drills to be "one of the most effective means of strength development" representing "a new era in the development of human strength-potential".

The elite of the US military and law enforcement instantly recognized the power of the Russian kettlebell, ruggedly simple and deadly effective as an AK-47. You can find Pavel's certified RKC instructors among Force Recon Marines, Department of Energy nuclear security teams, the FBI's Hostage Rescue Team, the Secret Service Counter Assault Team, etc.

Once the Russian kettlebell became a hit among those whose life depends on their strength and conditioning, it took off among hard people from all walks of life: martial artists, athletes, regular hard comrades.

"I can't think of a more practical way of special operations training... I was extremely skeptical about kettlebell training and now wish that I had known about it fifteen years ago..."

—*Name withheld, Special Agent, U.S. Secret Service Counter Assault Team*

Am I kettlebell material?

Kettlebell training is extreme but not elitist. At the 1995 Russian Championship the youngest contestant was 16, the oldest 53! And we are talking elite competition here; the range is even wider if you are training for yourself rather than for the gold. Dr. Krayevskiy, the father of the kettlebell sport, took up training at the age of forty-one and twenty years later he was said to look fresher and healthier than at forty.

Only 8.8% of top Russian gireviks, members of the Russian National Team and regional teams, reported injuries in training or competition (Voropayev, 1997). A remarkably low number, especially if you consider that these are elite athletes who push their bodies over the edge. Many hard men with high mileage have overcome debilitating injuries with kettlebell training (get your doctor's approval). Acrobat Valentin Dikul fell and broke his back at seventeen. Today, in his mid-sixties, he juggles 180-pound balls and breaks powerlifting records!

"... kettlebells are a unique conditioning tool and a powerful one as well that you should add to your arsenal of strength... my experience with them has been part of what's led me to a modification in my thoughts on strength and bodyweight exercises... I'm having a blast training with them and I think you will as well."

—Bud Jeffries, the author of *How to Squat 900lbs. without Drugs, Powersuits, or Kneewraps*

How do I learn to use the kettlebell?

From Pavel's books and videos: *The Russian Kettlebell Challenge* or *From Russia with Tough Love* for comrades ladies. From an RKC certified instructor; find one in your area on RussianKettlebell.com. Kettlebell technique can be learned in one or two sessions and you can start intense training during the second or even first week (Dvorkin, 2001).

"...I felt rejuvenated and ready to conquer the world. I was sold on the kettlebells, as the exercises were fun and challenging, and demanded coordination, explosion, balance, and power... I am now on my way to being a better, fitter, and more explosive grappler, and doing things I haven't done in years!"

—Kid Peligro, *Grappling* magazine

What is the right kettlebell size for me?

Kettlebells come in 'poods'. A pood is an old Russian measure of weight, which equals 16kg, or roughly 35 lbs. An average man should start with a 35-pounder. It does not sound like a lot but believe it; it feels a lot heavier than it should! Most men will eventually progress to a 53-pounder, the standard issue size in the Russian military. Although available in most units, 70-pounders are used only by a few advanced guys and in elite competitions. 88-pounders are for mutants.

An average woman should start with an 18-pounder. A strong woman can go for a 26-pounder. Some women will advance to a 35-pounder. A few hard women will go beyond.

"Kettlebells are like weightlifting times ten."

"Kettlebells are like weightlifting times ten. ...If I could've met Pavel in the early '80s, I might've won two gold medals. I'm serious."

—Dennis Koslowski, D.C., RKC,
Olympic Silver Medalist in Greco-Roman Wrestling

Classic RKC Kettlebells (Cast Iron/E-Coated)

Item	Weight	Price	MAIN USA	PUERTO RICO	AK&HI	CAN
#P10N	10 lb	$41.75	S/H $14.00	$47.00	$53.00	$35.00
#P10P	14 lb	$54.95	S/H $16.00	$51.00	$57.00	$41.00
#P10M	18 lb	$65.95	S/H $22.00	$65.00	$71.00	$46.00
#P10T	10 kg (22 lb)	$71.45	S/H $25.00	$73.00	$79.00	$52.00
#P10G	12 kg (27 lb)	$76.95	S/H $28.00	$80.00	$86.00	$58.00
#P10U	14 kg (31 lb)	$87.95	S/H $34.00	$93.00	$99.00	$64.00
#P10A	16 kg (35 lb)	$96.75	S/H $38.00	$104.00	$110.00	$72.00
#P10S (Women's)	16 kg (35 lb)	$96.75	S/H $38.00	$104.00	$110.00	$72.00
#P10H	20 kg (45 lb)	$107.75	S/H $44.00	$123.00	$122.00	$85.00
#P10B	24 kg (53 lb)	$118.75	S/H $49.00	$141.00	$139.00	$94.00
#P10J	28 kg (62 lb)	$142.95	S/H $53.00	$162.00	$157.00	$107.00
#P10C	32 kg (70 lb)	$153.95	S/H $55.00	$186.00	$193.00	$121.00
#P10Q	36 kg (80 lb)	$175.95	S/H $58.00	$203.00	$209.00	$134.00
#P10F	40 kg (89 lb)	$197.95	S/H $64.00	$223.00	$229.00	$148.00
#P10R	44 kg (97 lb)	$241.95	S/H $69.00	$241.00	$247.00	$160.00
#P10L	48 kg (106 lb)	$263.95	S/H $75.00	$261.00	$267.00	$175.00

SAVE! ORDER A SET OF CLASSIC KETTLEBELLS & SAVE $$$

	Item	Set	Price	MAIN USA	PUERTO RICO	AK&HI	CAN
Save $37.00	#SP10	Classic Set–35, 53 & 70 lb.	$332.50	S/H $142.00	$431.00	$450.00	$287.00
Save $16.00	#SP11	Women's Set–10, 14 & 18 lb.	$146.37	S/H $52.00	$163.00	$181.00	$122.00

ALASKA/HAWAII KETTLEBELL ORDERING
Dragon Door now ships to all 50 states, including Alaska and Hawaii, via UPS Ground.

CANADIAN KETTLEBELL ORDERING
Dragon Door now accepts online, phone and mail orders for Kettlebells to Canada, using UPS Standard service. UPS Standard to Canada service is guaranteed, fully tracked ground delivery, available to every address in all of Canada's ten provinces. Delivery time can vary between 3 to 10 days.

IMPORTANT – International shipping quotes & orders do not include customs clearance, duties, taxes or other non-routine customs brokerage charges, which are the responsibility of the customer.

- **KETTLEBELLS ARE SHIPPED VIA UPS GROUND SERVICE, UNLESS OTHERWISE REQUEST**
- **KETTLEBELLS RANGING IN SIZE FROM 4KG TO 24 CAN BE SHIPPED TO P.O. BOXES OR MILITARY ADDDRESSES VIA THE U.S. POSTAL SERVICE, BUT REQUIRE PHYSICAL ADDDRESSES FOR UPS DELIVERIES FOR THE 32KG AND 40KG KETTLEBEL**
- **NO RUSH ORDERS ON KETTLEBELLS!**

www.dragondoor.com
1-800-899-5111

Order Dragon Door Kettlebells online:
www.dragondoor.com/shop-by-department/kettlebells/

1·800·899·5111

24 HOURS A DAY

FAX YOUR ORDER (866) 280-7619

ORDERING INFORMATION

Customer Service Questions? Please call us between 9:00am– 11:00pm EST Monday to Friday at 1-800-899-5111. Local and foreign customers call 513-346-4160 for orders and customer service

100% One-Year Risk-Free Guarantee. If you are not completely satisfied with any product—we'll be happy to give you a prompt exchange, credit, or refund, as you wish. Simply return your purchase to us, and please let us know why you were dissatisfied—it will help us to provide better products and services in the future. *Shipping and handling fees are non-refundable.*

Telephone Orders For faster service you may place your orders by calling Toll Free 24 hours a day, 7 days a week, 365 days per year. When you call, please have your credit card ready.

Complete and mail with full payment to: Dragon Door Publications, P.O. Box 1097, West Chester, OH 45071

Please print clearly

Sold To: **A**

Name ______________________

Street ______________________

City ______________________

State ______________ *Zip* ________

*Day phone** ______________________

* *Important for clarifying questions on orders*

Please print clearly

SHIP TO: ***(Street address for delivery)*** **B**

Name ______________________

Street ______________________

City ______________________

State ______________ *Zip* ________

Email ______________________

ITEM #	QTY.	ITEM DESCRIPTION	ITEM PRICE	A OR B	TOTAL

HANDLING AND SHIPPING CHARGES • NO COD'S

Total Amount of Order Add (Excludes kettlebells and kettlebell kits):

$00.00 to 29.99	Add $6.00	$100.00 to 129.99	Add $14.00
$30.00 to 49.99	Add $7.00	$130.00 to 169.99	Add $16.00
$50.00 to 69.99	Add $8.00	$170.00 to 199.99	Add $18.00
$70.00 to 99.99	Add $11.00	$200.00 to 299.99	Add $20.00
		$300.00 and up	Add $24.00

Canada and Mexico add $6.00 to US charges. All other countries, flat rate, double US Charges. See Kettlebell section for Kettlebell Shipping and handling charges.

Total of Goods	
Shipping Charges	
Rush Charges	
Kettlebell Shipping Charges	
OH residents add 6.25% sales tax	
MN residents add 7.125% sales tax	
TOTAL ENCLOSED	

METHOD OF PAYMENT ❒ CHECK ❒ M.O. ❒ MASTERCARD ❒ VISA ❒ DISCOVER ❒ AMEX

Account No. *(Please indicate all the numbers on your credit card)* EXPIRATION DATE

☐☐☐☐ ☐☐☐☐ ☐☐☐☐ ☐☐☐☐ ☐☐/☐☐

Day Phone: (   ) ______________

Signature: ______________________ **Date:** ______________

NOTE: *We ship best method available for your delivery address. Foreign orders are sent by air. Credit card or International M.O. only. For* **RUSH** *processing of your order, add an additional $10.00 per address. Available on money order & charge card orders only.*

Errors and omissions excepted. Prices subject to change without notice.

Warning to foreign customers:

The Customs in your country may or may not tax or otherwise charge you an additional fee for goods you receive. Dragon Door Publications is charging you only for U.S. handling and international shipping. Dragon Door Publications is in no way responsible for any additional fees levied by Customs, the carrier or any other entity.

Do You Have A Friend Who'd Like To Receive The Hard-Style Catalog?

We would be happy to send your friend a free copy. Make sure to print and complete in full:

Name ....

Address ....

City .... **State** .... **Zip** ....

1·800·899·5111

24 HOURS A DAY

FAX YOUR ORDER (866) 280-7619

DISCOVER NOVUS

ORDERING INFORMATION

Customer Service Questions? Please call us between 9:00am– 11:00pm EST Monday to Friday at 1-800-899-5111. Local and foreign customers call 513-346-4160 for orders and customer service

100% One-Year Risk-Free Guarantee. If you are not completely satisfied with any product—we'll be happy to give you a prompt exchange, credit, or refund, as you wish. Simply return your purchase to us, and please let us know why you were dissatisfied—it will help us to provide better products and services in the future. *Shipping and handling fees are non-refundable.*

Telephone Orders For faster service you may place your orders by calling Toll Free 24 hours a day, 7 days a week, 365 days per year. When you call, please have your credit card ready.

Complete and mail with full payment to: Dragon Door Publications, P.O. Box 1097, West Chester, OH 45071

Please print clearly

Sold To: **A**

Name ______________________

Street ______________________

City ______________________

State ______________ *Zip* ________

*Day phone** ______________________

** Important for clarifying questions on orders*

Please print clearly

SHIP TO: ***(Street address for delivery)*** **B**

Name ______________________

Street ______________________

City ______________________

State ______________ *Zip* ________

Email ______________________

ITEM #	QTY.	ITEM DESCRIPTION	ITEM PRICE	A OR B	TOTAL

HANDLING AND SHIPPING CHARGES • NO COD'S

Total Amount of Order Add (Excludes kettlebells and kettlebell kits):

$00.00 to 29.99	**Add $6.00**	**$100.00 to 129.99**	**Add $14.00**
$30.00 to 49.99	**Add $7.00**	**$130.00 to 169.99**	**Add $16.00**
$50.00 to 69.99	**Add $8.00**	**$170.00 to 199.99**	**Add $18.00**
$70.00 to 99.99	**Add $11.00**	**$200.00 to 299.99**	**Add $20.00**
		$300.00 and up	**Add $24.00**

Canada and Mexico add $6.00 to US charges. All other countries, flat rate, double US Charges. See Kettlebell section for Kettlebell Shipping and handling charges.

Total of Goods	
Shipping Charges	
Rush Charges	
Kettlebell Shipping Charges	
OH residents add 6.25% sales tax	
MN residents add 7.125% sales tax	
TOTAL ENCLOSED	

METHOD OF PAYMENT ❒ CHECK ❒ M.O. ❒ MASTERCARD ❒ VISA ❒ DISCOVER ❒ AMEX

Account No. *(Please indicate all the numbers on your credit card)* EXPIRATION DATE

☐☐☐☐ ☐☐☐☐ ☐☐☐☐ ☐☐☐☐ ☐☐/☐☐

Day Phone: ( ) ______________

Signature: ______________________ **Date:** ______________

NOTE: *We ship best method available for your delivery address. Foreign orders are sent by air. Credit card or International M.O. only. For* **RUSH** *processing of your order, add an additional $10.00 per address. Available on money order & charge card orders only.*

Errors and omissions excepted. Prices subject to change without notice.

Warning to foreign customers:

The Customs in your country may or may not tax or otherwise charge you an additional fee for goods you receive. Dragon Door Publications is charging you only for U.S. handling and international shipping. Dragon Door Publications is in no way responsible for any additional fees levied by Customs, the carrier or any other entity.

Do You Have A Friend Who'd Like To Receive The Hard-Style Catalog?

We would be happy to send your friend a free copy. Make sure to print and complete in full:

Name ....

Address ....

City .... **State** .... **Zip** ....

1·800·899·5111

24 HOURS A DAY

FAX YOUR ORDER (866) 280-7619

ORDERING INFORMATION

Customer Service Questions? Please call us between 9:00am– 11:00pm EST Monday to Friday at 1-800-899-5111. Local and foreign customers call 513-346-4160 for orders and customer service

100% One-Year Risk-Free Guarantee. If you are not completely satisfied with any product—we'll be happy to give you a prompt exchange, credit, or refund, as you wish. Simply return your purchase to us, and please let us know why you were dissatisfied—it will help us to provide better products and services in the future. *Shipping and handling fees are non-refundable.*

Telephone Orders For faster service you may place your orders by calling Toll Free 24 hours a day, 7 days a week, 365 days per year. When you call, please have your credit card ready.

Complete and mail with full payment to: Dragon Door Publications, P.O. Box 1097, West Chester, OH 45071

Please print clearly

Sold To: **A**

Name ______

Street ______

City ______

State ______ *Zip* ______

*Day phone** ______

** Important for clarifying questions on orders*

Please print clearly

SHIP TO: ***(Street address for delivery)*** **B**

Name ______

Street ______

City ______

State ______ *Zip* ______

Email ______

ITEM #	QTY.	ITEM DESCRIPTION	ITEM PRICE	A OR B	TOTAL

HANDLING AND SHIPPING CHARGES • NO COD'S

Total Amount of Order Add (Excludes kettlebells and kettlebell kits):

$00.00 to 29.99	Add $6.00	$100.00 to 129.99	Add $14.00
$30.00 to 49.99	Add $7.00	$130.00 to 169.99	Add $16.00
$50.00 to 69.99	Add $8.00	$170.00 to 199.99	Add $18.00
$70.00 to 99.99	Add $11.00	$200.00 to 299.99	Add $20.00
		$300.00 and up	Add $24.00

Canada and Mexico add $6.00 to US charges. All other countries, flat rate, double US Charges. See Kettlebell section for Kettlebell Shipping and handling charges.

Total of Goods	
Shipping Charges	
Rush Charges	
Kettlebell Shipping Charges	
OH residents add 6.25% sales tax	
MN residents add 7.125% sales tax	
TOTAL ENCLOSED	

METHOD OF PAYMENT ❒ CHECK ❒ M.O. ❒ MASTERCARD ❒ VISA ❒ DISCOVER ❒ AMEX

Account No. *(Please indicate all the numbers on your credit card)* EXPIRATION DATE

☐☐☐☐ ☐☐☐☐ ☐☐☐☐ ☐☐☐☐ ☐☐/☐☐

Day Phone: ( ) ______

Signature: ______ **Date:** ______

NOTE: *We ship best method available for your delivery address. Foreign orders are sent by air. Credit card or International M.O. only. For* **RUSH** *processing of your order, add an additional $10.00 per address. Available on money order & charge card orders only.*

Errors and omissions excepted. Prices subject to change without notice.

Warning to foreign customers:

The Customs in your country may or may not tax or otherwise charge you an additional fee for goods you receive. Dragon Door Publications is charging you only for U.S. handling and international shipping. Dragon Door Publications is in no way responsible for any additional fees levied by Customs, the carrier or any other entity.

Do You Have A Friend Who'd Like To Receive The Hard-Style Catalog?

We would be happy to send your friend a free copy. Make sure to print and complete in full:

Name ______

Address ______

City ______ **State** ______ **Zip** ______

1·800·899·5111

24 HOURS A DAY

FAX YOUR ORDER (866) 280-7619

ORDERING INFORMATION

Customer Service Questions? Please call us between 9:00am– 11:00pm EST Monday to Friday at 1-800-899-5111. Local and foreign customers call 513-346-4160 for orders and customer service

100% One-Year Risk-Free Guarantee. If you are not completely satisfied with any product—we'll be happy to give you a prompt exchange, credit, or refund, as you wish. Simply return your purchase to us, and please let us know why you were dissatisfied—it will help us to provide better products and services in the future. *Shipping and handling fees are non-refundable.*

Telephone Orders For faster service you may place your orders by calling Toll Free 24 hours a day, 7 days a week, 365 days per year. When you call, please have your credit card ready.

Complete and mail with full payment to: Dragon Door Publications, P.O. Box 1097, West Chester, OH 45071

Please print clearly

Sold To: **A**

*Name*__________

Street __________

City __________

State ______ *Zip* ______

*Day phone**__________

** Important for clarifying questions on orders*

Please print clearly

SHIP TO: ***(Street address for delivery)*** **B**

*Name*__________

Street __________

City __________

State ______ *Zip* ______

Email __________

ITEM #	QTY.	ITEM DESCRIPTION	ITEM PRICE	A OR B	TOTAL

Total of Goods	
Shipping Charges	
Rush Charges	
Kettlebell Shipping Charges	
OH residents add 6.25% sales tax	
MN residents add 7.125% sales tax	
TOTAL ENCLOSED	

HANDLING AND SHIPPING CHARGES • NO COD'S

Total Amount of Order Add (Excludes kettlebells and kettlebell kits):

$00.00 to 29.99	**Add $6.00**	**$100.00 to 129.99**	**Add $14.00**
$30.00 to 49.99	**Add $7.00**	**$130.00 to 169.99**	**Add $16.00**
$50.00 to 69.99	**Add $8.00**	**$170.00 to 199.99**	**Add $18.00**
$70.00 to 99.99	**Add $11.00**	**$200.00 to 299.99**	**Add $20.00**
		$300.00 and up	**Add $24.00**

Canada and Mexico add $6.00 to US charges. All other countries, flat rate, double US Charges. See Kettlebell section for Kettlebell Shipping and handling charges.

METHOD OF PAYMENT ❒ CHECK ❒ M.O. ❒ MASTERCARD ❒ VISA ❒ DISCOVER ❒ AMEX

Account No. *(Please indicate all the numbers on your credit card)* EXPIRATION DATE

□□□□ □□□□ □□□□ □□□□ □□/□□

Day Phone: ( )________

Signature: __________ **Date:** ______

NOTE: *We ship best method available for your delivery address. Foreign orders are sent by air. Credit card or International M.O. only. For* **RUSH** *processing of your order, add an additional $10.00 per address. Available on money order & charge card orders only.*

Errors and omissions excepted. Prices subject to change without notice.

Warning to foreign customers:

The Customs in your country may or may not tax or otherwise charge you an additional fee for goods you receive. Dragon Door Publications is charging you only for U.S. handling and international shipping. Dragon Door Publications is in no way responsible for any additional fees levied by Customs, the carrier or any other entity.

Do You Have A Friend Who'd Like To Receive The Hard-Style Catalog?

We would be happy to send your friend a free copy. Make sure to print and complete in full:

Name ....

Address ....

City .... **State** .... **Zip** ....